Student Solutions Manual to Accompany

CHEMISTRY

Science of Change

SECOND EDITION

Oxtoby / Nachtrieb / Freeman

Donald J. Wink

The University of Illinois at Chicago

D1412473

Saunders Golden Sunburst Series

SAUNDERS COLLEGE PUBLISHING

Harcourt Brace College Publishers

Fort Worth Philadelphia San Diego New York Orlando San Antonio

Toronto Montreal London Sydney Tokyo

Printed in the United States of America.

Wink: Student Solutions Manual to accompany CHEMISTRY: SCIENCE OF CHANGE, 2/E, by Oxtoby/Nachtrieb/Freeman

ISBN 0-03-096805-4

345 021 987654321

PREFACE

Recall how John Paxson described the play that put the Chicago Bulls on the brink of winning their third NBA championship in June, 1993: "It's a shot I've practiced hundreds of thousands of times in my driveway...catch and shoot." The lesson is simple: if you want to perform your best under pressure, then practice, practice, and practice some more when you are *not* under pressure. That is the reason why chemistry textbooks contain so many dozens -- even hundreds or thousands -- of problems. Neither I nor any other instructor I know will ask the exact same questions as the sole component on an exam. But by working the assigned problems diligently a student can prepare very well for the questions that are on an exam.

The second edition of *Chemistry: Science of Change* contains several types of problems to make it easier to learn chemistry. "Building" problems greatly assist students as they learn to use the calculation and analytical skills discussed in each chapter. Multi-step problems then help students practice using different pieces of information to solve a single probem. Finally, the many problems drawn from the original literature enable students to test their comprehension of a subject on a problem more closely connected to the real world of practical chemistry. Working many -- perhaps even most -- of each of these types of problems will give students the practice they need to truly master the many different angles presented by general chemistry.

It is easy for students to become overly anxious about the use of significant figures in their computations. But reliable rules are easy to remember and, with rare exceptions, always useful. In this manual, I have followed the authors' conventions presented in Appendix A-3. This includes carrying additional significant figures in intermediate stages of a calculation, and using extra significant figures when they are available. A telling example is given in the table on the next page. In calculating the mass of a given chemical amount of water, one might think to use a mass with the same precision as the number of moles -- in the example, three significant figures. This does not cause a problem when the number of moles of H_2O is 0.251 mol. But just slightly different values for the number of moles (in the second and third columns) do give values that exhibit round-off errors with less accurate values for the molar mass of H_2O. The rule I suggest students use -- and which I have tried to follow -- is to use at least *two* extra significant figures where they are available. The true answer is then obtained by rounding off *after all calculations*, not in the middle.

	moles of H_2O		
molar mass of H_2O	0.251 mol	0.253 mol	0.255 mol
18.01528 g mol^{-1}	4.52 g	4.56 g	4.59 g
18.0153 g mol^{-1}	4.52 g	4.56 g	4.59 g
18.015 g mol^{-1}	4.52 g	4.56 g	4.59 g
18.02 g mol^{-1}	4.52 g	4.56 g	**4.60 g**
18.0 g mol^{-1}	4.52 g	**4.55 g**	4.59 g

One of the issues that also affects the presentation in this book is the need for clarity. I have tried to always indicate how I am using the information in the problem to get to the answer. The only exceptions are where the method used to obtain the answer is specified by the wording of the problem. Clarity is also concerned with the question of layout. Neat presentation does more than make it easy for the reader (or grader) to understand what a student is doing. It makes it easier for the student to review his or her work. I suggest students get into the habit of clearly indicating the answer to a problems in some manner, as I have tried to do with boldface type in all the problems in the book that have distinct one-word or one-number answers.

The final point I'd like to make deals with consistency of method. There can be many different ways to solve a problem, and where possible I discuss the options.

Which method someone uses may just be a question of taste and experience. In any case, I think students should seek out alternate ways of solving a problem to see which is most comfortable, and then to stick with that method. It will make it easier to take the myriad problems this book -- and an instructor -- give and to make sense of them quickly and to answer them accurately.

For those of you who are interested, the manual was prepared almost entirely using *Microsoft Word for Windows*, including the auxiliary Equation Editor and Draw programs. The only exception is are the drawings in Chapters 25 and 26, prepared with the program *Chemdraw*. The entire text occupies over 6.5 MB of disk space.

I would like to close by acknowledging those people who have helped me in this project in a significant way. My wife, Mary, did extensive work inputting many of the chapters into the computer. Her patience, with my writing and with the program, were critical to getting the job done neatly and on time. Messrs. Brian Cadre and Ismail Bobat proofread almost all of the chapters, and my colleague Wade Freeman served beyond the call of duty as a final checker of numbers and style. I have long credited Prof. Freeman with the production of one of the first modern solutions manuals some years ago in his work on an auxiliary for Saunders' *Principles of Modern Chemistry*. His advice and constructive criticism were, therefore, an honor for me to receive. Finally, many of these solutions bear the stamp of the questions and struggles of the students I have taught at NYU and UIC over the last six years, using this text and the *Principles* text. Their willingness to hold me to a standard of clarity and thoroughness have probably been one of the most important influences on me as a teacher of chemistry. Where possible, I have let my answers in this manual reflect my memory of how those students approached the subject. In turn, I hope students and instructors who use this manual will let me know where they think the text can be improved.

TABLE OF CONTENTS

CHAPTER 1 - THE ATOMIC NATURE OF MATTER

1-1. Table salt - Heterogeneous mixture of mostly sodium chloride and small amounts of other substances.

Wood - Heterogeneous mixture of tree cells, themselves mixtures of water and many thousands of substances.

Mercury - A substance and an element.

Air - Homogeneous mixture of gases.

Water - A substance with the molecular formula H_2O.

Seawater - Homogeneous mixture of water and dissolved substances.

Sodium chloride - A substance with the formula NaCl.

Mayonnaise - Heterogeneous mixture of oil. eggs, vinegar (itself a mixture of water and acetic acid) and seasoning.

1-3. Some examples are: Warm water and a small amount of ice

Liquid in a seltzer bottle right after the bottle is opened

1-5. Elements are substances that can't be changed into any simpler substances. Proof that something is *not* an element simply requires that it can be changed into something simpler. But failure to change it into something simpler does not *definitely* prove it is an element; the experiment may just have been inadequate to the task.

1-7. The number of compounds made of a combination of C, H, and O are almost countless. Vodka contains only two, water (H_2O) and ethanol (C_2H_5OH), and it is therefore a mixture.

1-9. If the sample is 99.44% Si by weight, then it is 100.00 - 99.44 = 0.56% C by weight. This is equal to a mass fraction of 0.0056. The mass of C in the 10.0 g sample is then:

$$\text{g C} = 10.0\text{ g sample} \times \left(\frac{0.0056\text{ g C}}{1\text{ g sample}}\right) = \mathbf{0.056\ g\ C}$$

1-11. The burning of paper yields many products. A few form the solid ash that remains. But most, in particular carbon dioxide and water vapor, are gases. They comprise the rest of the mass.

1-13. The law of the conservation of mass says that the mass of the system before reaction must equal the mass after the reaction. Therefore:

$$\text{mass}_{\textit{(potassium sulfite)}} + \text{mass}_{\textit{(hydrochloric acid)}} = \text{mass}_{\textit{(flask contents)}} + \text{mass}_{\textit{(sulfur dioxide)}}$$

$$1.50\text{ g} + 20.00\text{ g} = 21.09\text{ g} + \text{mass}_{\textit{(sulfur dioxide)}}$$

$$\mathbf{0.41\ g} = \text{mass}_{\textit{(sulfur dioxide)}}$$

1-15. Any sample of pure ascorbic acid will have the same chemical composition, whatever the source. So the ratio of carbon to oxygen in the sample from lemons will be the same as from the laboratory sample. In the laboratory sample the ratio is:

$$\frac{\text{mass O}}{\text{mass C}} = \frac{40.0\text{g}}{30.0\text{g}} = \frac{4}{3} \Rightarrow \text{mass O} = \frac{4}{3} \times \text{mass C}$$

Therefore, in the natural sample: $\text{mass O} = \frac{4}{3} \times 12.7\text{ g} = \mathbf{16.9\ g}$

1-17

	Substance	O : Ca ratio
(a)	CaO	1 :1
(b)	$Ca_3(PO_4)_2$	8 :3
(c)	$Ca(H_2PO_2)_2$	4 :1
(d)	$Ca(MnO_4)_2$	8 :1
(e)	$Ca_5(PO_4)_3OH$	13 :5

1-19.

Compound	Mass of Si combined with 1.00 g of N	Ratio of masses of Si in each compound
A	2.005 g	1.333 g
B	1.504 g	1.000 g

We must compare the masses of Si combined with 1.00 g of N in each compound. These are found to stand as 1.333 : 1.000, or 4 : 3. Therefore, these data are consistent with the law of multiple proportions.

1-21. (a) MoS_3: Sulfur weighs (within the accuracy of this experiment) $^1/_3$rd of what molybdenum weighs. But since there are three sulfur atoms for every molybdenum atom, **1.0 g of S** combines with 1.0 g of Mo.

MoS_4: In this compound there are four sulfur atoms for every molybdenum atom. So the mass of sulfur per mass of molybdenum is 4 × 1/3 = 4/3. There are **1.3 g of S** combined with 1.0 g of molybdenum.

Mo_2S_3: In this compound there are three sulfur atoms for every two molybdenum atoms. So the mass of sulfur per mass of molybdenum is 3/2 × 1/3 = 1/2. There is **0.5 g of S** combined with 1.0 g of molybdenum.

(b) The ratio $^{(g\ S)}/_{(g\ Mo)}$ is the reciprocal of the ratio $^{(g\ Mo)}/_{(g\ S)}$.

For these compounds:

MoS_3: **1.0 g Mo** to 1.0 g S. MoS_4: **0.75 g Mo** to 1.0 g S.

Mo_2S_3: **2.0 g Mo** to 1.0 g S.

1-23. (a) The results of this experiment are clearly consistent with the law of combining volumes, for the ratios of the volumes of gaseous products are 14:4 : 14.4 = 1 : 1. The 1 : 1 ratio further indicates that the compound has a 1 : 1 ratio of H_2:O_2. The simplest formula for the compound is then **HO**.

(b) The law of combining volumes only tells us the simplest possible formula. Any formula with a 1 : 1 H : O ratio is possible, so H_2O_2, H_3O_3, etc. are all possible formulas.

1-25. The chemical reaction is: $2\ N_2O + 3\ O_2 \rightarrow 4\ NO_2$. We can use the law of Gay-Lussac and recall that the coefficients on the substances indicate the volumes of gases that will be involved at constant temperature and pressure. So, for 4.0 L of NO_2 one needs **2.0 L of N_2O** and **3.0 L of O_2**.

1-27. Heavier molecules will form a denser gas than lighter molecules. So a smaller volume of products can weigh the same as the larger volume of reactants if the product molecules are, on average, heavier than the reactant molecules.

1-29. The ratio of the mass of 1 atom of X to the mass of 1 atom of Y is:

$$\frac{\text{at. mass X}}{3 \times \text{at. mass Y}} = \frac{10.000\text{ lb.}}{0.9763\text{ lb.}} = 10.243$$

We rearrange this to:

$$\text{at. mass X} = 3 \times 10.243 \times \text{at. mass Y} = 30.73 \times \text{at. mass Y}$$

When we set the atomic mass of X equal to 1, we obtain:

$$\text{at. mass X} = 30.73 \times 1 = \mathbf{30.73}$$

1-31. The value of the relative atomic masses of the combined oxygen isotopes was larger in the pre-1961 scale, by a factor of $\frac{16.0000}{15.9994} = 1.0000375$. *All* atomic masses were larger by that factor on the pre-1961 scale. So ^{12}C then had a relative atomic mass of $12 \times 1.0000375 =$ **12.0004**.

1-33. The average mass of any two marbles does not reflect the true distribution of marble types in the sack. The true average is a weighted average over all marbles. In this case: average marble mass = $m_r f_r + m_g f_g$

Where: m_r = mass of a red marble f_r = fraction of marbles that are red

m_g = mass of a green marble f_g = fraction of marbles that are green

The fractions are given by the relative numbers of each type:

$$f_r = \frac{10{,}051}{10{,}051 + 24{,}351} = 0.29216 \qquad f_g = \frac{24{,}351}{10{,}051 + 24{,}351} = 0.70784$$

average marble mass = $(11.50\text{ g})(0.29216) + (12.70\text{ g})(0.70784) =$ **12.35 g.**

1-35. For the relative atomic mass, one calculates a weighted average of the masses of the isotopes: relative mass boron = $A_{10}p_{10} + A_{11}p_{11}$

Where: A_{10} = atomic mass of ^{10}B p_{10} = fractional abundance of ^{10}B

A_{11} = atomic mass of ^{11}B p_{11} = fractional abundance of ^{11}B

1-35. (continued)

In this problem, the unknown is A_{11}:

$$10.811 = (10.013)(0.1961) + A_{11}(0.8039)$$

$$10.811 = 1.9635 + 0.8039\ A_{11}$$

$$8.8475 = 0.8039\ A_{11}$$

$$\mathbf{11.01} = A_{11}$$

1-37. (a) Each of the naturally occurring isotopes will give a separate signal in the mass spectrum, so tin will have **ten** separate signals.

(b) The relative abundances of the isotopes dictate the magnitude of the signal for each. So for tin the largest and smallest will stand in a $^{0.3285}/_{0.0035}$ = **94** ratio.

1-39. The fractional abundance of regular chocolate-covered cherries, p_{reg}, is 0.95 and the fractional abundance of "mutant" chocolate-covered cherries, p_{mut}, is 0.050. The average mass is therefore,

$$A = A_{reg}p_{reg} + A_{mut}\,p_{mut}$$

$$= (21.4\text{g})(0.95) + (4.0\text{ g})(0.050)$$

$$= 20.5\text{ g}$$

For a box of 100: mass = no. of cherries x average mass

= 100 x 20.5 g = **2000 g** (to 2 significant figures)

1-41. (a) 4(30.974) + 10(15.999) = **283.89**

(b) 79.904 + 35.453 = **115.357**

(c) 40.078 + 2[14.007 +3(15.999)] = **164.09**

(d) 2(39.098) + 54.938 + 4(15.999) = **197.13**

(e) 2[14.007 + 4(1.0079)] + 32.066 + 4(15.999) = **132.13**

1-43. First, find the number of seconds in 80 years:

$$80\,\text{yr} \times \frac{365.25\,\text{day}}{\text{yr}} \times \frac{24\,\text{hr}}{\text{day}} \times \frac{60\,\text{min}}{\text{hr}} \times \frac{60\,\text{sec}}{\text{min}} = 2.52 \times 10^9\ \text{sec}$$

(365.25 days per year is needed to include leap years)

1-43. (continued)

At one atom per second, this means the person counted out 2.53×10^9 atoms of gold (2.53 billion). To figure out the mass of this number of atoms, we convert to moles and then to grams:

$$2.53\times10^9\text{atoms}\times\frac{1\text{ mol Au}}{6.022\times10^{23}\text{atoms Au}}\times\frac{196.97\text{ g Au}}{1\text{ mol Au}}=\mathbf{8.3\times10^{-13}\text{ g Au}}$$

The most sensitive analytical balances detect down to about 10 μg (10^{-5} g). Sophisticated quartz crystal microbalances detect down to about 100 pg (10^{-10} g). There is literally no way to detect the efforts of this person's life.

1-45. (a) $12.000\text{g }SF_2\times\frac{1\text{ mol }SF_2}{70.062\text{g }SF_2}\times\frac{6.0221\times10^{23}\text{ molecules }SF_2}{1\text{ mol }SF_2}$

$$=\mathbf{1.031\times10^{23}\text{ molecules }SF_2}$$

(b) 1.000 g of fluorine equals: $1.000\text{g F}\times\frac{1\text{ mol F}}{18.998\text{ g F}}=0.052637\text{ mol F}$

The chemical formula indicates: $\frac{n_S}{n_F}=\frac{1}{2}$

so: $n_S = 0.50000\times n_F = 0.02632\text{ mol S}$

We can now convert to mass: $0.2632\text{ mol S}\times\frac{32.066\text{g S}}{1\text{ mol S}}=\mathbf{0.8440\text{ g S}}$.

(c) $12.000\text{ g }S_2F_4\times\frac{1\text{ mol }S_2F_4}{140.124\text{ g }S_2F_4}\times\frac{6.0221\times10^{23}\text{ molecules }S_2F_4}{1\text{ mol }S_2F_4}$

$$=\mathbf{5.157\times10^{22}\text{ molecules }S_2F_4}$$

1.000 g of F (again) corresponds to 0.052637 mol F.

The chemical formula indicates: $\frac{n_S}{n_F}=\frac{2}{4}=\frac{1}{2}$

so: $n_S = 0.50000\times n_F = 0.02632\text{ mol S}$

This is the same chemical amount of S as in part (b), so mass S = **0.8440 g S.**

(d) The number of SF_2 and S_2F_4 molecules in 12.000 g of each of these compounds is different because the molar masses are different.

1-45. (continued)

Because the mass of an S_2F_4 molecule is twice the mass of an SF_2 molecule, a given mass of SF_2 will contain twice as many molecules as the same mass of S_2F_4. But since the ratio $\frac{n_S}{n_F} = \frac{1}{2}$ is the same in each molecule, the relative masses contributed by S and by F are the same in each case.

1-47. In 1.00 mol of vitamin B_{12} there are 6.022 X 10^{23} molecules of vitamin B_{12}. For each molecule of vitamin B_{12} there are 63 C atoms, 88 H atoms, 1 Co atom, 14 N atoms, 14 O atoms, and 1 P atom.

Therefore: $$6.022 \times 10^{23} \text{ molecules } B_{12} \times \frac{181 \text{ atoms}}{1 \text{ molecule } B_{12}} = \mathbf{1.09 \times 10^{26} \text{ atoms}}$$

1-49. Iodine has only one naturally occurring isotope, so dividing the mass of one mole of iodine atoms by Avogadro's number gives us the actual mass of one I atom.

$$\frac{126.90447 \text{ g of I}}{N_o \text{ atoms of I}} = \frac{126.90447 \text{ g of I}}{6.022137 \times 10^{23} \text{ atoms of I}} = \mathbf{2.1072997 \times 10^{-22} \frac{g}{\text{atom I}}}$$

1-51. For the molar mass of ferrocene:

$$\text{molar mass} = (55.847 \frac{\text{g Fe}}{\text{mol Fe}}) + 10 \times (12.011 \frac{\text{g C}}{\text{mol C}}) + 10 \times (1.00794 \frac{\text{g H}}{\text{mol H}})$$

$$= 186.036 \frac{\text{g Fe}(C_5H_5)_2}{\text{mol Fe}(C_5H_5)_2}$$

(a) $$\text{mol Fe}(C_5H_5)_2 = 100.0 \text{ g Fe}(C_5H_5)_2 \times \left(\frac{1 \text{ mol Fe}(C_5H_5)_2}{186.04 \text{ g Fe}(C_5H_5)_2}\right)$$

$$= \mathbf{0.5375 \text{ mol Fe}(C_5H_5)_2}$$

(b) molecules $Fe(C_5H_5)_2$

$$= 0.5375 \text{ mol Fe}(C_5H_5)_2 \times \left(\frac{6.022 \times 10^{23} \text{ molecules Fe}(C_5H_5)_2}{1 \text{ mol Fe}(C_5H_5)_2}\right)$$

$$= \mathbf{3.237 \times 10^{23} \text{ molecules Fe}(C_5H_5)_2}$$

1-53. (a) The number of moles of LiF in 65.4 g of Li is:

$$65.4\,\text{g LiF} \times \left(\frac{1\ \text{mol LiF}}{25.939\ \text{g LiF}}\right) = 2.52\,\text{mol LiF}$$

For the number of moles of Li: $2.53\,\text{mol LiF} \times \left(\frac{1\,\text{mol Li}}{1\,\text{mol LiF}}\right) = 2.53\ \text{mol Li}$

For the number of grams of Li: $2.53\,\text{mol Li} \times \left(\frac{6.941\,\text{g Li}}{1\,\text{mol Li}}\right) = \mathbf{17.5\ g\ Li}$

(b) The only difference in the two parts of this problem are the units for mass - grams and pounds. The relative weights of Li in LiF is independent of the units for mass. Therefore, if there are 17.5 g Li in 65.4 g of LiF, then there are **17.5 lb Li** in 65.4 lb LiF.

1-55. Some unit conversions is in order first: There are 10 deciliters (10 dL) in 1 liter and there are 1000 milliliters (1000 mL) in 1 liter. Therefore the sample size is:

$$500\ \text{mL} \times \left(\frac{1\ \text{L}}{1000\ \text{mL}}\right) \times \left(\frac{10\ \text{dL}}{1\ \text{L}}\right) = 5.00\ \text{dL}.$$

For this patient: $5.00\,\text{dL} \times \left(\frac{5.1\times10^{-9}\,\text{g Hg}}{\text{dL}}\right) = 2.6 \times 10^{-8}\ \text{g} = \mathbf{26\ ng}$

1-57. The molar mass is the number of grams per mole of the substance. This is a ratio that the problem gives, with only 0.750 mol of this element. To get the atomic mass, we set the number of moles in the ratio to 1:

$\frac{112.77\ \text{g X}}{0.750\ \text{mol X}} = \frac{\mathbf{150.\ g\ X}}{\mathbf{1\,mol\ X}}$. The element is **samarium** (Sm).

1-59. The mass of a sample is the product of the volume and the density:

$$5.12\ \text{cm}^3\ AsF_3 \times \left(\frac{2.163\text{g}\ AsF_3}{1\ \text{cm}^3\ AsF_3}\right) = \mathbf{11.1\ g}$$

$$\text{molar mass of } AsF_3 = (74.9216\frac{\text{g As}}{\text{mol As}}) + 3 \times (18.9984\frac{\text{g F}}{\text{mol F}}) = 131.9168\frac{\text{g } AsF_3}{\text{mol} AsF_3}$$

$$\text{moles } AsF_3 = 11.07\,\text{g}\ AsF_3 \times \left(\frac{1\ \text{mol}\ AsF_3}{131.9168\ \text{g}\ AsF_3}\right) = \mathbf{0.0840\ moles\ AsF_3}$$

1-61. Density is defined as the mass of a substance per unit volume. Therefore,

$$\text{density of nerf} = \left(\frac{50.0\text{g nerf}}{549\text{ cm}^3\text{ nerf}}\right) = \mathbf{0.0911\ g\ cm^{-3}}$$

1-63. This problem requires two conversions: from kg to g and from g to cm^3:

$$34.5\text{ kg} \times \left(\frac{1000\text{ g}}{1\text{ kg}}\right) \times \left(\frac{1\text{ cm}^3\text{ Hg}}{13.6\text{ g Hg}}\right) = \mathbf{2540\ cm^3}$$

1-65. In this problem, conversions use density (the ratio of mass to volume), molar mass (the ratio of mass and chemical amount) and Avogadro's number (the ratio of chemical amount and the amount of particles):

$$\left(\frac{1\text{ cm}^3\text{ Lu}}{9.84\text{ g Lu}}\right) \times \left(\frac{174.967\text{ g Lu}}{1\text{ mol Lu}}\right) \times \left(\frac{1\text{ mol Lu}}{6.0221 \times 10^{23}\text{ atom Lu}}\right) = \mathbf{2.95 \times 10^{-23}\ \frac{cm^3}{atom\ Lu}}$$

1-67. If the rose-hip vitamin C is simply pure vitamin C, then there could be no difference. But the naturally-derived material may in fact be a mixture of vitamin C and small amounts of other substances with some health effects.

1-69. The chemist is discussing substances when the term "simple bodies" is used. This sentence expresses the fact that substances -- compounds and/or elements -- can be separated ("resolved") by physical means.

1-71. (a)

MATERIAL	CLASSIFICATION
Soft-wood chips	A complex heterogeneous mixture.
Water	A pure compound with the molecular formula H_2O.
Iron	An element (Fe)
Sodium Hydroxide	A pure compound with the formula NaOH.

(b) The iron vessel is a sealed system. All of the mass in it at the start remains in it at the end. The total mass at the end is the same as that at the beginning: 17.2 + 150.1 + 22.43 = **189.7 kg.**

1-73. The lightest of the objects are the grebes: the krulls are listed as heavier than the grebes and the grebes are listed as having a fraction of the mass of the stoats. The listed ratios are the basis for the calculation of the mass of a stoat and of a krull:

$$\text{mass of grebe} = 0.780 \times \text{mass of stoat}$$

$$1.000\text{ g} = 0.780 \times \text{mass of stoat}$$

$$\frac{1.000\text{g}}{0.780} = \text{mass of stoat} = \mathbf{1.28\ g}$$

$$\text{mass of krull} = 4.60 \times \text{mass of grebe}$$

$$= 4.60 \times 1.000\text{g} = \mathbf{4.60\ g}$$

$$\text{mass of collection} = (17 \times 4.60\text{ g}) + (19 \times 1.00\text{ g}) + (11 \times 1.28\text{ g}) = \mathbf{111.30\ g}$$

1-75. This suggestion is entirely consistent with Gay-Lussac's observations. The student would write the equation for the decomposition of water as:

$$2\,H_4O_2 \rightarrow 2\,H_4 + O_4$$

In volumes, this is the same as saying:

2 volumes water → 2 volumes hydrogen + 1 volume oxygen.

Compare this with the "conventional" equation:

$$2\,H_2O \rightarrow 2\,H_2 + O_2,$$

which predicts the same relative volumes of the gases.

1-77 1. *Matter consists of indivisible atoms.* There are two ways scientists have seen that atoms are divisible: in spontaneous radioactive decay (for example with all isotopes of uranium or radium) and in "atom smashing" events, for example in a nuclear reactor.

2. *All atoms of a given chemical element are identical in mass and in all other properties.* Isotopes were not discovered until almost 100 years after Dalton's work. Isotopes have virtually identical chemical properties but have different masses.

1-77. (continued)

3. *Different chemical elements have different kinds of atoms, and in particular, such atoms have different masses.* This statement (so far) needs no modification or extension.

4. *Atoms are indestructible, and retain their identity in chemical reactions.* It is still true that there are no instances where elements are destroyed in a chemical reaction. Atoms are destroyed in nuclear reactions (which we do not consider chemical reactions), discussed in Chapter 16 of the text.

5. *The formation of a compound from its elements occurs through combining atoms of unlike elements in small whole-number ratios.* Some solid compounds in fact do have fractional elemental composition. A few of these were known in Dalton's time, but experimental imprecision prevented their recognition.

1-79. The mass fraction of Zr in both gems must be the same. In the first gem this is:

$$\text{mass fraction Zr} = \frac{5.474}{5.474 + 1.685 + 3.840} = 0.4977.$$

In the second gem, the mass fraction of Zr is the same, so the mass of Zr is

$$\text{mass Zr} = \text{total mass} \times 0.4977 = \mathbf{22.31\ g}$$

1-81. (a) The molecular mass of UF_6 is 238.03 + 6(18.998) = 352.02, so the molar mass is 352.02 g mol^{-1}. The average mass of one molecule of UF_6 is:

$$\left(\frac{352.02\text{ g }UF_6}{1\text{ mol }UF_6}\right) \times \left(\frac{1\text{ mol }UF_6}{6.0221 \times 10^{23}\text{ molecule }UF_6}\right) = \mathbf{5.8454 \times 10^{-22}\ \frac{g}{molecule\ UF_6}}$$

(b) The mass of uranium used to determine the molar mass of UF_6 is *average* mass for this element, taking into account the relative masses and abundances of the isotopes. There is no molecule that has this average mass. The actual masses of molecules of UF_6 will be distributed amongst several possible values, determined by the isotope of U that is present.

1-83. The ratios of the isotopes can be used to get the relative fractional amounts of the elements. First, we note that in a typical sample there are 498.7 parts of ^{16}O, 0.1832 parts ^{17}O, and 1.000 part ^{18}O, for a total of 499.8832 parts. Then the fractional abundances are:

$^{16}O = {}^{498.7}/_{499.8832} = 0.99763$ $\quad$ $^{17}O = {}^{0.1832}/_{499.8832} = .00036649$

$^{18}O = {}^{1.000}/_{499.8832} = 0.002005$

Then these fractional abundances can be applied to the 10 million atom sample:

No. ^{18}O atoms = $10{,}000{,}000 \times 0.002005$ = **20,050 ^{18}O atoms**

No. ^{17}O atoms = $10{,}000{,}000 \times 0.0003665$ = **3,665 ^{17}O atoms**

No. ^{16}O atoms = $10{,}000{,}000 \times 0.9976$ = **9,976,000 ^{16}O atoms**

1-85. (a) This problem reminds us that the mass scale we use may be arbitrary, but the relative masses of the elements are not arbitrary. Similarly, the counting numbers -- like the mole -- that we employ may be different for the scientists on another planet. But a molecule is still a molecule.

32 margs of sulfur is actually 32×4.8648 g = 155.67 g of sulfur. This corresponds to $155.67\,\text{g}\ {}^{32}\text{S} \times \left(\frac{1\ \text{mol}\ {}^{32}\text{S}}{31.972\ \text{g}\ {}^{32}\text{S}}\right) = 4.8691\,\text{mol}\ {}^{32}\text{S}$.

The number of ^{32}S atoms in this quantity of ^{32}S is:

$$4.8691\,\text{mol}\ {}^{32}\text{S} \times \left(\frac{6.0221 \times 10^{23}\ \text{atom}\ {}^{32}\text{S}}{1\,\text{mol}\ {}^{32}\text{S}}\right) = 2.9322 \times 10^{24}\ \frac{\text{atom}\ {}^{32}\text{S}}{1\,\text{mol}\ {}^{32}\text{S}}$$

Therefore, N_{or} = **2.9321 X 10^{24}**.

(b) On earth, the atomic mass of P is 30.9738 g/mol, so 6.0221 X 10^{23} atoms of P weigh 30.9738 g. Therefore, an average P atom weighs:

$$\left(\frac{30.938\ \text{g P}}{1\ \text{mol P}}\right) \times \left(\frac{1\ \text{mol P}}{6.0221 \times 10^{23}\ \text{atoms P}}\right) = 5.1434 \times 10^{-23}\ \text{g}.$$

1-85. (continued)

Finally, we can convert from our units to the units on planet HTRAE because we know the values of their counting unit N_{Or} and their mass unit, the marg:

$$\left(\frac{5.1434\times10^{-23}\text{ g}}{\text{atom P}}\right)\times\left(\frac{2.9321\times10^{24}\text{ atoms P}}{\text{elom }^{32}\text{P}}\right)\times\left(\frac{1\text{ marg}}{4.8648\text{ g}}\right)=31.001\frac{\text{marg P}}{\text{elom P}}$$

A chemist on HTRAE would write the relative atomic mass of phosphorus as **31.001**.

1-87. The blue line corresponds to iridium and the red line to hydrogen. The data given indicate that the volume per gram of the elements are 0.04423 $cm^3\ g^{-1}$ for Ir and 12,100 $cm^3\ g^{-1}$ for hydrogen. Clearly, hydrogen occupies much more volume per gram than Ir.

CHAPTER 2 - CHEMICAL EQUATIONS AND REACTION YIELDS

2-1. The C:H ratio in cyclohexane is 6:12 = 1:2, so the empirical formula is CH_2. Cyclopropane has the same C:H ratio as cyclohexane, so cyclopropane has the same empirical formula as cyclohexane.

2-3. (a) The empirical formula is the smallest whole number ratio of atoms in a compound. Dividing the subscripts in the molecular formula each by twelve gives the empirical formula $C_3H_3N_2O$.

(b) The molar mass of a compound is the sum of the molar masses of the elements in the compound, each multipled by its occurrence in the formula.

(36 × at. mass C) + (36 × at. mass H) + (24 × at. mass N) + (12 × at. mass O)

$$= \left(36 \times 12.011 \frac{\text{g C}}{\text{mol C}}\right) + \left(36 \times 1.00794 \frac{\text{g H}}{\text{mol H}}\right) + \left(24 \times 14.00674 \frac{\text{g N}}{\text{mol N}}\right) + \left(12 \times 15.9994 \frac{\text{g O}}{\text{mol O}}\right)$$

$= 432.396 + 36.2858 + 336.1617 + 191.993 = \mathbf{996.84\ g\ mol^{-1}}$

2-5. From the molecular formula there are 6 atoms of carbon for every 6 atoms of oxygen. Therefore:

$$3.0 \times 10^{24} \text{atoms O} \times \left(\frac{6 \text{ atoms C}}{6 \text{ atoms O}}\right) = \mathbf{3.0 \times 10^{24} atoms\ C}.$$

2-7. (a) Metallic silver consists of silver atoms in a solid lattice. The number of repetitions of the basic formula unit is *variable* (Ag_2, Ag_{10}, Ag_{1000}, and so forth). The term "silver molecule," is therefore meaningless.

(b) The formula unit of solid silver is Ag

2-9. Water is one portion of the compound. Its amount can be determined by considering three different values: (i) the number of moles of compound, (ii) the number of moles of water per mole of cmompound, and then (iii) the number of molecules of water per mole of water. We start with the molar mass of one mole of $MgSO_4 \cdot 7H_2O$, which is 247 g mol^{-1} (to three significant digits).

2-9. (continued)

(i) moles of salt: $55\ \text{g MgSO}_4 \bullet 7H_2O \times \left(\frac{1\ \text{mol MgSO}_4 \bullet 7H_2O}{247\ \text{g MgSO}_4 \bullet 7H_2O}\right)$

$= 0.223\text{mol MgSO}_4 \bullet 7H_2O$

(ii) moles of water: $0.223\ \text{mol MgSO}_4 \bullet 7\ H_2O \times \left(\frac{7\ \text{mol } H_2O}{1\ \text{mol MgSO}_4 \bullet 7H_2O}\right)$

$= 1.651\ \text{mol } H_2O$

(iii) molecules of water: $1.651\ \text{mol } H_2O \times 6.0221 \times 10^{23}\ \frac{\text{molecules}}{\text{mol}}$

$= \mathbf{9.4 \times 10^{23}}$ **molecules of H_2O.**

2-11. (a) We will need to know the mass of one mole of the drug. This is:

$1\ \text{mol AuC}_4H_4O_4Na_2S = 196.96654 + (4 \times 12.011) + (4 \times 1.0074)$

$+ (4 \times 15.9994) + (2 \times 22.9898) + 32.066 = 391.09\ \text{g}$

Within this amount of the drug, there is *one* mole of gold, which weighs 196.96654 g. The mass of Au administered over the course of the therapy is:

$$\left(\frac{0.0500\ \text{g AuC}_4H_4O_4Na_2S}{\text{week}}\right) \times \left(\frac{196.96654\ \text{g Au}}{391.09\ \text{g AuC}_4H_4O_4Na_2S}\right) \times 20\ \text{weeks}$$

$$= 0.504\ \text{g Au} \times \left(\frac{1000\ \text{mg}}{1\ \text{g}}\right) = \mathbf{504\ mg\ Au.}$$

(b) Because the subscripts in the molecular formula are integral multiples of the subscripts in the empirical formula, the *ratios* of the amounts of elements given by an empirical formula and by a molecular formula are *identical.* This is true for chemical amounts as well as for the masses of the elements. If there is one gram of Au per *x* grams of the compound when we calculate using the empirical formula, there will be one gram of Au per *x* grams of compound using the molecular formula. Because this problem relies on the ratios of the masses of Au and the drug, the answer would be the **same** with the empirical or the molecular formula.

2-13. To obtain a mass percentage (or mass fraction) of an element in a compound, we divide the mass of the element in one mole of the compound by the molar mass of the compound.

Molar mass of Cu_2Sb is: (2×63.546) + 121.757 = 248.85 g mol^{-1}.

To obtain mass % for Sb:

$$\% \text{ Sb} = \left(\frac{121.75 \text{ g Sb}}{1 \text{ mol } Cu_2Sb}\right) \times \left(\frac{1 \text{ mol } Cu_2Sb}{248.85 \text{ g } Cu_2Sb}\right) = 0.4893 \text{ Sb} = \mathbf{48.93\% \ Sb}$$

2-15. This is a good point to introduce a tabular layout for mass % problems.

	MOLAR MASS (g mol^{-1})	MASS OF H IN ONE MOLE OF COMPOUND	MASS % H
H_2O	18.0153	$\left(\frac{2 \text{ mol H}}{1 \text{ mol } H_2O}\right) \times \left(\frac{1.00794 \text{ g H}}{1 \text{ mol H}}\right) = \frac{2.0159 \text{ g H}}{1 \text{ mol } H_2O}$	$\left(\frac{2.0159 \text{ g H}}{1 \text{ mol } H_2O}\right) \times \left(\frac{1 \text{ mol } H_2O}{18.0153 \text{ g } H_2O}\right) = \frac{0.1111 \text{ g H}}{1 \text{ g } H_2O} = 11.11\% \text{ H}$
$C_{12}H_{26}$	170.34	$\left(\frac{26 \text{ mol H}}{1 \text{ mol } C_{12}H_{26}}\right) \times \left(\frac{1.00794 \text{ g H}}{1 \text{ mol H}}\right) = \frac{26.2064 \text{ g H}}{1 \text{ mol } C_{12}H_{26}}$	$\left(\frac{26.206 \text{ g H}}{1 \text{ mol } C_{12}H_{26}}\right) \times \left(\frac{1 \text{ mol } C_{12}H_{26}}{170.34 \text{ g } C_{12}H_{26}}\right) = \frac{0.1538 \text{ g H}}{1 \text{ g } C_{12}H_{26}} = 15.38\% \text{ H}$
N_4H_6	62.0746	$\left(\frac{6 \text{ mol H}}{1 \text{ mol} N_4H_6}\right) \times \left(\frac{1.00794 \text{ g H}}{1 \text{ mol H}}\right) = \frac{6.0476 \text{ g H}}{1 \text{ mol } N_4H_6}$	$\left(\frac{6.0476 \text{ g H}}{1 \text{ mol } N_4H_6}\right) \times \left(\frac{1 \text{ mol } N_4H_6}{62.0746 \text{ g } N_4H_6}\right) = \frac{0.09743 \text{ g H}}{1 \text{ g } N_4H_6} = 9.743\% \text{ H}$
LiH	7.949	$\left(\frac{1 \text{ molH}}{1 \text{ molLiH}}\right) \times \left(\frac{1.00794 \text{gH}}{1 \text{molH}}\right) = \frac{1.00794 \text{g H}}{1 \text{ molLiH}}$	$\left(\frac{1.00794 \text{g H}}{1 \text{ mol LiH}}\right) \times \left(\frac{1 \text{ mol LiH}}{7.949 \text{ g LiH}}\right) = \frac{0.1268 \text{ g H}}{1 \text{ g LiH}} = 12.68\ \% \text{ H}$

In order of increasing mass % H: **N_4H_6 < H_2O < LiH < $C_{12}H_{26}$.**

2-17. Molar mass= 19 × at. mass C + 28 × at. mass H + 2 × at. mass O

$$= 19 \times 12.011 + 28 \times 1.00794 + 2 \times 15.9994 = 288.43 \text{ g mol}^{-1}$$

$$\left(\frac{\text{g C in 1 mol}}{\text{molar mass}}\right) = \left(\frac{19 \times 12.011}{288.43}\right) = 0.7912 = \mathbf{79.12\% \ C}$$

2-19. The masses of each element in one mole of the compound are:

$$\text{mass of Cl} = 1\text{ mol Cl} \times \left(\frac{35.4527\text{ g Cl}}{1\text{ mol Cl}}\right) = 35.4527\text{ g Cl}$$

$$\text{mass of F} = 8\text{ mol F} \times \left(\frac{18.9984\text{ g F}}{1\text{ mol F}}\right) = 151.987\text{ g F}$$

$$\text{mass of O} = 2\text{ mol O} \times \left(\frac{15.9994\text{ g O}}{1\text{ mol O}}\right) = 31.9988\text{ g O}$$

$$\text{mass of Pt} = 1\text{ mol Pt} \times \left(\frac{195.08\text{ g Pt}}{1\text{ mol Pt}}\right) = 195.08\text{ g Pt}$$

Total mass of one mole of compound = 414.52 g.

The mass percentages are:

$$\left(\frac{35.4527\text{ g Cl}}{414.52\text{ g compound}}\right) = 0.08553 = \mathbf{8.553\%\ Cl}$$

$$\left(\frac{151.987\text{ g F}}{414.52\text{ g compound}}\right) = 0.3667 = \mathbf{36.67\%\ F}$$

$$\left(\frac{31.9988\text{ g O}}{414.52\text{ g compound}}\right) = 0.07220 = \mathbf{7.720\%\ O}$$

$$\left(\frac{195.08\text{ g Pt}}{414.52\text{ g compound}}\right) = 0.4706 = \mathbf{47.06\%\ Pt}$$

2-21. The molar mass of $PbCrO_4$ is 323.2 g mol^{-1}. The molar mass of $PbCrO_4{\bullet}PbO$ is 546.4 g mol^{-1}. The mass percentages are:

$$\text{for } PbCrO_4: \left(\frac{207.2\text{ g Pb}}{323.2\text{ g compound}}\right) = 0.6411 = \mathbf{64.11\%\ Pb}$$

$$\text{for } PbCrO_4{\bullet}PbO: \left(\frac{414.4\text{ g Pb}}{546.4\text{ g compound}}\right) = 0.7584 = \mathbf{75.84\ \%\ Pb}$$

2-23. This problem is done by assuming a sample size of 100.00 g, made of 98.70 g He and 1.30 g C_4H_{10}. The mass of H in that 1.30 g of C_4H_{10} is:

$$1.30\text{ g } C_4H_{10} \times \left(\frac{1\text{ mol } C_4H_{10}}{58.12\text{ g } C_4H_{10}}\right) \times \left(\frac{10\text{ mol H}}{1\text{ mol } C_4H_{10}}\right) \times \left(\frac{1.00794\text{ g H}}{1\text{ mol H}}\right) = 0.225\text{ g H}$$

The percentage of H in Q-gas is: $\left(\frac{0.225\text{ g H}}{100\text{ g Q-gas}}\right) = 0.00225 = \mathbf{0.225\%\ H}$

2-25. The number of moles of each element in the sample is:

O: $16.58 \text{ mg O} \times \left(\frac{1 \text{ g O}}{1000 \text{mg O}}\right) \times \left(\frac{1 \text{ mol O}}{15.9994 \text{ g O}}\right) = 1.036 \times 10^{-3} \text{ mol O}$

P: $8.02 \text{ mg P} \times \left(\frac{1 \text{ g P}}{1000 \text{ mg P}}\right) \times \left(\frac{1 \text{ mol P}}{30.974 \text{ g P}}\right) = 2.589 \times 10^{-4} \text{ mol P}$

Zn: $25.40 \text{ mg Zn X} \left(\frac{1 \text{ g Zn}}{1000 \text{ mg Zn}}\right) \times \left(\frac{1 \text{ mol Zn}}{65.39 \text{ g Zn}}\right) = 3.884 \times 10^{-4} \text{ mol Zn}$

The element present least chemical amount is phosphorus. It will serve as our "key element" for this problem, for only it has the chance to have a subscript of 1 in the empirical formula. To determine the empirical formula, we divide the number of moles of P into the number of moles of O and Zn:

$$\frac{3.884 \times 10^{-4} \text{ mol Zn}}{2.589 \times 10^{-4} \text{ mol P}} = \frac{1.500 \text{ mol Zn}}{1 \text{ mol P}} = \frac{3 \text{ mol Zn}}{2 \text{ mol P}}$$

$$\frac{1.036 \times 10^{-3} \text{ mol O}}{2.589 \times 10^{-3} \text{ mol P}} = \frac{4.002 \text{ mol O}}{1 \text{ mol P}} = \frac{4 \text{ mol O}}{1 \text{ mol P}} = \frac{8 \text{ mol O}}{2 \text{ mol P}}$$

The numbers of moles stand in the whole number ratio

2 mol P : 8 mol O : 3 mol Zn, so the empirical formula is $\mathbf{Zn_3P_2O_8}$.

Note that we were not able to keep the P with a subscript of 1. We had to give it a subscript of 2 to make the other subscripts whole numbers.

2-27. We determine the number of moles of each of the elements, assuming a hypothetical 100.0 g sample. In a such a sample, the mass of each element in grams equals its mass percentage in the compound. Hence:

Element	Grams in 100.00 g	Moles in 100 g	Relative # of moles
Si	28.37 g	$28.37 \text{ g Si} \times \left(\frac{1 \text{ mol Si}}{28.0855 \text{ g Si}}\right) = 1.010 \text{ mol Si}$	1.000
Cl	100.00-28.37= 71.63 g	$71.63 \text{ g Cl} \times \left(\frac{1 \text{ mol Cl}}{35.4527 \text{ g Cl}}\right) = 2.020 \text{mol Cl}$	2.000

The empirical formula of the compound is $\mathbf{SiCl_2}$.

2-29.

Element	Grams in 100.00 g	Moles in 100 g	Relative # of moles
Si	53.99 g	$53.99\text{ g Si}\times\left(\frac{1\text{ mol Si}}{28.0855\text{ g Si}}\right) = 1.922\text{mol Si}$	2.333
Fe	100.00 - 53.99 = 46.01 g	$46.01\text{ g Fe}\times\left(\frac{1\text{ mol Fe}}{55.847\text{ g Fe}}\right) = 0.8239\text{mol Fe}$	1.000

The empirical formula must have whole number subscripts. We note that 2.333 × 3 = 7.00 and 1.00 × 3 = 3.00 (see text Appendix C-4). So the correct empirical formula is $\mathbf{Fe_3Si_7}$.

2-31. For compound #1:

Element	Grams in 100.00 g	Moles in 100 g	Relative # of moles
Ba	90.745 g	$90.745\text{ g Ba}\times\left(\frac{1\text{ mol Ba}}{137.327\text{ g Ba}}\right) = 0.66080\text{mol Ba}$	1.000
N	100.000 g - 90.745 g 9.255 g	$9.255\text{ g N}\times\left(\frac{1\text{ mol N}}{14.00674\text{ g N}}\right) = 0.66075\text{ mol N}$	1.000

The empirical formula is **BaN**.

For compound #2:

Element	Grams in 100.00 g	Moles in 100 g	Relative # of moles
Ba	93.934 g	$93.634\text{ g Ba}\times\left(\frac{1\text{ mol Ba}}{137.327\text{ g Ba}}\right) = 0.68183\text{mol Ba}$	1.500
N	100.000 g - 93.934 g 6.336 g	$6.366\text{ g N}\times\left(\frac{1\text{ mol N}}{14.00674\text{ g N}}\right) = 0.45450\text{ mol N}$	1.000

The empirical formula is $\mathbf{Ba_3N_2}$.

2-33. In a 100.00 g hypothetical sample, the number of atoms of the elements are:

$$48.0\text{ g Au}\times\left(\frac{1\text{ mol Au}}{196.97\text{ g Au}}\right)\times\left(\frac{6.0221\times10^{23}\text{ atoms Au}}{1\text{ mol Au}}\right) = 1.467\times10^{23}\text{ atoms Au}$$

$$45.0\text{g Pt}\times\left(\frac{1\text{ mol Pt}}{195.08\text{ g Pt}}\right)\times\left(\frac{6.0221\times10^{23}\text{ atoms Pt}}{1\text{ mol Pt}}\right) = 1.389\times10^{23}\text{ atoms Pt}$$

$$7.0\text{ g Ag}\times\left(\frac{1\text{ mol Ag}}{107.87\text{ g Ag}}\right)\times\left(\frac{6.0221\times10^{23}\text{ atoms Ag}}{1\text{ mol Ag}}\right) = 3.908\times10^{22}\text{ atoms Ag}$$

2-33. (continued)

Total atoms in 100.00 g: = 3.247×10^{23} atoms.

$$\text{atom fraction Au} = \frac{1.467 \times 10^{23} \text{atoms Au}}{3.247 \times 10^{23} \text{ atoms elements}} = 0.452.$$

For a 1000 atom sample:

$$\text{atoms Au} = \text{total No. of atoms} \times \text{atom fraction Au}$$
$$= 1000 \text{ total atoms} \times 0.452 \frac{\text{atoms Au}}{\text{total atoms}} = \mathbf{452 \text{ atoms Au}}$$

2-35. In this problem, we are given the masses (not percentages) of two of the elements in a sample of definite (not hypothetical) size. The third mass, of oxygen, is found by difference:

mass oxygen = total mass - mass Na - mass S

= 65.32 g - 21.14 g - 14.74 g = 29.44 g O

Element	Grams in sample	Moles in sample	Relative # of moles
Na	21.14 g	$21.14 \text{ g Na} \times \left(\frac{1 \text{ mol Na}}{22.9898 \text{ g Na}}\right) = 0.9195 \text{ mol Na}$	2.000
S	14.74 g	$14.74 \text{ g S} \times \left(\frac{1 \text{ mol S}}{32.066 \text{ g S}}\right) = 0.4597 \text{ mol S}$	1.000
O	29.44 g	$29.44 \text{ g O} \times \left(\frac{1 \text{ mol O}}{15.9994 \text{ g O}}\right) = 1.840 \text{ mol N}$	4.003

Within the precision of the measurements, the empirical formula is $\mathbf{Na_2SO_4}$.

2-37. In a combustion problem:

moles C in sample = moles C in CO_2 = moles of CO_2 after combustion

moles H in sample = moles H in H_2O = 2 × moles H_2O after combustion

For this problem:

$$\text{mol C} = 3.701 \text{ g } CO_2 \times \left(\frac{1 \text{ mol } CO_2}{44.021 \text{ g } CO_2}\right) \times \left(\frac{1 \text{ mol C}}{1 \text{ mol } CO_2}\right) = 0.0841 \text{ mol C}$$

$$\text{mol H} = 1.082 \text{g } H_2O \times \left(\frac{1 \text{ mol } H_2O}{18.015 \text{ g } H_2O}\right) \times \left(\frac{2 \text{ mol H}}{1 \text{ mol } H_2O}\right) = 0.1201 \text{ mol H}$$

moles H : moles C = 0.1201 : 0.08410 = 1.428 : 1.

2-37. (continued)

To determine the nearest whole number ratio equal to this value, we note that $0.427 \sim {}^{3}/_{7}$. Therefore:

$$\text{moles H : moles C} = (1 + {}^{3}/_{7}) : 1 = ({}^{10}/_{7}) : 1 = 10 : 7.$$

To the precision of the data, the empirical formula is $\mathbf{C_7H_{10}}$.

2-39. All of the carbon in the sample produces CO when broken down. We can therefore relate the number of grams of CO produced with the number of moles C initially present. A similar relationship exists between grams of CO and moles of O, and grams of Cl_2 and moles of Cl.

$$\text{moles C} = \text{moles O} = \text{moles CO} = 32.21 \text{ g CO} \times \left(\frac{1 \text{ mol CO}}{28.010 \text{ g CO}}\right) = 1.150$$

$$\text{moles Cl} = 2 \times \text{moles } Cl_2 = 2 \times 81.55 \text{ g } Cl_2 \times \left(\frac{1 \text{ mol } Cl_2}{70.906 \text{ g } Cl_2}\right) = 2.300$$

The relative numbers of moles in the compound are:

moles C: moles O: moles Cl = 1.150 : 1.150 : 2.300 = 1 : 1 : 2.

So the empirical formula is $\mathbf{COCl_2}$.

2-41. The molecular formula of a compound is always an integral multiple of the empirical formula, so we can write:

molecular formula = (empirical formula)$_n$ where n = 1,2,3....

The same integer n relates the molar mass of a compound with the "empirical mass". The empirical mass of C_3H_5 is 41.07 g mol^{-1}.

$$\text{Molar mass} = n\,(\text{Empirical mass}),$$

$$n = \frac{\text{Molar mass}}{\text{Empirical mass}} = \frac{410.7 \text{ g mol}^{-1}}{41.07 \text{ g mol}^{-1}} = 10.00$$

Therefore: molecular formula = $(C_3H_5)_{10} = \mathbf{C_{30}H_{50}}$.

2-43. (a) $N_2 + O_2 \rightarrow 2\ NO$

(b) $2\ N_2 + O_2 \rightarrow 2\ N_2O$

(c) $K_2SO_3 + 2\ HCl \rightarrow 2\ KCl + H_2O + SO_2$

(d) $2\ NH_3 + 3\ O_2 + 2\ CH_4 \rightarrow 2\ HCN + 6\ H_2O$

2-45. (a) $3\ H_2 + N_2 \rightarrow 2\ NH_3$

(b) $2\ K + O_2 \rightarrow K_2O_2$

(c) $PbO_2 + Pb + 2\ H_2SO_4 \rightarrow 2\ PbSO_4 + 2\ H_2O$

(d) $2\ BF_3 + 3\ H_2O \rightarrow B_2O_3 + 6\ HF$

(e) $2\ KClO_3 \rightarrow 2\ KCl + 3\ O_2$

(f) $CH_3COOH + 2\ O_2 \rightarrow 2\ CO_2 + 2\ H_2O$

(g) $2\ K_2O_2 + 2\ H_2O \rightarrow 4\ KOH + O_2$

(h) $3\ PCl_5 + 5\ AsF_3 \rightarrow 3\ PF_5 + 5\ AsCl_3$

2-47. (a) $2\ C_6H_6 + 15\ O_2 \rightarrow 12\ CO_2 + 6\ H_2O$

(b) $2\ F_2 + H_2O \rightarrow OF_2 + 2\ HF$

(c) $CaC_2 + 2\ H_2O \rightarrow Ca(OH)_2 + C_2H_2$

(d) $7\ O_2 + 4\ NH_3 \rightarrow 4\ NO_2 + 6\ H_2O$

(e) $2\ Al + 6\ NaOH \rightarrow 3\ H_2 + 2\ Na_3AlO_3$

2-49. (a) $Fe_2O_3 + 3\ H_2 \rightarrow 2\ Fe + 3\ H_2O$

(b) $3\ Fe_2O_3 + H_2 \rightarrow 2\ Fe_3O_4 + H_2O$

2-51. The chemical equation indicates that for every 4 moles of H_2O_2 there is one mole of PbS, so: $\dfrac{x\ \text{mol}\ H_2O_2}{2.47\ \text{mol PbS}} = \dfrac{4\ \text{mol}\ H_2O_2}{1\ \text{mol PbS}}$

$$x\ \text{mol}\ H_2O_2 = \left(\frac{4\ \text{mol}\ H_2O_2}{1\ \text{mol PbS}}\right) \times 2.47\ \text{mol PbS}$$

$$= \mathbf{9.88\ mol\ H_2O_2}$$

2-53. The chemical equation indicates that for every one mole of C_2H_6 there are two moles of H_2. By Avogadro's postulate, this means the ratio of *liters* of C_2H_6 gas to liters of H_2 gas is also 1 : 2. Therefore:

$$\frac{x \text{ L } C_2H_6}{14.2 \text{ L } H_2} = \frac{1 \text{ L } C_2H_6}{2 \text{ L } H_2} \Rightarrow x \text{ L } C_2H_6 = \left(\frac{1 \text{ L } C_2H_6}{2 \text{ L } H_2}\right) \times 14.2 \text{ L } H_2 = \mathbf{7.10 \text{ L } C_2H_6}$$

2-55. As indicated in the textbook, one can work this kind of problem step-wise or in a single calculation (after calculating the molar masses of the substances). Here, (a) and (b) are done step-wise and (c) and (d) are done in a single calculation using the calculated molar masses.

(a) Molar mass of CH_4: $12.011 + 4(1.00794) = 16.042 \text{ g mol}^{-1}$.

Molar mass of O_2: $2(15.9994) = 31.9988 \text{ g mol}^{-1}$.

Chemical amount of O_2: $1.000 \text{ g } O_2 \times \left(\frac{1 \text{ mol } O_2}{31.9988 \text{ g } O_2}\right) = 0.31251 \text{ mol } O_2$

Chemical amount of CH_4: $0.031251 \text{ mol } O_2 \times \left(\frac{1 \text{ mol } CH_4}{2 \text{ mol } O_2}\right) = 0.15626 \text{ mol } CH_4$

Mass of CH_4: $0.015626 \text{ mol } CH_4 \times \left(\frac{16.042 \text{ g } CH_4}{1 \text{ mol } CH_4}\right) = \mathbf{0.2507 \text{ g } CH_4}$.

(b) Molar mass of $TiCl_2$: $47.88 + 2(35.4527) = 118.785 \text{ g mol}^{-1}$

Molar mass of $TiCl_4$: $47.88 + 4(35.4527) = 189.691 \text{ g mol}^{-1}$

Chemical amount of $TiCl_4$: $1.000 \text{ g } TiCl_4 \times \left(\frac{1 \text{ mol } TiCl_4}{189.691 \text{ g } TiCl_4}\right) = 5.2717 \times 10^{-3} \text{ mol}$

Chemical amount of $TiCl_2$: $5.2717 \times 10^{-3} \text{ mol} \times \left(\frac{1 \text{ mol } TiCl_2}{1 \text{ mol } TiCl_4}\right) = 5.2717 \times 10^{-3} \text{ mol}$

Mass of $TiCl_4$: $5.2717 \times 10^{-3} \text{ mol } TiCl_2 \times \left(\frac{118.785 \text{ g } TiCl_2}{1 \text{ mol } TiCl_2}\right) = \mathbf{0.6262 \text{ g } TiCl_2}$.

(c) Molar mass of Na_3VO_4: $3(22.990) + 50.942 + 4(15.9994) = 183.910 \text{ g mol}^{-1}$

Molar mass of H_2O: $2(1.0079) + 15.9994 = 18.0153 \text{ g mol}^{-1}$

Done in one line, the calculation for mass of Na_3VO_4 is:

$$1.000 \text{ g } H_2O \times \left(\frac{1 \text{ mol } H_2O}{18.0153 \text{ g } H_2O}\right) \times \left(\frac{2 \text{ mol } Na_3VO_4}{1 \text{ mol } H_2O}\right) \times \left(\frac{183.910 \text{ g } Na_3VO_4}{1 \text{ mol } Na_3VO_4}\right) = \mathbf{20.42 \text{ g } Na_3VO_4}$$

2-55. (continued)

(d)Molar mass of K_2O_2: $2(39.0983) + 2(15.9994) = 110.1954 \text{ g mol}^{-1}$.

Molar mass of H_2O: $2(1.00794) + 15.9994 = 18.0153 \text{ g mol}^{-1}$

Done in one line, the calculation for grams of K_2O_2 is:

$$1.000 \text{ g } H_2O \times \left(\frac{1 \text{ mol } H_2O}{18.0153 \text{ g } H_2O}\right) \times \left(\frac{2 \text{ mol } K_2O_2}{4 \text{ mol } H_2O}\right) \times \left(\frac{110.1954 \text{ g } K_2O_2}{1 \text{ mol } K_2O_2}\right) = \mathbf{3.058 \text{ g } K_2O_2}$$

2-57. Molar mass of Al_2O_3: $2(26.98156) + 3(15.9994) = 101.9613 \text{ g mol}^{-1}$.

Molar mass of Na_3AlF_6: $3(22.9898) + 26.98159 + 6(18.998) = 209.939 \text{ g mol}^{-1}$

Done in one line, the calculation for the number of grams of Na_3AlF_6 is:

$$287 \text{ g } Al_2O_3 \times \left(\frac{1 \text{ mol } Al_2O_3}{101.96 \text{ g } Al_2O_3}\right) \times \left(\frac{2 \text{ mol } Na_3AlF_6}{1 \text{ mol } Al_2O_3}\right) \times \left(\frac{209.94 \text{ g } Na_3AlF_6}{1 \text{ mol } Na_3AlF_6}\right) = \mathbf{1180 \text{ g } Na_3AlF_6}$$

2-59. When a problem requires the determination of the chemical or mass amounts of *two or more* substances based on one other key substance, it is easiest to calculate the chemical amount of the key substance, then use this amount in calculations of the other two.

Molar mass of KCl: $39.0983 + 35.4527 = 74.551 \text{ g mol}^{-1}$

Molar mass of KNO_3: $39.0983 + 14.00674 + 3(15.9994) = 101.103 \text{ g mol}^{-1}$

Molar mass of Cl_2: $2(35.4527) = 70.9054 \text{ g mol}^{-1}$.

The chemical amount of KNO_3, the "key" substance in this case, is:

$$567 \text{ g } KNO_3 \times \left(\frac{1 \text{ mol } KNO_3}{101.1032 \text{ g } KNO_3}\right) = 5.6081 \text{ mol } KNO_3$$

The mass of KCl that will give this amount of KNO_3 is:

$$5.6081 \text{ mol } KNO_3 \times \left(\frac{4 \text{ mol KCl}}{4 \text{ mol } KNO_3}\right) \times \left(\frac{74.551 \text{ g KCl}}{1 \text{ mol KCl}}\right) = \mathbf{418 \text{ g KCl}}$$

The mass of Cl_2 by-product is:

$$5.6081 \text{ mol } KNO_3 \times \left(\frac{2 \text{ mol } Cl_2}{4 \text{ mol } KNO_3}\right) \times \left(\frac{70.9054 \text{ g } Cl_2}{1 \text{ mol } Cl_2}\right) = \mathbf{199 \text{ g } Cl_2}$$

2-61. The formula $K_2Zn_3[Fe(CN)_6]_2$ indicates that there are *twelve* carbons per formula unit. Therefore, the formation of one mole of $K_2Zn_3[Fe(CN)_6]_2$ would require twelve moles of K_2CO_3. Then, for the mass of $K_2Zn_3[Fe(CN)_6]_2$

$$= 18.6 \text{ g } K_2CO_3 \times \left(\frac{1 \text{ mol } K_2CO_3}{138.20 \text{ g } K_2CO_3}\right) \times \left(\frac{1 \text{ mol } K_2Zn_3[Fe(CN)_6]_2}{12 \text{ mol } K_2CO_3}\right) \times \left(\frac{698.3\text{g } K_2Zn_3[Fe(CN)_6]_2}{1 \text{ mol } K_2Zn_3[Fe(CN)_6]_2}\right)$$

$$= \mathbf{7.83 \text{ g } K_2Zn_3[Fe(CN)_6]_2}$$

2-63. We can find the value for *x* by determining the number of moles of water that were produced in producing the final amount of Na_3RhCl_6.

$$\text{mass } H_2O = \text{original mass } Na_3RhCl_6 \bullet x\, H_2O - \text{mass of final } Na_3RhCl_6$$

$$= 2.1670 - 1.3872 = 0.7798 \text{ g}$$

$$\text{moles } H_2O \text{ given off} = 0.7798 \text{ g } H_2O \times \left(\frac{1 \text{ mol } H_2O}{18.015 \text{ g } H_2O}\right)$$

$$= 0.04329 \text{ mol } H_2O$$

$$\text{moles } Na_3RhCl_6 \text{ remaining} = 1.3872 \text{ g } Na_3RhCl_6 \times \left(\frac{1 \text{ mol } Na_3RhCl_6}{384.6 \text{ g } Na_3RhCl_6}\right)$$

$$= 0.003607 \text{ mol}$$

$$x = \frac{\text{moles } H_2O \text{ given off}}{\text{moles } Na_3RhCl_6 \text{ remaining}}$$

$$= \frac{0.04329}{0.003607} = \mathbf{12}$$

2-65. The words of the problem give the information needed for the balanced chemical equation relating Si_2H_6 and SiO_2: $6\, Si_2H_6 + 21\, O_2 \rightarrow 12\, SiO_2 + 18\, H_2O$

In this problem the measured amount of disilane starting material is given as a volume. With this information, the density, and the molar mass of disilane, we can calculate the mass of silica:

$$25.0 \text{ cm}^3 \text{ } Si_2H_6 \times \left(\frac{2.78 \times 10^{-3} \text{ g } Si_2H_6}{1 \text{ cm}^3 \text{ } Si_2H_6}\right) \times \left(\frac{1 \text{ mol } Si_2H_6}{62.220 \text{ g } Si_2H_6}\right) \times \left(\frac{12 \text{ mol } SiO_2}{6 \text{ mol } Si_2H_6}\right) \times \left(\frac{60.084 \text{ g } SiO_2}{1 \text{ mol } SiO_2}\right)$$

$$= \mathbf{0.134 \text{ g } SiO_2}.$$

2-67. We start by calculating how many cheeseburgers might be made using all of each ingredient. The ingredient that gives the fewest cheeseburgers limits the process.

Patties: $600 \text{ patties} \times \left(\dfrac{1 \text{ cheeseburger}}{2 \text{ patties}}\right) = 300 \text{ cheeseburgers}$

Cheese: $400 \text{ cheese slices} \times \left(\dfrac{1 \text{ cheeseburger}}{1 \text{ cheese slice}}\right) = 400 \text{ cheeseburgers}$

Tomato: $1000 \text{ tomato slices} \times \left(\dfrac{1 \text{ cheeseburger}}{4 \text{ tomatoslices}}\right) = 250 \text{ cheeseburgers}$

Buns: $350 \text{ buns} \times \left(\dfrac{1 \text{ cheeseburger}}{1 \text{ hamburger bun}}\right) = 350 \text{ cheeseburgers}$

The least product comes from the supply of **tomato slices**. That will make **250 cheeseburgers.** For these, 500 hamburger patties are required, so **100 hamburger patties** will be left over.

2-69.

Parts	# available - dozens	# available - units	conversion to tables	# of tables that can be made
legs	25.25	303	$\dfrac{1 \text{ table}}{4 \text{ legs}}$	75
leaves	20.00	240	$\dfrac{1 \text{ table}}{2 \text{ leaves}}$	120
frames	11.00	132	$\dfrac{1 \text{ table}}{1 \text{ frame}}$	132
tops	7.00	84	$\dfrac{1 \text{ table}}{1 \text{ top}}$	84

Note: the tables are only useful as units, so the number available from the legs is rounded *down* from 75.75.

The least amount of product is given by the legs, so the legs are the "limiting reactant", and a maximum of 75 tables can be assembled.

2-71. The molar masses we need for this calculation are:

NH_3: 17.0306 g mol^{-1} O_2: 31.9988 g mol^{-1} H_2O: 18.0153 g mol^{-1}

The amount of NH_3 present in the reaction mixture is:

$$34.0 \text{ g } NH_3 \times \left(\frac{1 \text{ mol } NH_3}{17.03056 \text{ g } NH_3}\right) = 1.996 \text{ mol } NH_3$$

2-71. (continued)

If it all reacted, the yield of H_2O would be:

$$1.996 \text{ mol } NH_3 \times \left(\frac{6 \text{ mol } H_2O}{4 \text{ mol } NH_3} \right) = 2.995 \text{ mol } H_2O$$

The amount of O_2 present in the reaction mixture is:

$$50.0 \text{ g } O_2 \times \left(\frac{1 \text{ mol } O_2}{31.9989 \text{ g } O_2} \right) = 1.5626 \text{ mol } O_2$$

If it all reacted, the yield of H_2O would be:

$$1.5626 \text{ mol } O_2 \times \left(\frac{6 \text{ mol } H_2O}{3 \text{ mol } O_2} \right) = 3.1252 \text{ mol } H_2O$$

The NH_3 would give *less* of the H_2O product; hence, **NH_3 is the limiting reactant.** The mass of water that could form is:

$$2.995 \text{ mol } H_2O \times \left(\frac{18.0153 \text{ g } H_2O}{1 \text{ mol } H_2O} \right) = \mathbf{53.9 \text{ g } H_2O}$$

2-73. The molar masses we need for this calculation are:

$BaCl_2$: 208.232 g mol^{-1} Na_2SO_4: 142.043 g mol^{-1} $BaSO_4$: 233.391 g mol^{-1}

The stoichiometry of the reaction is $BaCl_2$:Na_2SO_4:$BaSO_4$ = 1: 1: 1. This means that the limiting reactant is simply the reactant present in the least chemical amount - there is no need to convert moles of reactants into moles of product.

$BaCl_2$ present in the reaction mixture:

$$6.500 \text{ g } BaCl_2 \times \left(\frac{1 \text{mol } BaCl_2}{208.232 \text{g } BaCl_2} \right) = 0.031215 \text{ mol } BaCl_2.$$

Na_2SO_4 present in the reaction mixture:

$$9.420 \text{g } Na_2SO_4 \times \left(\frac{1 \text{ mol } Na_2SO_4}{142.043 \text{ g } Na_2SO_4} \right) = 0.066318 \text{ mol } Na_2SO_4$$

There is less $BaCl_2$ present, so **$BaCl_2$ is the limiting reagent.** It will form 0.031215 moles of $BaSO_4$. The mass of $BaSO_4$ that will form is:

$$0.031215 \text{ mol } BaSO_4 \times \left(\frac{233.391 \text{ g } BaSO_4}{1 \text{ mol } BaSO_4} \right) = \mathbf{7.285 \text{ g } BaSO_4}$$

2-75. The theoretical yield is always controlled by the limiting reactant. A limiting reactant calculation is done first, and then the theoretical yield is calculated from the limiting reactant. In tabular format (see problems 2-71 and 2-73 for a "linear" layout), the limiting reactant calculation is:

Reactant	Molar mass	Amount available - grams	Amount available - moles	Conversion factor to moles H_2O	Moles H_2O formed
H_2	2.0158 g mol^{-1}	2.000	0.9922 mol H_2	$\frac{1\,mol\,H_2O}{1\,mol\,H_2}$	0.9922 mol H_2O
O_2	31.9988 g mol^{-1}	1.000	0.03125 mol O_2	$\frac{2\,mol\,H_2O}{1\,mol\,O_2}$	0.06250 mol H_2O

The limiting reactant is O_2, so the theoretical yield is 0.06250 mol H_2O. This will equal (for a molar mass of 18.0153 g mol^{-1} for H_2O) **1.126 g H_2O**

2-77. This limiting reactant problem is also done by determining how many moles of the CO_2 product could form from each reactant. But in this problem the amounts of the reactants are given as *volumes.* Because the temperature and pressure are constant, the product can be predicted based on the law of combining volumes.

Calculating from the C_2H_4:40.0 L C_2H_4 $\times\left(\frac{4\text{ L }CO_2}{1\text{ L }C_2H_4}\right)$ = 160 L CO_2

Calculating from O_2: 20.0 L C_2H_4 $\times\left(\frac{4\text{ L }CO_2}{6\text{ L }O_2}\right)$ = 13.3 L CO_2

The O_2 is the limiting reactant. The theoretical yield of CO_2 is **13.3 L CO_2.**

2-79. The necessary molar masses are: Fe_2O_3: 159.69 g mol^{-1} Fe: 55.847 g mol^{-1}

Chemical amount of Fe_2O_3:

$$433.2\text{ g }Fe_2O_3 \times\left(\frac{1\text{ mol }Fe_2O_3}{159.69\text{ g }Fe_2O_3}\right) = 2.713\text{ mol }Fe_2O_3$$

2-79. (continued)

Theoretical yield of Fe in moles :

$$2.713 \text{ mol } Fe_2O_3 \times \left(\frac{2 \text{ mol Fe}}{1 \text{ mol } Fe_2O_3}\right) = 5.426 \text{ mol Fe}$$

The theoretical yield of Fe in g: $5.426 \text{ mol Fe} \times \left(\frac{55.847 \text{ g Fe}}{1 \text{ mol Fe}}\right) = \mathbf{303.0\ g\ Fe}$

The percentage yield: $\left(\frac{254.3 \text{ g Fe}}{303.0 \text{ g Fe}}\right) = 0.8393 = \mathbf{83.93\%}$

2-81. (a) If 8.0% of the cookies are broken (and eaten) then 92.0% can be sold. You must make enough cookies so that 92% of them will equal 200 dozen (or 2400) cookies. (0.92) x = 2400 cookies ⇒ x = **2609 cookies**

(b) 2609 cookies made - 2400 cookies delivered = **209 cookies** eaten

2-83. The number of molecules of water and TCDD must be determined separately.

$$1 \text{ kg } H_2O \times \left(\frac{1000 \text{ g } H_2O}{1 \text{ kg } H_2O}\right) \times \left(\frac{1 \text{ mol } H_2O}{18.0153 \text{ g } H_2O}\right) \times \left(\frac{6.0221 \times 10^{23} \text{molecules } H_2O}{1 \text{ mol } H_2O}\right)$$

$$= 3 \times 10^{25} \text{ molecules } H_2O$$

$$6 \mu g \text{ TCDD} \times \left(\frac{10^{-6} \text{ gTCDD}}{1 \ \mu g \text{ TCDD}}\right) \times \left(\frac{1 \text{ mol TCDD}}{322.0 \text{ g TCDD}}\right) \times \left(\frac{6.0221 \times 10^{23} \text{ moleculesTCDD}}{1 \text{ molTCDD}}\right)$$

$$= 1 \times 10^{15} \text{ molecules TCDD.}$$

Percentage of TCDD molecules: $\left(\frac{1 \times 10^{15}}{3 \times 10^{25}}\right) = 3 \times 10^{-11} \times 100\% = \mathbf{3 \times 10^{-9}\%}$.

2-85. The balanced reaction for the chlor-alkali process is

$2 \text{ NaCl} + 2 \text{ } H_2O \rightarrow H_2 + 2 \text{ NaOH} + Cl_2$.

For simplicity, since the reactant and the product are both present *in metric tons*, we do not convert to and from grams. The mass *ratio* of Cl_2 : 2 NaOH is 70.906 : 79.994 regardless of the units of mass. Therefore:

$$660 \text{ metric tons } Cl_2 \times \left(\frac{79.994 \text{ tons NaOH}}{70.906 \text{ tons } Cl_2}\right) = 745 \text{ metric tons NaOH.}$$

2-87.

Name	Molecular Formula	Empirical Formula	Molar Mass in g mol^{-1}
Tetralin	$C_{10}H_{12}$	**C_5H_6**	**132.21**
Quinine	**$C_{20}H_{24}N_2O_2$**	$C_{10}H_{12}NO$	324.41
d-Ribose	**$C_5H_{10}O_2$**	CH_2O	150.13
Cubane	C_8H_8	**CH**	**104.15**
Benzene	**C_6H_6**	CH	78.11

2-89. The mass of reactant OsO_4 is 17.6 mg, or 0.0176 g OsO_4.

$$0.0176\text{ g } OsO_4 \times \left(\frac{1\text{ mol } OsO_4}{254.228\text{ g } OsO_4}\right) \times \left(\frac{1\text{ mol Os}}{1\text{ mol } OsO_4}\right) \times \left(\frac{190.23\text{ g Os}}{1\text{ mol Os}}\right)$$

$= 0.0132$ g Os = **13.2 mg Os**

2-91. For $InCl_2$: $\dfrac{114.818\text{ g In}}{185.723\text{g } InCl_2} = 0.61823 = \mathbf{61.82\%\ In}$

For $In_3[In_2Cl_9]$ (= In_5Cl_9): $\dfrac{574.09\text{ g In}}{893.164\text{ g } In_5Cl_9} = 0.64276 = \mathbf{64.28\%\ In}$

The compositions of the two compounds are quite similar.

2-93. The mass of potassium is the difference between the mass of the sample and the mass of the cesium: mass K in sample = mass sample - mass Cs

= 0.03151 g - 0.02346 g = 0.00805 g

Element	Grams in sample	Moles in sample	Relative # of moles
Cs	0.02346	$0.02346\text{ g Cs} \times \left(\frac{1\text{ mol Cs}}{132.91\text{ g Cs}}\right) = 1.765 \times 10^{-4}\text{ mol Cs}$	1.000
K	0.00805	$0.00805\text{ g K} \times \left(\frac{1\text{ mol K}}{39.098\text{ g K}}\right) = 2.06 \times 10^{-4}\text{ mol K}$	1.167

The K:Cs ratio of 1.167:1 is equivalent to 7:6. Thus, the formula is **K_7C_6**.

2-95. We may again assume 100.000 g.

Element	grams in 100.00 g	moles in 100 g	relative # of moles
Fe	62.613 g	$62.613\ g\ Fe \times \left(\frac{1\ mol\ Fe}{55.847 g\ Fe}\right) = 1.12115\ mol\ Fe$	1.000
S	37.387 g	$37.387\ g\ S \times \left(\frac{1\ mol\ S}{32.066 g\ S}\right) = 1.16594\ mol\ S$	1.0400

The Fe : S ratio is 1 Fe : 1.0400 S. 0.0400 is equal to $\frac{1}{25}$. We can rewrite this ratio as $1\ Fe : 1\frac{1}{25}\ S = \frac{25}{25}\ Fe : \frac{26}{25}\ S = 25\ Fe : 26\ S$,

The formula is **$Fe_{25}S_{26}$**. Note that this is very close to FeS, but that compound would have Fe 62.352% and S 36.475%. These values are too far away from the experimental numbers for the compound to be FeS.

2-97. This real sample contains all of the 0.7200 g of Ba and an additional mass of 0.1678 g of O. Then:

Element	grams in sample	moles in sample	relative # of moles
Ba	0.7200 g	$0.7200\ g\ Ba \times \left(\frac{1\ mol\ Ba}{137.327\ g\ Ba}\right) = 0.0052439\ mol\ Ba$	1.0000
O	0.1678g	$0.1678\ g\ O \times \left(\frac{1\ mol\ O}{15.9994\ g\ O}\right) = 0.010488\ mol\ O$	1.9924

The compound is **BaO_2** (barium peroxide).

2-99. The balanced chemical reaction, in words, is:

Aspartame + 2 water [yields] aspartic acid + methanol + phenylalanine.

In formulas:

$$C_{14}H_{18}N_2O_5 + 2\ H_2O \rightarrow C_4H_7NO_4 + CH_3OH + C_wH_xN_yO_z$$

The values for w, x, y, and z are obtained by using the fact that the number of C, H, N, and O atoms must balance.

2-99. (continued)

As written, we have:

14C / 22H / 2N / 7O [yields] 5C / 1H / 1N / 5O + wC / xH / yN / zO

The values for w, x, y, and z are w = 10, x = 11, y = 1, z = 2.

The formula for phenylalanine is $\mathbf{C_{10}H_{11}NO_2}$.

2-101. The chemical amount of K_2O product is:

$$8.34\ \text{g}\ K_2O \times \left(\frac{1\ \text{mol}\ K_2O}{94.196\ \text{g}\ K_2O}\right) = 0.8854\ \text{mol}\ K_2O$$

The amount of K required is:

$$0.08854\ \text{mol}\ K_2O \times \left(\frac{10\ \text{mol K}}{6\ \text{mol}\ K_2O}\right) \times \left(\frac{39.0983\ \text{g K}}{1\ \text{mol K}}\right) = \mathbf{5.77\ g\ K}$$

The amount of KNO_3 required is:

$$0.08854\ \text{mol}\ K_2O \times \left(\frac{2\ \text{mol}\ KNO_3}{6\ \text{mol}\ K_2O}\right) \times \left(\frac{101.103\ \text{g}\ KNO_3}{1\ \text{mol}\ KNO_3}\right) = \mathbf{2.98\ g\ KNO_3}$$

2-103. The key insight required for this problem is that the nitrogen in 3'-methylphthalanilic acid appears *entirely* in the *m*-toluidine. And the 3'-methylphtalanilic acid is 5.49% N, meaning that for every 100 g of the acid there are 5.49 g N. Working from 5.23 g of *m*-toluidine:

$$5.23\ \text{g}\ m\text{-toluidine} \times \left(\frac{14.00674\ \text{g N}}{1\ \text{mol N}}\right) \times \left(\frac{1\ \text{mol N}}{1\ \text{mol}\ m\text{-toluidine}}\right) \times \left(\frac{1\ \text{mol}\ m-\text{toluidine}}{107.16\ \text{g}\ m-\text{toluidine}}\right)$$

$$= 0.684\ \text{g N}$$

This is the amount of N in the mass of the fruit set. The mass of the fruit set is:

$$0.684\ \text{g N} \times \left(\frac{100\ \text{g fruit set}}{5.49\ \text{g N}}\right) = \mathbf{12.5\ g}\ \text{fruit set}$$

2-105.

Element	grams in sample	moles in sample	relative # of moles
C	48.044 g	$48.044\ \text{g C} \times \left(\frac{1\ \text{mol C}}{12.011\ \text{g C}}\right) = 4.000\ \text{mol C}$	1
H	12.09 g	$12.09\ \text{g H} \times \left(\frac{1\ \text{mol H}}{1.00794\ \text{g H}}\right) = 12.00\ \text{mol H}$	3

The empirical formula is $\mathbf{CH_3}$.

2-107. The reactant P_4 yields the P in the product P_4O_{10}, so by determining the mass of P_4 in 5.40 g of P_4O_{10} we can determine the mass of P in the sample.

$$5.40 \text{ g } P_4O_{10} \times \frac{4 \times (30.9738 \text{ g P})}{283.8892 \text{ g } P_4O_{10}} = 2.3567 \text{ g P}$$

$$2.3567 \text{ g P} / 2.50 \text{ g sample} = 0.943 \text{ P} = \mathbf{94.3\%} \text{ P}$$

2-109. (a) $Nb + 4\ NbCl_5 \rightarrow 5\ NbCl_4$

(b) Potential yield from Nb:

$$0.50 \text{ g Nb x} \left(\frac{1 \text{ mol Nb}}{92.606 \text{g Nb}}\right) \times \left(\frac{5 \text{ mol } NbCl_4}{1 \text{ mol Nb}}\right) = 0.027 \text{ mol } NbCl_4$$

Potential yield from $NbCl_5$:

$$5.0 \text{ g } NbCl_5 \times \left(\frac{1 \text{ mol } NbCl_5}{269.87 \text{ g } NbCl_5}\right) \times \left(\frac{5 \text{ mol } NbCl_4}{4 \text{ mol } NbCl_5}\right) = 0.023 \text{ mol } NbCl_4$$

The limiting reagent is $\mathbf{NbCl_5}$.

(c) This wouldn't matter, because Nb_2Cl_{10} has the same empirical formula as $NbCl_5$.

2-111. The chemical reaction for the combustion of octane is:

$$2\ C_8H_{18} + 25\ O_2 \rightarrow 16\ CO_2 + 18\ H_2O$$

We assume the car gets 30 miles per gallon, in which case 20 fewer miles saves 0.67 gallons of gasoline. This equals approxiumately 2.7 liters, or 2700 cm^3. The density of octane should be around that given in the Chapter 1 for benzene, another hydrocarbon, say 0.85 g cm^{-3}, so this volume of gasoline contains approximately 2700 × 0.85 = 2300 g of octane. Octane has a molar mass of 114 g mol^{-1}, so the gasoline contains roughly $^{2300}/_{114}$ = 20 moles of octane. This much octane would yield $(^{16}/_{2})\times 20$ = 160 moles of CO_2 per week, or 8300 moles CO_2 per year. The mass of 8300 moles of CO_2 in pounds is:

$$8300 \text{ mol } CO_2 \times \left(\frac{44 \text{ g } CO_2}{1 \text{ mol } CO_2}\right) \times \left(\frac{1 \text{ lb}}{453 \text{g}}\right) = 800 \text{ lb } CO_2.$$

Within the (considerable) assumptions of this calculation, the article is correct.

CHAPTER 3 -CHEMICAL PERIODICITY

AND THE FORMATION OF SIMPLE COMPOUNDS

3-1. We can predict a new formula based on a formula for a compound in the same group of the periodic table. Here, the matches are:

Element	Group	Related Compound	Predicted Formula
P	V	NH_3	PH_3
Cl	VII	HF	HCl
Si	IV	CH_4	SiH_4
S	VI	H_2O	H_2S

3-3. In this problem (compared to #3-1) there are no compounds to refer to for the listed elements. Instead, we just look at the group numbers. A binary compound will have a formula A_aX_x. One set of values of *a* and *x* that will be stable is given by the formula:

a = (8-Group # for X) $\quad$ x = (Group # for A)

(a) Potassium - Group I $\quad$ Polonium - Group VI

Formula: $K_{(8-6)}Po_1 = K_2Po_1 = \mathbf{K_2Po}$

(b) Strontium - Group II $\quad$ Chlorine - Group VII

Formula: $Sr_{(8-7)}Cl_2 = Sr_1Cl_2 = \mathbf{SrCl_2}$.

(c) Barium - Group II $\quad$ Sulfur - Group VI

Formula: $Ba_{(8-6)}S_2 = Ba_2S_2 = \mathbf{BaS}$.

3-5. The tabulated melting points are:

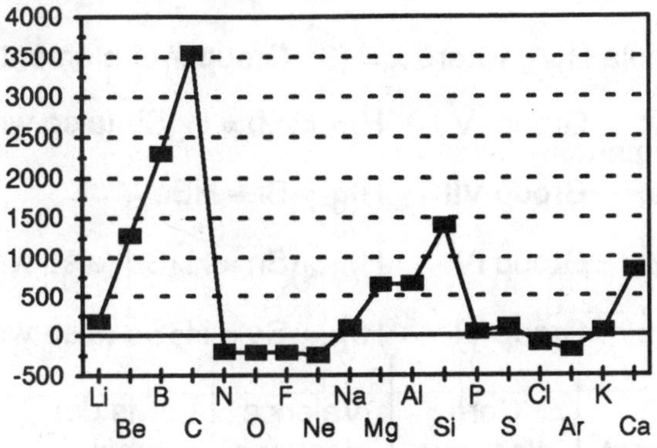

The periodic pattern has a consistent increase in the boiling point up to Group IV then a rapid drop to much lower values for Groups V, VI, VII, and VIII.

3-7. (a) The formation of a 1:2 chloride and 1:1 oxide indicates a **Group II** element.

(b) As in chapter 2, this empirical formula problem can be solved using a hypothetical 100.00 g sample. This sample contains 44.7 grams of Cl, which (at 35.4527 g mol^{-1} for Cl) is equal to 1.27 mol Cl. This means there must be 0.635 mol of the unknown element present, weighing 55.3 g. The molar mass of the element is then $\frac{55.3 \text{ g}}{0.635 \text{ mol}} = 87.2 \text{ g mol}^{-1}$. It is **strontium (Sr)**.

3-9. (a) Six elements that are gases at room temperature are nitrogen, oxygen, fluorine, chlorine, helium, neon, and n.

(b) Yes, these elements are clustered at the top right of the periodic table, where they form diatomic or monatomic gases of small molecular mass.

3-11. The simple averages of the quantities are:

Melting point: **1250 °C** Boiling point: **2386 °C** Density: **3.02 g cm^{-3}**

3-13. Hydrogen forms compounds of the elements on the right side of the periodic table of the formula H_xA, where x = (8 - Group # of element A). Therefore:

Antimony:	Group V	$H_{(8-5)}Sb \equiv H_3Sb$ (also written as SbH_3)
Bromine:	Group VII	$H_{(8-7)}Br \equiv HBr$
Tin:	Group IV	$H_{(8-4)}Sn \equiv H_4Sn$ (also written as SnH_4)
Selenium:	Group VI	$H_{(8-6)}Se \equiv H_2Se$ (also written as SeH_2).

3-15.

	Element	Core electrons	Valence electrons	Lewis dot symbol
(a)	P	10	5	·Ṗ̣:
(b)	I	46	7	:İ: (with two dots below)
(c)	Al	10	3	·Ȧl·
(d)	Sr	36	2	Ṡr·

3-17.

(a) Kr	Group VIII	8 valence electrons	:K̤̈r:
(b) Te^{2-}	Group VI + 2 e-	8 valence electrons	:T̤̈e: (-2)
(c) S^+	Group VI - 1 e-	5 valence electrons	·Ṡ̤: (+1)
(d) Mg^+	Group II - 1 e-	1 valence electron	Mg· (+1)

3-19.

		Total e^-	Core e^-	Valence e^-
(a)	Kr	36	28	8
(b)	Te^{2-}	54	46	8
(c)	S^+	15	10	5
(d)	Mg^+	11	10	1

3-21. (a) SrSe strontium selenide $\cdot Sr \cdot + :\dot{\underset{\cdot}{Se}}: \longrightarrow Sr^{(+2)}\ :\ddot{\underset{\cdot\cdot}{Se}}:^{(-2)}$

(b) RbI; rubidium iodide $Rb^{\cdot} + :\dot{\underset{\cdot\cdot}{I}}: \longrightarrow Rb^{(+1)} + :\ddot{\underset{\cdot\cdot}{I}}:^{(-1)}$

(c) Na_2S; sodium sulfide $2\ Na^{\cdot} + :\dot{\underset{\cdot}{S}}: \longrightarrow 2Na^{(+1)} + :\ddot{\underset{\cdot\cdot}{S}}:^{(-2)}$

(d) $GaCl_3$; Gallium chloride $\dot{\underset{\cdot}{Ga}}^{\cdot} + 3\ :\dot{\underset{\cdot\cdot}{Cl}}: \longrightarrow Ga^{(+3)} + 3\ :\ddot{\underset{\cdot\cdot}{Cl}}:^{(-1)}$

(e) Fr_2O; Francium oxide $2\ Fr^{\cdot} + :\dot{\underset{\cdot}{O}}: \longrightarrow 2Fr^{(+1)} + :\ddot{\underset{\cdot\cdot}{O}}:^{(-2)}$

3-23. (a) Aluminum oxide (b) Rubidium selenide

(c) Ammonium sulfide (d) Calcium nitrate

(e) Cesium sulfate (f) Potassium hydrogen carbonate

3-25. (a) AgCN (b) $Ca(OCl)_2$

(c) K_2CrO_4 (d) Ga_2O_3

(e) KO_2 (f) $Ba(HCO_3)_2$

3-27. **Na_3PO_4**. The systematic name is **sodium phosphate**; the name phosphate suffices to indicate that there must be three sodium ions in the formula.

3-29. Potassium dihydrogen phosphate.

3-31. (a) Iodine and fluorine each have seven valence electrons. Hence, the Lewis structure must show $3 \times 7 = 21$ valence electrons. **Only 20 are shown.**

(b) Carbon has four valence electrons, oxygen six, and nitrogen five. The Lewis structure must therefore have $4 + 6 + 5 = 15$ electrons. **Sixteen are shown.**

(c) Carbon has four valence electrons, oxygen six, and hydrogen one. The Lewis structure must therefore have $4 + 6 + (2 \times 1) = 12$ electrons. **Fourteen are shown.**

3-33. The formula for formal charges is:

FORMAL CHARGE = Group No. - 2 ×(No. of lone pairs) - (No. of bonds)

Formula	ATOM	Group No.	No. of lone pairs	No. of bonds	Formal charge
(a) SO_4^{2-}	S	6	0	4	+2
	O	6	3	1	-1
(b) $S_2O_3^{2-}$	central S	6	0	4	+2
	outer S	6	3	1	-1
	O	6	3	1	-1
(c) SbF_3	Sb	5	1	3	0
	F	7	3	1	0
(d) SCN^-	S	6	3	1	-1
	C	4	0	4	0
	N	5	1	3	0

3-35.

Formula	ATOM	Group No.	No. of lone pairs	No. of bonds	Formal charge
HNO	H	1	0	1	0
	N	5	1	3	0
	O	6	2	2	0
HON	H	1	0	1	0
	O	6	1	3	1+
	N	5	2	2	1-

The first formula has no formal charges on any of the atoms. It is therefore the favored structure.

3-37. This problem is solved by noting the formal charge, the number of bonds, and the number of lone pairs on the element Z in each case. We can then determine the Group Number for the element, and then we can name the group.

Group No. = formal charge + (2 × No. of lone pairs) + (No. of bonds)

The determination of the formal charge on Z requires that we determine the formal charge on each of the oxygens and (in (d)), hydrogen. Then we determine the formal charge on Z by subtracting the formal charges on the other atoms from the total charge per atom of Z:

Formal charge on Z = total charge per Z - formal charges on other atoms

(a) Formal charges on oxygens = 0

Total charge on molecule = 0

Formal charge on Z = 0 - (2 × 0) = 0

Group No. of Z: = 0 + (2 × 0) + 4 = 4

The element comes from **Group IV** of the periodic table.

(b) Formal charges on outer oxygens = -1

Formal charges on inner oxygen = 0

Total charge on molecule = 0

Formal charge on Z = 1/2 × [0 - (6 × -1) - (0)] = + 3

Group # of Z: = 3 + (2 × 0) + 4 = + 7

The element comes from **Group VII** of the periodic table (the halogens).

(c) Formal charges on singly bonded oxygens = -1

Formal charges on doubly bonded oxygen = 0

Total charge on molecule = -1

Formal charge on Z = -1 - (2 × -1) - (0) = + 1

Group # of Z: = 1 + (2 × 0) + 4 = + 5

The element comes from **Group V** of the periodic table.

3-37. (continued)

(d)

Formal charges on outer oxygens = -1
Formal charges on inner oxygen = 0
Formal charges on hydrogen = 0
Total charge on molecule = 0
Formal charge on Z = 0 - (3 × -1) - (0) = + 3
Group # of Z: = 3 + (2 × 0) + 4 = + 7

The element comes from **Group VII** of the periodic table (the halogens).

3-39. (a) 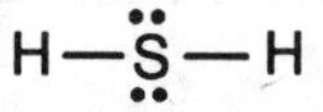 (b) 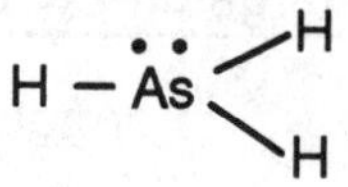

(c) 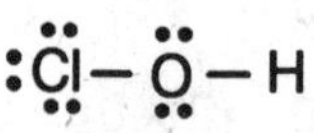

3-41. 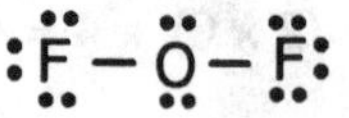

3-43. 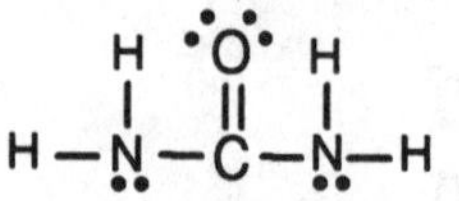

N-H: 1.01×10^{-10} m

C=O: 1.20×10^{-10} m

N-C: 1.47×10^{-10} m

3-45. (a) i 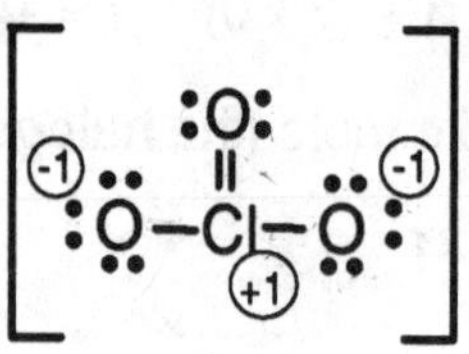

ii 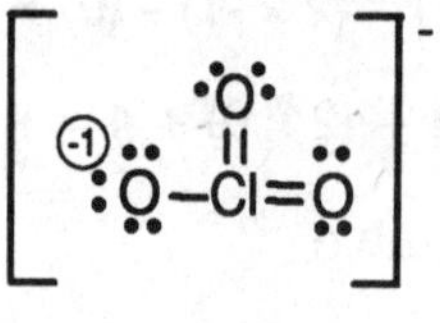

There are two possible Lewis structures for ClO_3^-, which differ in that one has an octet around each of the atoms (structure **i**) while the other has an octet for all the outer atoms and an expanded octet for the chlorine, but fewer formal charges (structure **ii**). As noted in the text for $POCl_3$, which Lewis structure is "correct" is ambiguous, and this is a limitation of the Lewis model.

3-45. (b) 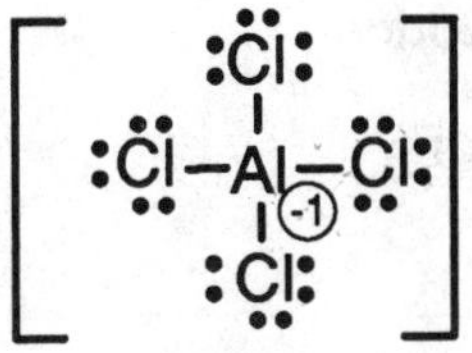 (c) 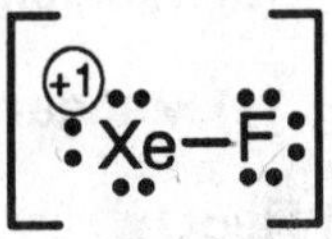

3-47. 

3-49. 

3-51 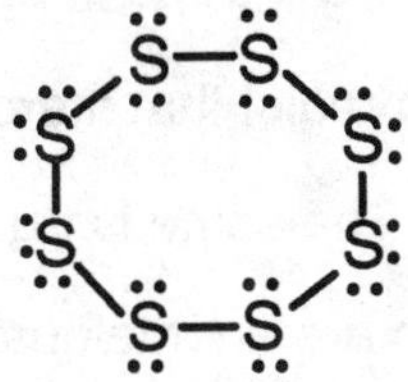

3-53 (a) 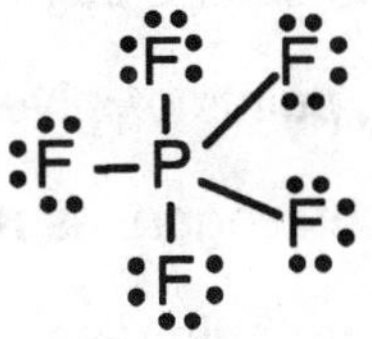 (b) 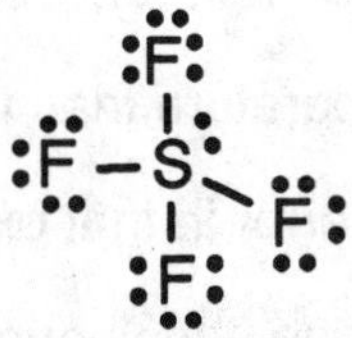 (c) 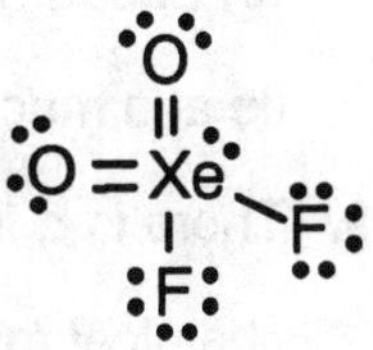

3-55. (a) N_2O_5 (b) HI (c) BN (d) PH_3

3-57. (a) Hydrogen telluride (b) Phosphorus trichloride

(c) Ammonia (d) Tetrasulfur tetranitride

3-59. Tetraphosphorus decaoxide = P_4O_{10}

Phosphorus pentachloride = PCl_5

$$P_4O_{10} + 6\ PCl_5 \rightarrow 10\ POCl_3$$

3-61. (a) Iron(III) oxide (b) Titanium(IV) bromide (c) Tungsten(VI) oxide
(d) Lead(IV) chloride (e) Manganese(III) fluoride

3-63. (a) SnF_2 (b) Re_2O_7 (c) CoF_3
(d) WCl_5 (e) $Cu(NO_3)_2$

3-65. Rhenium (VII) sulfide = Re_2S_7 Rhenium (VI) sulfide = ReS_3

$$Re_2S_7 + H_2 \rightarrow H_2S + 2\ ReS_3$$

3-67. (a) The average of the boiling points of copper and gallium is 2485 ^{o}C, which is a poor estimate for the boiling point of zinc (907 ^{o}C).

(b) The information in this part of the problem about the melting points, not the boiling points, of the elements. But if we assume that the trend in boiling points matches the trend in melting points, then we predict that mercury would have a much lower boiling point than its neighbors. The same is true of zinc. We conclude that the boiling points of the zinc group are anomalously low.

(c) Based on the conclusion in (b), we expect the boiling point of cadmium to lie at a much lower temperature than the boiling points of silver and indium.

3-69. There is a fundamental error in that oxygen, a chalcogen, is *not* in the same chemical family as chlorine and fluorine, which are halogens. Hydrogen fluoride is strongly corrosive, but the compound of oxygen most similar to HF is H_2O (plain water)! Although oxygen *is* a corrosive gas, especially with metals and at elevated temperatures and pressures, the reasons the character advances are invalid.

3-71. (a) Na_3CO_3 is not expected to be stable. The stable compound related to this formula is Na_2CO_3, sodium carbonate.

(b) MgCl is not expected to be stable. The stable compound related to this formula is $MgCl_2$, magnesium chloride.

(c) $(NH_4)_2SO_4$ is expected to be stable. Its name is ammonium sulfate.

3-71. (continued)

(d) BaCN is not expected to be stable. The stable compound related to this formula is $Ba(CN)_2$, barium cyanide.

(e) $Sr(OH)_2$ is expected to be stable. Its name is strontium hydroxide.

3-73. (a) Ammonium phosphate, $(NH_4)_3PO_4$.

Potassium nitrate, KNO_3.

Ammonium sulfate, $(NH_4)_2SO_4$.

(b)

COMPOUND	$(NH_4)_3PO_4$	KNO_3	$(NH_4)_2SO_4$
Molar mass (g mol^{-1})	149.087	101.103	132.262
Mass of N in one mole of compound	42.202 g	14.0067 g	28.0135 g
Mass % N	28.307%	13.854%	21.18%
Mass of P in one mole of compound	30.974 g	0.00 g	0.00 g
Mass % P	20.776%	0.00%	0.00%
Mass of K in one mole of compound	0.00 g	39.0983 g	0.00 g
Mass % K	0.00%	38.672%	0.00%

3-75. Both water and ammonia have one or more lone pairs. The hydrogen ion encountering one of them will "attach itself" to the lone pair, and the oxygen (in water) or nitrogen (in ammonia) will gain a formal charge, as indicated.

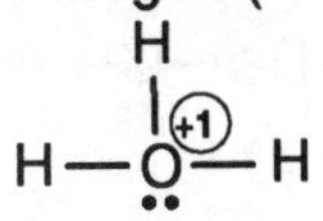

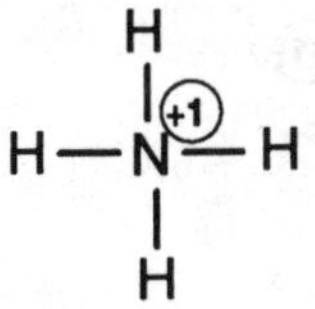

3-77. (a)

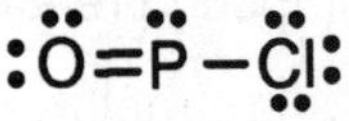

(b) No formal charges Octet rule satisfied

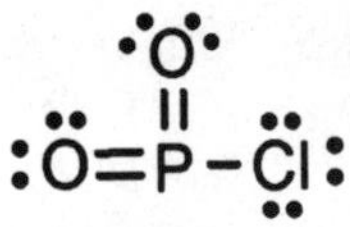

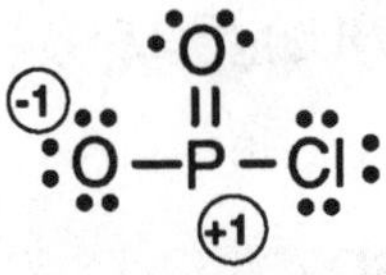

3-79 (a) Central S Central N

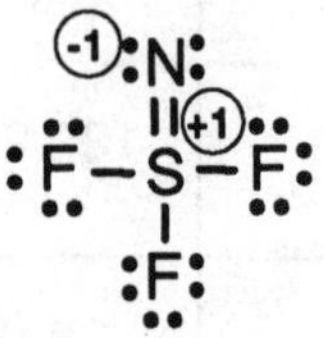

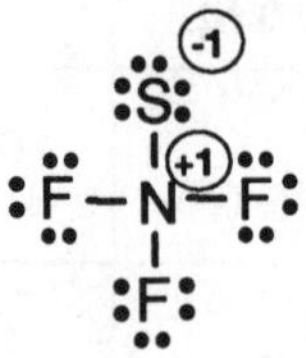

(b) Both structures have a separation of formal charge, but in the case with nitrogen in the center the negative charge is on an element (sulfur) to the right in the periodic table, where elements are known to prefer negative charges. It should be more likely.

3-81.

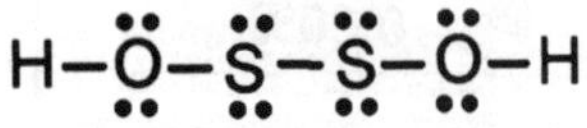

There are no resonance structures available in this case.

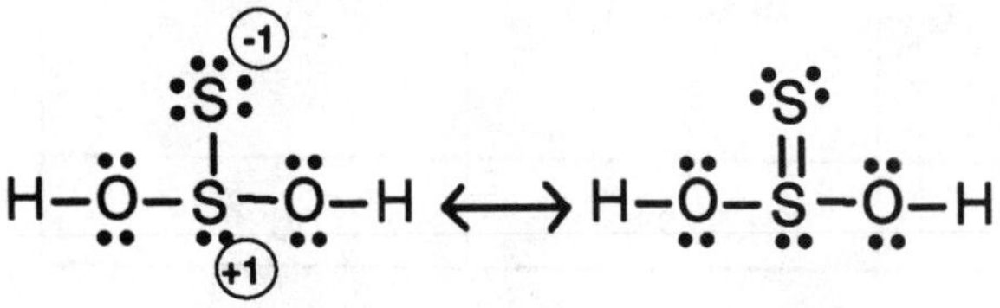

This isomer has the disadvantage of one resonance form possessing formal charge separation and the other an expanded octet.

But it has the advantage of multiple resonance forms.

3-83. (a)

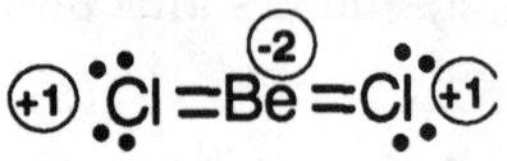

(b)

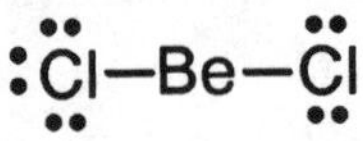

3-85. 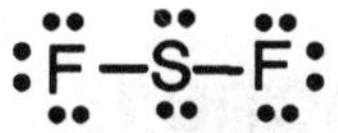 There are no formal charges in this structure.

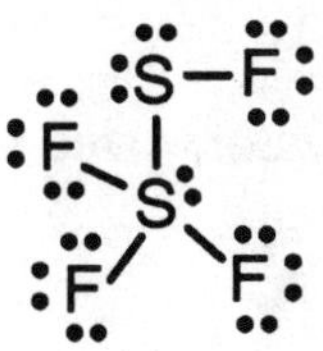

There are no formal charges in this structure. Note that the central S atom has an expanded octet. No Lewis structure can be drawn in this skeleton withough violating the octet rule.

3-87. Recall that elemental sulfur has a formula of S_8.

(a) $10\ In + S_8 \rightarrow 2\ In_5S_4$

(b) Pentaindium tetrasulfide.

3-89. $Na_2[CuCl_4]$: transition metal is copper; ligands are 4 chlorides, Cl^-.

$[Co(H_2O)_6]Br_2$: transition metal is cobalt; ligands are six waters, H_2O.

$K_2[Pt(CN)_4]$: transition metal is platinum; ligands are four cyanides, CN^-.

$Cr(CO)_6$: transition metal is chromium; ligands are six carbon monoxides, CO.

CHAPTER 4 - TYPES OF CHEMICAL REACTIONS

4-1. Strong electrolyte: A substance that, upon dissolution in water, gives a solution that conducts electricity well.

Weak electrolyte: A substance that, upon dissolution in water, gives a solution that conducts electricity poorly.

Nonelectrolyte: A substance that, upon dissolution in water, gives a solution that does not conduct electricity.

4-3. $Mg(ClO_4)_2\ (s) \rightarrow Mg^{2+}\ (aq) + 2\ ClO_4^-\ (aq)$

4-5. The first two parts of the problem are worked in steps through (i) separation of all *aqueous* salts into ions and then (ii) elimination of common ions from the two sides of the equation. Common ions found in the intermediate equation (i) are marked in bold to make them clearer. The last two parts of the problem have just the answer.

(a) START: $NaCl\ (aq) + AgNO_3\ (aq) \rightarrow AgCl\ (s) + NaNO_3\ (aq)$

(i) $\mathbf{Na^+}\ (aq) + Cl^-\ (aq) + Ag^+\ (aq) + \mathbf{NO_3^-}\ (aq)$

$\rightarrow AgCl\ (s) + \mathbf{Na^+}\ (aq) + \mathbf{NO_3^-}\ (aq)$

(ii) $Cl^-\ (aq) + Ag^+\ (aq) \rightarrow AgCl\ (s)$

(b) START: $K_2CO_3\ (s) + 2\ HCl\ (aq) \rightarrow 2\ KCl\ (aq) + CO_2\ (g) + H_2O\ (l)$

(i) $K_2CO_3\ (s) + 2\ H^+\ (aq) + \mathbf{2\ Cl^-}\ (aq)$

$\rightarrow 2\ K^+\ (aq) + \mathbf{2\ Cl^-}\ (aq) + CO_2\ (g) + H_2O\ (l)$

(ii) $K_2CO_3\ (s) + 2\ H^+\ (aq) \rightarrow 2\ K^+\ (aq) + CO_2\ (g) + H_2O\ (l)$

(c) $2\ Cs\ (s) + 2\ H_2O\ (l) \rightarrow 2\ Cs^+\ (aq) + 2\ OH^-\ (aq) + H_2\ (g)$

(d) $10\ Cl^-\ (aq) + 2\ MnO_4^-\ (aq) + 16\ H^+\ (aq)$

$\rightarrow 5\ Cl_2\ (g) + 2\ Mn^{2+}\ (aq) + 8\ H_2O\ (l)$

4-7. Balanced reaction: $NaBr\ (aq) + AgNO_3\ (aq) \rightarrow AgBr\ (s) + NaNO_3\ (aq)$

Net ionic reaction: $Br^-\ (aq) + Ag^+\ (aq) \rightarrow AgBr\ (s)$

4-9. (a) Balanced reaction: $Zn(NO_3)_2\ (aq) + K_2S\ (aq) \rightarrow ZnS\ (s) + 2\ KNO_3\ (aq)$

Net ionic reaction: $Zn^{2+}\ (aq) + S^{2-}\ (aq) \rightarrow ZnS\ (s)$

(b) Balanced reaction:

$$2\ AgClO_3\ (aq) + CaCl_2\ (aq) \rightarrow 2\ AgCl\ (s) + Ca(ClO_3)_2\ (aq)$$

Net ionic reaction: $2\ Ag\ (aq) + 2\ Cl^-\ (aq) \rightarrow 2\ AgCl\ (s)$

(c) Balanced reaction:

$$3\ NaOH\ (aq) + Fe(NO_3)_3\ (aq) \rightarrow Fe(OH)_3\ (s) + 3\ NaNO_3\ (s)$$ (aq)

Net ionic reaction: $3\ OH^-\ (aq) + Fe^{3+}\ (aq) \rightarrow Fe(OH)_3\ (s)$

(d) Balanced reaction:

$$3\ Ba(CH_3COO)_2(aq) + 2\ Na_3PO_4(aq) \rightarrow Ba_3(PO_4)_2\ (s) + 6\ NaCH_3COO\ (aq)$$

Net ionic reaction: $3\ Ba^{2+}\ (aq) + 2\ PO_4^{3-}\ (aq) \rightarrow Ba_3(PO_4)_2\ (s)$

4-11. (a) $Be^{2+}\ (aq) + 2\ CH_3COO^-\ (aq) \rightarrow Be(CH_3COO)_2\ (s)$

(b) $Ba^{2+}\ (aq) + SO_4^{2-}\ (aq) \rightarrow BaSO_4\ (s)$

(c) $Ca^{2+}\ (aq) + 2\ OH^-\ (aq) \rightarrow Ca(OH)_2\ (s)$

(d) N. R.

4-13. Two precipitation reactions could occur given the starting solutions:

$$Na^+\ (aq) + Cl^-\ (aq) \rightarrow NaCl\ (s)$$

$$K^+\ (aq) + NO_3^-\ (aq) \rightarrow KNO_3\ (s)$$

Both of the possible solid products are soluble compounds. Though solutions of different salts were mixed, there were no insoluble substances generated.

4-15. She needs an anion that forms a soluble salt with magnesium and an insoluble salt with barium. A good candidate is sulfate, SO_4^{2-}. It must be delivered as a salt with a cation that will not precipitate nitrate. There are many soluble sulfates; sodium sulfate is a good choice.

4-17. For clarity we write the balanced equation and the net ionic equation for each (note that the acids are left in their undissociated form in the net ionic reaction).

(a) $2\ HNO_3\ (aq) + K_2CO_3\ (s) \rightarrow 2\ KNO_3\ (aq) + CO_2\ (g) + H_2O\ (l)$

$2\ HNO_3\ (aq) + K_2CO_3\ (s) \rightarrow 2\ K^+\ (aq) + 2\ NO_3^-\ (aq) + CO_2\ (g) + H_2O\ (l)$

(b) $HBr\ (aq) + Zn\ (s) \rightarrow H_2\ (s) + ZnBr_2\ (aq)$

$HBr\ (aq) + Zn\ (s) \rightarrow H_2\ (s) + Zn^{2+}\ (aq) + 2\ Br^-\ (aq)$

(c) $H_2SO_4\ (aq) + ZnO\ (s) \rightarrow H_2O\ (l) + ZnSO_4\ (aq)$

$H_2SO_4\ (aq) + ZnO\ (s) \rightarrow H_2O\ (l) + Zn^{2+}\ (aq) + SO_4^{2-}\ (aq)$

4-19. (a) Hydrosulfuric acid (b) Periodic acid

(c) Carbonic acid (d) Hydrobromic acid

4-21. (a) PF_3 - phosphorus trifluoride H_3PO_3 - phosphorous acid

HF - hydrofluoric acid

(b) $PF_3\ (aq) + 3\ H_2O\ (l) \rightarrow H_3PO_3\ (aq) + 3\ HF\ (aq)$

4-23. (a) $HClO_3\ (aq) + KOH\ (aq) \rightarrow H_2O\ (l) + K^+\ (aq) + ClO_3^-\ (aq)$

(b) $N_2O_5\ (g) + 2\ NaOH\ (aq) \rightarrow 2\ NO_3^-\ (aq) + 2\ Na^+\ (aq) + H_2O\ (l)$

(c) $(NH_4)_2SO_4\ (aq) + Ba(OH)_2\ (aq) \rightarrow 2\ NH_3\ (g) + 2\ H_2O\ (l) + BaSO_4\ (s)$

Note that this is both a precipitation and an acid-base reaction.

4-25. (a) $2\ HBr\ (aq) + Ca(OH)_2\ (s) \rightarrow 2\ H_2O\ (l) + Ca^{2+}\ (aq) + 2\ Br^-\ (aq)$

(b) $NH_3\ (aq) + H_2SO_4\ (aq) \rightarrow NH_4^+\ (aq) + HSO_4^-\ (aq)$

A further reaction can take place between ammonia and the hydrogen sulfate, *if the ammonia is present in excess*:

$NH_3\ (aq) + HSO_4^-\ (aq) \rightarrow NH_4^+\ (aq) + SO_4^{2-}\ (aq)$

(c) $LiOH\ (aq) + HNO_3\ (aq) \rightarrow Li^+\ (aq) + NO_3^-\ (aq) + H_2O\ (l)$

4-27. The base is the hydrogen carbonate ion, HCO_3^-, which can accept a hydrogen ion to give carbonic acid, H_2CO_3.

4-29. (a) $Ca(OH)_2\ (aq) + 2\ HF\ (aq) \rightarrow CaF_2\ (s) + 2\ H_2O\ (l)$

Acid: hydrofluoric acid — Salt: calcium fluoride

Base: calcium hydroxide

(b) $2\ RbOH\ (aq) + H_2SO_4\ (aq) \rightarrow Rb_2SO_4\ (s) + 2\ H_2O\ (l)$

Acid: sulfuric acid — Salt: rubidium sulfate

Base: rubidium hydroxide

(c) $Zn(OH)_2\ (s) + 2\ HNO_3\ (aq) \rightarrow Zn(NO_3)_2\ (aq) + 2\ H_2O\ (l)$

Acid: nitric acid — Salt: zinc nitrate

Base: zinc hydroxide

(d) $KOH\ (aq) + CH_3COOH\ (aq) \rightarrow KCH_3COO\ (aq) + H_2O\ (l)$

Acid: acetic acid — Base: potassium hydroxide

Salt: potassium acetate

4-31. The salt is sodium sulfide, Na_2S. The other product is water.

4-33. (a) Cl^- cannot act as a Brønsted-Lowry acid

(b) HSO_4^- can act as a Brønsted-Lowry acid. Its conjugate base is SO_4^{2-}.

(c) NH_4^+ can act as a Brønsted-Lowry acid. Its conjugate base is NH_3.

(d) NH_3 can act as a Brønsted-Lowry acid. Its conjugate base is NH_2^-.

(d) H_2O can act as a Brønsted-Lowry acid. Its conjugate base is OH^-.

4-35. (a), (c), and (d) are conjugate acid-base pairs.

(b) The substances in this part each have a possible conjugate acid and conjugate base. H_2O is the conjugate *acid* to the *base* OH^-, H_2O_2 is the conjugate *acid* to the *base* HO_2^-, and H_2O is the conjugate *base* to the *acid* H_3O^+.

4-37. (a) $NH_4Br\ (aq) + H_2O\ (l) \rightarrow H_3O^+\ (aq) + NH_3\ (aq) + Br^-\ (aq)$

(b) $H_2S\ (aq) + H_2O\ (l) \rightarrow H_3O^+\ (aq) + HS^-\ (aq)$

(c) $(NH_4)_2SO_4\ (aq) + H_2O\ (l) \rightarrow 2\ H_3O^+\ (aq) + 2\ NH_3\ (aq) + SO_4^{2-}\ (aq)$

4-39.

	Lewis Acid	Lewis Base
(a)	Ag^+ *(aq)*	NH_3 *(aq)*
(b)	BF_3 *(g)*	$N(CH_3)_3$ *(g)*
(c)	$B(OH)_3$ *(aq)*	OH^- *(aq)*

4-41. (a) $CaO\ (s) + H_2O\ (l) \rightarrow Ca(OH)_2\ (s)$

(b) Yes; the calcium oxide acts as a Lewis base, donating electrons to a hydrogen ion on a water molecule, which acts as a Lewis acid.

4-43. (a) The fluoride ion has a closed shell, octet configuration. It can only act as an electron pair donor, so by extension any compound that donates fluoride is acting as an electron pair donor. Therefore, the **base** is the fluoride **donor** and the **acid** is the fluoride **donor.**

(b) Acid: BF_3 Base: ClF_3O_2

Acid: TiF_4 Base: KF.

Note that the acids already have some fluorides attached; but they still act as an acid in *accepting* an additional fluoride.

4-45. Some elements have their oxidation number fixed by the rules and some have their oxidation number determined by the other elements. The oxidation numbers must add to the total charge on the formula (rule 1). Here all compounds are neutral, to the oxidation numbers must add to zero.

(a) CH_2O. By rule 4: **Ox. No. H = +1**· By rule 5: **Ox. No. O = -2** .

[Ox No. O] + 2 × [Ox. No. H] + [Ox. No. C] = 0

[Ox. No. C] = -([Ox No. O] + 2 × [Ox. No. H])

[Ox. No. C] = - (-2 + 2 × 1) = **0**

Note that there is nothing wrong with the carbon (or any other element, for that matter) in a compound having an oxidation number of zero.

4-45. (continued)

(b) H_2CO_3. By rule 4: **Ox. No. H = +1**· By rule 5: **Ox. No. O = -2** .

3 × [Ox No. O] + 2 × [Ox. No. H] + [Ox. No. C] = 0

[Ox. No. C] = -(3 × [Ox No. O] + 2 × [Ox. No. H])

[Ox. No. C] = - (-3 × 2 + 2 × 1) = **+4**

(c) RbH. By rule 2: **Ox. No. Rb = +1**. By rule 4 **Ox. No. H = -1** (Rb is a metal).

(d) N_2O_5. By rule 5: **Ox. No. O = -2** .

2 × [Ox No. N] + 5 × [Ox. No. O] = 0

[Ox No. N] = -1/2 × (5 × [Ox. No. O])

[Ox No. N] = -1/2 × (5 × -2) = **+5.**

4-47. $\overset{+3}{As_2O_3}\ (aq) + 2\ \overset{0}{I_2}\ (aq) + 2\ H_2O\ (l) \rightarrow \overset{+5}{As_2O_5}\ (aq) + 4\ \overset{-1}{HI}(aq)$

Oxidized: 2 As from +3 to +5 .... 4 electrons transferred

Reduced: 4 I from 0 to -1 .... 4 electrons transferred.

4-49. (a) $2\ \overset{+3}{PF_2I}\ (l) + 2\ \overset{0}{Hg}\ (l) \rightarrow \overset{+2}{P_2F_4}\ (g) + \overset{+1}{Hg_2I_2}\ (s)$

(b) $2\ \overset{+5/-2}{KClO_3}\ (aq) \rightarrow 2\ \overset{-1}{KCl}\ (s) + 3\ \overset{0}{O_2}(g)$

(c) $4\ \overset{-3}{NH_3}\ (g) + 5\ \overset{0}{O_2}\ (g) \rightarrow 4\ \overset{+2/-2}{NO}\ (g) + 6\ \overset{-2}{H_2O}\ (g)$

(d) $2\ \overset{0}{As}\ (s) + 6\ \overset{+1}{NaOH}\ (l) \rightarrow 2\ \overset{+3}{Na_3AsO_3}\ (s) + 3\ \overset{0}{H_2}(g)$

4-51. (a) Oxidized: 2 Hg from 0 to +1 .... **2** electrons transferred

Reduced: 2 P in 2 PF_2I's from +3 to +2 .... **2** electrons transferred

(b) Oxidized: 6 O in 2 $KClO_3$'s from -2 to 0 .... **12** electrons transferred

Reduced: 2 Cl in 2 $KClO_3$'s from +5 to -1 ...... **12** electrons transferred

(c) Oxidized: 4 N in 4 NH_3's from -3 to +2 .... **20** electrons transferred

Reduced: 10 O in 5 O_2's from 0 to -2 .... **20** electrons transferred

(d) Oxidized: 2 As from 0 to +3 .... **6** electrons transferred

Reduced: 6 H in 6 NaOH's from +1 to 0 .... **6** electrons transferred

4-53. The H and O atoms in this reaction are all in compounds where the rules predetermine their oxidation numbers to be +1 (H) and -2 (O). For the others:

REACTANTS: **Au** has an oxidation number of **0.**

Se in H_2SeO_4 has an oxidation number of **+6.**

PRODUCTS: It is important to recognize the presence of selenate ion, SeO_4^{2-}, in the compound $Au_2(SeO_4)_3$. Then we have:

Se in SeO_4^{2-} has an oxidation number of **+6.**

Se in H_2SeO_3 has an oxidation number of **+4.**

Au in $Au_2(SeO_4)_3$ has an oxidation number equal and opposite to $^1/_2$ of the charge on 3 SeO_3^{2-} ions, or an oxidation number of **+3 on each Au.**

The species oxidized is the Au; *some* of the H_2SeO_4 is reduced.

4-55. The reaction: $2\ Al_2O_3\ (s) + 3\ C\ (s) \rightarrow 2\ Al\ (s) + 3\ CO_2\ (g)$

The species oxidized is C; the species reduced is Al_2O_3.

4-57.

$$Ba\ (s) + H_2\ (g) \rightarrow BaH_2\ (s)$$

$$BaH_2\ (s) + 2\ H_2O\ (l) \rightarrow Ba^{2+}\ (aq) + 2\ OH^-\ (aq) + 2\ H_2\ (g)$$

$$BaH_2\ (s) + 2\ HCl\ (aq) \rightarrow Ba^{2+}\ (aq) + 2\ Cl^-\ (aq) + 2\ H_2\ (g)$$

In the last case, the reaction of water with barium hydride causes the formation of hydroxide ion, which precipitates with the zinc, and aqueous barium ion, which precipitates with the sulfate:

$$BaH_2\ (s) + 2\ H_2O\ (l) + Zn^{2+}\ (aq) + SO_4^{2-}\ (aq)$$
$$\rightarrow BaSO_4\ (s) + Zn(OH)_2\ (s) + 2\ H_2\ (g)$$

4-59. (a) $H_2Te\ (aq) + H_2O\ (l) \rightarrow HTe^-\ (aq) + H_3O^+\ (aq)$ acid-base

(b) $SrO\ (s) + CO_2\ (g) \rightarrow SrCO_3\ (s)$ Lewis acid-base

4-59. (continued)

Both (c) and (d) are acid-base reactions

(c) 2 HI *(aq)* + $CaCO_3$ *(s)* → H_2O *(l)* + Ca^{2+} *(aq)* + 2 I^- *(aq)* + CO_2 *(g)*

(d) Na_2O *(s)* + 2 NH_4Br *(s)* → 2 NH_3 *(g)* + H_2O *(l)* + 2 Na^+ *(aq)* + 2 Br^- *(aq)*

4-61 Note that in all cases once we have figured out the formula of the product, the name of the product reminds us whether the anhydride is basic ("hydroxide" in the product) or is acidic ("acid" in the product).

(a) MgO – base anhydride – $Mg(OH)_2$ – magnesium hydroxide $MgO + H_2O$

(b) Cl_2O – acid anhydride – $HOCl$ - hypochlorous acid $Cl_2O + H_2O$

(c) SO_3 – acid anhydride – H_2SO_4 – sulfuric acid

(d) Cs_2O – base anhydride – $CsOH$ – cesium hydroxide

4-63. (a) I_2O_5 – diiodine pentaoxide – acid anhydride

(b) BaO – barium oxide – base anhydride

(c) CrO_3 – chromium (VI) oxide – acid anhydride

(d) N_2O – dinitrogen oxide – acid anhydride

4-65.

SnO *(s)* + 2 HCl *(aq)* → Sn^{2+} *(aq)* + 2 Cl^- *(aq)* + H_2O *(l)*

SnO *(s)* + OH^- *(aq)* + H_2O *(l)* → $Sn(OH)_3^-$ *(aq)*

4-67. This problem consists of the generation of two different cations and two different anions; we must identify which combination might cause a precipitate.

CATIONS	ANIONS	POSSIBLE SOLIDS
ammonium,	carbonate	$(NH_4)_2CO_3$
NH_4^+	CO_3^{2-}	$(NH_4)_2SO_4$
calcium,	sulfate,	$CaCO_3$
Ca^{2+}	SO_4^{2-}	$CaSO_4$

4-67. (continued)

Tabulation in this manner helps one to systematically consider all possible combinations. For this set, the least soluble substance is calcium carbonate, $CaCO_3$. The appropriate ionic reaction is:

$$CO_3^{2-}\ (aq) + CaSO_4\ (s) \rightarrow CaCO_3\ (s) + SO_4^{2-}\ (aq)$$

The material left in solution will be ammonium sulfate, $(NH_4)_2SO_4$.

4-69. The observation that the product solution is a nonelectrolyte strongly suggests that the complex does not form charged ions in solution. This is the case with the complex $Co(NH_3)_3Cl_3$. The other substances dissociate into ions when they dissolve, and the ions would make the solution an electrolyte.

4-71. This fulfills the definition of a substance given in Chapter 1. There, the fundamental definition of a chemical substance was that it could not be "separated into portions that have different properties." In the case of water, its ionization is a basic property; dividing a sample of water into portions will always give a material with the same properties.

4-73. The heat comes from the reaction: $H_3O^+\ (aq) + OH^-\ (aq) \rightarrow 2\ H_2O\ (l)$

The white precipitate comes from the reaction:

$$K^+\ (aq) + ClO_4^-\ (aq) \rightarrow KClO_4\ (s)$$

$KClO_4$ is one of the very few substances containing potassium *or* perchlorate that is not very soluble.

4-75. (a) NF_4^+ acts as a base in this case; it is the source of fluoride, which accepts two hydrogen ions from water (see problem 43).

(b) The analogous reaction of NH_4^+ is: $NH_4^+ + H_2O \rightarrow NH_3 + H_3^+ + {}^1/_2\ O_2$.

The product H_2F^+ in the first reaction is a stable ion, largely because of the properties of fluoride that make it stable with two hydrogen ions attached. The H_3^+ ion is in fact known in the gas phase, but it will be unstable in the

4-75. (continued)

presence of O_2. Although the quoted reaction is a *redox* reaction, NF_4^+ is, in the sense that it increases the concentration of H_3O^+in water, an *acid*: NF_4^+ (aq) + H_2O (l) → NF_3 (aq) + H_2OF^+ (aq)

$$H_2OF^+ (aq) \rightarrow H_2F^+ (aq) + \tfrac{1}{2}\ O_2 (g)$$

$$2\ H_2O\ (l) + H_2F^+ (aq) \rightarrow 2\ H_3O^+ (aq) + F^- (aq)$$

4-77. (a) $2\ NaH + B_2H_6 \rightarrow 2\ NaBH_4$

(b) This is a Lewis acid-base reaction. The B_2H_6 acts as an acceptor of electron pairs on the hydride ion, itself a strong Lewis base. Therefore, B_2H_6 acts as a Lewis acid.

4-79. This is an unusual reaction because (i) the manganese ends up in two different oxidation numbers, both of which differ from the starting oxidation number and (ii) only some of the oxygen atoms change their oxidation number.

$$\overset{+1/+7/-2}{2\ KMnO_4\ (s)} \rightarrow \overset{+1/+6/-2}{K_2MnO_4\ (s)} + \overset{+4/-2}{MnO_2\ (s)} + \overset{0}{O_2\ (g)}$$

The analysis of the reaction is, nevertheless, straightforward:

Oxidized: 2 O from -2 to 0 4 electrons transferred

Reduced: 1 Mn from +7 to +6 1 electron transferred

1 Mn from +7 to +4 3 electrons transferred

There are four electrons lost from O's and four gained by Mn's. The reaction is balanced with respect to the change in oxidation number.

4-81. Reactants: H: +1 O: -2 Xe: +6

Products: H: +1 O: -2 *and* 0 Xe: +8 *and* 0.

Some Xe in the hydrogen xenate ions is being reduced to Xe(0) and some is being oxidized to Xe(8+). Also, oxygens (on the hydrogen xenate, the hydroxide ion, or on both) are being oxidized from -2 to 0.

4-83. We are told that the hydrate of P_4O_{10} that is formed is HPO_3 What remains to know is that the anhydride available from HNO_3 is N_2O_5.

$$4\ HNO_3 + P_4O_{10} \rightarrow 4\ HPO_3 + 2\ N_2O_5$$

4-85. (a) The barium ion has a +2 oxidation number in all its compounds, and therefore the perxenate anion is XeO_6^{4-}. This will combine with americium, Am^{3+} in a neutral compound with the formula: $\mathbf{Am_4(XeO_6)_3}$.

(b) Perxenic acid would be the compound formed by adding enough hydrogen ions to perxenate to neutralize its charge. The formula would be $\mathbf{H_4XeO_6}$.

(c) Because perxenic acid has an even number of hydrogen ions, it is straightforward to determine that its anhydride would be: XeO_4.

4-87. Recall problems No. 42 and No. 44 in this connection; the oxide in CaO acts as a strong Lewis base with many Lewis acids according to the general reaction:

$$O^{2-} + AO_x \rightarrow AO_{x+1}^{2-}$$

whereupon the new anion combines with the Ca^{2+} ion to form a new salt.

In this case: $CaO\ (s) + SO_3\ (g) \rightarrow CaSO_4\ (s)$

$CaO\ (s) + SO_2\ (g) \rightarrow CaSO_3\ (s)$

4-89. (a) $4\ KClO_3\ (s) \rightarrow KCl\ (s) + 3\ KClO_4\ (s)$ *redox reaction*

(b) $H_2S\ (aq) + H_2O\ (l) \rightarrow H_3O^+\ (aq) + HS^-\ (aq)$ *acid-base reaction*

(c) $H_2O_2\ (g) + 2\ HI\ (g) \rightarrow I_2\ (g) + 2\ H_2O\ (g)$ *redox reaction*

(d) $P_4O_{10}\ (s) + 10\ C\ (s) \rightarrow P_4\ (g) + 10\ CO\ (g)$ *redox reaction.*

CHAPTER 5 - THE GASEOUS STATE

5-1. $NH_4HS\ (s) + HCl\ (g) \rightarrow NH_4Cl\ (s) + \mathbf{H_2S\ (g)}$

5-3. $NH_4HS\ (s) \rightarrow NH_3\ (g) + H_2S\ (g)$

5-5. $NH_4Br\ (s) + NaOH\ (aq) \rightarrow NH_3\ (g) + H_2O\ (l) + NaBr\ (aq)$

5-7. $2\ BaO_2\ (s) \rightarrow 2\ BaO\ (s) + O_2\ (g)$. The gas is **oxygen.**

5-9. The situation described has the pressure of the gas equal to the pressure exerted by the water column. $P_{gas} = P_{water} = g\, d_{water}\, h_{water}$

The formula for the pressure exerted by the column of water -- $g\, d_{water}\, h_{water}$-- requires densities in kg m^{-3} and heights in meters to yield pressure in standard units of pascals. Conversions from the units of g cm^{-3} and cm should be done separately:

$$d_{water} = \left(1.00\frac{\text{g}}{\text{cm}^3}\right)\times\left(\frac{10^6\ \text{cm}^3}{\text{m}^3}\right)\times\left(\frac{1\ \text{kg}}{1000\ \text{g}}\right) = 1000\ \frac{\text{kg}}{\text{m}^3}$$

$$h_{water} = (44.5\ \text{cm})\ \text{x}\left(\frac{1\ \text{m}}{100\ \text{cm}}\right) = 0.445\ \text{m}$$

So:

$$P_{gas} = \left(9.80665\frac{\text{m}}{\text{s}^2}\right)\times\left(1000\frac{\text{kg}}{\text{m}^3}\right)\times(0.445\ \text{m})$$

$$= 4364\ \frac{\text{kg}}{\text{m}-\text{s}^2} = 4364\ \text{pascals}$$

$$= (4364\ \text{pascals})\ \text{x}\left(\frac{1\ \text{atm}}{101{,}325\ \text{pascals}}\right) = \mathbf{0.0431\ atm}$$

5-11. Pressure is important to this problem only because the equal pressures exerted by the oil and the mercury mean the mass of the oil and the mass of the mercury must be the same. We combine this insight with the definition of density to obtain the height of the oil. The comment "identical tube" tells us that the cross-sectional areas of the tubes are the same.

5-11. (continued):

$$\text{mass oil} = \text{mass of mercury}$$

$$d_{OIL}\,V_{OIL} = d_{Hg}\,V_{Hg}$$

$$d_{OIL}\,h_{OIL}\,area_{\,OIL} = d_{Hg}\,h_{Hg}\,area_{Hg}$$

$$d_{OIL}\,h_{OIL} = d_{Hg}\,h_{Hg}$$

$$h_{OIL} = \frac{d_{Hg}h_{Hg}}{d_{OIL}} = \frac{(13.6\text{ g cm}^{-3})\times(305\text{ mm})}{(1.60\text{g cm}^{-3})}$$

$$= \mathbf{259\ cm = 2.59\ m}$$

5-13. We know the hundreds of kilometers of the earth's atmosphere exert a pressure of about 1.00 atm at sea level. The standard atmosphere (Table 5-2) is equivalent to the pressure exerted by 760 mm Hg. So the mercury ocean would only have to be **760 mm** (about 30 inches) deep.

5-15. 172.00 MPa = 1.7200×10^8 Pa

$$1.7200 \times 10^8\text{ Pa} \times \left(\frac{1\text{ atm}}{101{,}325\text{ Pa}}\right) = \mathbf{1697.5\ atm}$$

$$1.7200 \times 10^8\text{ Pa} \times \left(\frac{1\text{ bar}}{100{,}000\text{ Pa}}\right) = \mathbf{1720.0\ bar}$$

5-17. The trapped nitrogen exerts a pressure equal to that of the room pressure added to the pressure exerted by the extra height of Hg.

$$P_{gas} = P_{room} + P_{Hg}$$

$$= 1.000\text{ atm} + (67.5\text{ mm Hg}) \times \left(\frac{1\text{ atm}}{760\text{ mm Hg}}\right)$$

$$= 1.000\text{ atm} + 0.0888\text{ atm} = \mathbf{1.09\ atm}$$

5-19. The experiment has nitrogen, at a pressure of 3.00 atm (= P_1) and a volume of 2.00 L (= V_1), expanding to a volume of 2.00 + 5.00 = 7.00 L (= V_2).
Applying Boyle's Law: $P_2V_2 = P_1\,V_1$

$$P_2 = \frac{P_1V_1}{V_2} = \frac{(3.00\text{atm})\times(2.00\text{L})}{7.00\text{ L}} = \mathbf{0.857\ atm.}$$

5-21.

	V_1	P_1	V_2	P_2	Calculations
(a)	0.235 L	1.00 atm	**0.0992 L**	2.37 atm	$V_2 = \frac{1.00\text{ atm} \times 0.235\text{ L}}{2.37\text{ atm}} = 0.992\text{ L}$
(b)	785 mL	1.50 atm	**1080 mL**	110.0 kPa	$P_2 = 110.0\text{ kPa} \times \frac{1000\text{Pa}}{1\text{ kPa}} \times \frac{1\text{ atm}}{101325\text{ Pa}} = 1.0856\text{atm}$; $V_2 = \frac{1.50\text{ atm} \times 785\text{ mL}}{1.0856\text{ atm}} = 1080\text{ mL}$
(c)	604 mL	995 torr	406 mL	**1480 torr**	$P_2 = \frac{604\text{ mL} \times 995\text{ torr}}{406\text{ mL}} = 1480\text{ torr}$
(d)	x mL	2.00 atm	$x/2$ mL	**4.00 atm**	$P_2 = \frac{2.00\text{ atm} \times x\text{ mL}}{x/2\text{ mL}} = 4.00\text{ atm}$

5-23.

$$^{o}C = \frac{5}{9}(^{o}F - 32{\cdot}0) = \frac{5}{9}(98.6 - 32.0)$$

$$= 37.0\ ^{o}C$$

$$T\text{ (Kelvin)} = 273.15 + {}^{o}C = 273.15 + 37.0 = 310.1\text{ K}$$

5-25. $\frac{V_2}{T_2} = \frac{V_1}{T_1}$; $\quad V_2 = \left(\frac{T_2}{T_1}\right) \text{x } V_1 = 2 \text{ x } V_1 = 2 \text{ x } 4.00 = 8.00\text{ L}$

5-27. Charles' Law is always easiest to use with the Kelvin as the temperature.

$$T_1 = 273.15 + \frac{5}{9}(^{o}F - 32)$$

$$= 273.15 + \frac{5}{9}(100 - 32) = 310.9\text{ K}$$

$$T_2 = 273.15 + \frac{5}{9}(0 - 32) = 255.4\text{ K}$$

As above: $\quad V_2 = \left(\frac{T_2}{T_1}\right) \text{x } V_1 = \left(\frac{255.4\text{ K}}{310.9\text{ K}}\right) \text{x } 17.4\text{ gills} = 14.3\text{ gills}$

5-29. The same number of moles of CaC_2 reacts in both cases and the pressure stays constant. As a result, Charles' Law applies. Note $T_1 = 50^oC + 273 = 323$ K.

$$T_2 = 400^oC + 273 = 673 \text{ K}$$

$$V_2 = \left(\frac{T_2}{T_1}\right) \times V_1 = \left(\frac{673 \text{ K}}{323 \text{ K}}\right) \times 64.5 \text{ L} = \mathbf{134\ L}$$

5-31.

	T_1	V_1	T_2	V_2	Calculations
(a)	0.0^oC = 273.15 K	185 L	100.0^oC = 373.15 K	**253 L**	$V_2 = \left(\frac{373.15 \text{ K}}{273.15 \text{ K}}\right) \times 185 \text{ L} = 253 \text{ L}$
(b)	400 K	18 quarts	200 K	**9.0 quarts**	$V_2 = \left(\frac{200 \text{ K}}{400 \text{ K}}\right) \times 18 \text{ quarts} = 9.0 \text{ quarts}$
(c)	1000 K	1000 mL	100^oC = 373.15K	**373 mL**	$V_2 = \left(\frac{373.15 \text{ K}}{1000 \text{ K}}\right) \times 1000 \text{ mL} = 373 \text{ mL}$
(d)	200^oC = 473.15K	*y* mL	1540 K = **1260^oC**	3.25 *y* mL	$T_2 = \left(\frac{3.25 \text{ y mL}}{\text{y mL}}\right) \times 473.15 \text{ K} = 1540 \text{ K}$

5-33. It is useful to recognize that when one or more variable in an ideal gas law calculation remains constant -- here it is the number of moles and R -- one can analyze the remaining variables as an equal pair of ratios in a "stripped" form of the idea gas law :

$$\frac{P_2V_2}{T_2} = \frac{P_1V_1}{T_1}$$

$$P_2 = \left(\frac{V_1}{T_1}\right) \times \left(\frac{T_2}{V_2}\right) \times P_1 = \left(\frac{V_1}{V_2}\right) \times \left(\frac{T_2}{T_1}\right) \times P_1$$

$$= \left(\frac{1}{3.25}\right) \times \left(\frac{2}{1}\right) \times 5.50 \text{ atm} = \mathbf{3.38\ atm}$$

5-35. **(a)** Presumably the temperature of the gas doesn't change when the bottle is filled. Then, this problem is a simple Boyle's Law problem.

$$P_2V_2 = P_1V_1 \Rightarrow \quad P_2 = \left(\frac{V_1}{V_2}\right) \times P_1 = \left(\frac{20.6\ \text{L}}{1.05\ \text{L}}\right) \times 1.01\ \text{atm} = \mathbf{19.8\ atm}$$

(b) Now we apply the ideal gas law. Under conditions of constant volume and number of moles: $\frac{P_2}{T_2} = \frac{P_1}{T_1}$

$$P_2 = \left(\frac{T_2}{T_1}\right)P_1 = \left(\frac{273.15 + 21.0}{273.15 - 20.0}\right) \times 19.8 = \mathbf{23.0\ atm}$$

5-37. The "pressure difference" across the walls refers to the difference in pressure inside and outside the bottle.

$$P_{inside} - P_{outside} = \text{pressure difference}$$

At bursting, for a $P_{outside} = 0.98$ atm

$$P_{inside} - P_{outside} = 1.25\ \text{atm}$$

$$P_{inside} = 1.25\ \text{atm} + P_{outside} = 1.25\ \text{atm} + 0.98\ \text{atm}$$

$$= 2.23\ \text{atm}$$

This is P_2. We already know $P_1 = 0.98$ atm, $T_1 = 68^{\circ}\text{F} = 293$ K.

Therefore: $\frac{T_2}{P_2} = \frac{T_1}{P_1}$

$$T_2 = \left(\frac{P_2}{P_1}\right) \times T_1 = \left(\frac{2.23\ \text{atm}}{0.98\ \text{atm}}\right) \times 293\ \text{K} = 667\ \text{K}$$

The bottle will burst at an oven temperature of 667 K. This is equal to **741°F.**

5-39. The only quantity given in the problem that cannot be plugged into the ideal gas law is the mass of O_2. This is equivalent to:

$$29.8\ \text{g}\ O_2 \times \left(\frac{1\ \text{mol}\ O_2}{31.9988\ \text{g}\ O_2}\right) = 0.931\ \text{mol}\ O_2$$

Then: $$T = \frac{PV}{nR} = \frac{(2.00\ \text{atm})\ (10.0\ \text{L})}{(0.931\ \text{mol}) \times \left(0.08206\ \frac{\text{L}-\text{atm}}{\text{mol}-\text{K}}\right)} = \mathbf{262\ K}$$

5-41. The handbook gives values for volume, the mass, and the molecular formula of the gas. But it omits any data on temperature and pressure. Given a pressure of 1 atm, and knowing that the molar mass of H_2Te is 129.62 g mol^{-1}, though, we can calculate the temperature of the gas:

$$T = \frac{PV}{nR} = \frac{(1.00 \text{ atm}) \times (1.00 \text{ L})}{\left(\dfrac{6.234 \text{ g}}{129.62 \text{ g mol}^{-1}}\right) \times \left(0.08206 \dfrac{\text{L}-\text{atm}}{\text{mol}-\text{K}}\right)} = \mathbf{253\ K}$$

This is equal to **-20°C.**

5-43. The data allow a calculation of the total number of molecules in the 15 cm^3 (= 0.015 L) sample, 21 °C (= 294.2 K). The ideal gas law will give us the number of moles of gas, and we convert separately to molecules.

$$n = \frac{PV}{RT} = \frac{(0.95 \text{ atm}) \times (0.015 \text{ L})}{\left(0.08206 \dfrac{\text{L}-\text{atm}}{\text{mol}-\text{K}}\right) \times (294.2 \text{ K})} = 5.94 \times 10^{-4} \text{ moles air}$$

The atoms of Kr is a fraction of this:

$$\begin{aligned} \text{atoms Kr} &= (\text{molecules air}) \times (\text{fraction Kr}) \\ &= (5.94 \times 10^{-4} \times 6.0221 \times 10^{23} \text{ molecules air}) \times \frac{1140 \text{ atoms Kr}}{10^9 \text{ molecules air}} \\ &= \mathbf{4.1 \times 10^{14}\ Kr\ atoms.} \end{aligned}$$

5-45. This calculation requires the molar mass of SF_6, 146.05 g mol^{-1}. The ideal gas law yields density is in units of grams per liter, where the mass of the gas in grams is determined by mass = (moles, n) × (molar mass, $\mathcal{M}$)

$$\text{density} = \frac{n\mathcal{M}}{V}$$

The ideal gas law gives us $\dfrac{n}{V} = \dfrac{P}{RT}$, so:

$$\text{density} = \frac{P\mathcal{M}}{RT} = \frac{(0.942 \text{ atm})\left(146.05 \text{ g mol}^{-1}\right)}{\left(0.08206 \dfrac{\text{L}-\text{atm}}{\text{mol}-\text{K}}\right) \times (288.15 \text{ K})} = \mathbf{5.82\ \frac{g}{L}}$$

5-47. The gas data permit a calculation of the molar mass,

$$\mathcal{M} = \frac{\text{mass of substance, } m}{\text{moles of substance, } n} = \frac{m}{n} = \frac{m}{\left(\frac{PV}{RT}\right)} = \frac{mRT}{PV}$$

$$= \frac{(1.55\text{ g}) \times \left(0.08206 \frac{\text{L-atm}}{\text{mol-K}}\right) \times (273.15\text{ K})}{(1.00\text{ atm}) \times (0.174\text{ L})} = 199.7\text{ g mol}^{-1}.$$

The molar mass of "CF_2" is 50.01 g mol^{-1}. The molar mass for the compound is 199.7 g mol^{-1} = 4 × 50.01 g mol^{-1}. The molecular formula is $(CF_2)_4$ = **C_4F_8**.

5-49. Note the 1:1 stoichiometry of HCl : NaCl. Therefore:

$$\text{mol HCl} = 2500\text{ kg NaCl} \times \left(\frac{1000\text{ g NaCl}}{1\text{ kg NaCl}}\right) \times \left(\frac{1\text{ mol NaCl}}{58.44\text{ g NaCl}}\right) \times \left(\frac{1\text{ mol HCl}}{1\text{ mol NaCl}}\right)$$

$$= 42{,}800\text{ mol HCl}$$

Then we may use the ideal gas law (note: 550 ^{o}C = 823.15 K):

$$V = \frac{nRT}{P} = \frac{(42{,}800\text{ mol}) \times \left(0.08206 \frac{\text{L-atm}}{\text{mol-K}}\right) \times (823.15\text{ K})}{0.97\text{ atm}}$$

= **3.0 x 10^{6} L** (3 million liters--about the size of a small house).

5-51. (a) 2 Na *(s)* + 2 HCl *(g)* → H_2 *(g)* + 2 NaCl *(s)*

(b) Note that 50.0^{o}C = 323.15 K

$$\text{mol } H_2 = 6.24\text{ g Na} \times \left(\frac{1\text{ mol Na}}{22.990\text{ g Na}}\right) \times \left(\frac{1\text{ mol } H_2}{2\text{ mol Na}}\right) = 0.1357\text{ mol } H_2$$

$$V = \frac{nRT}{P} = \frac{(0.1357\text{ mol}) \times \left(0.08206 \frac{\text{L-atm}}{\text{mol-K}}\right) \times (323.15\text{ K})}{0.850\text{ atm}} = \mathbf{4.23\text{ L}}$$

5-53. Note that 33°C = 306.15 K

$$\text{mol } Cl_2 = n = \frac{PV}{RT} = \frac{(0.953\text{ atm}) \times (5.32\text{ L})}{\left(0.08206 \frac{\text{L-atm}}{\text{mol-K}}\right) \times (306.15\text{ K})} = 0.2018\text{ mol } Cl_2$$

$$\text{mol } MnO_2 = \text{mol } Cl_2 = 0.2018\text{ mol}$$

$$\text{mass } MnO_2 = 0.2018\text{ mol } Cl_2 \times \left(\frac{86.9367\text{ g } MnO_2}{1\text{ mol } MnO_2}\right) = \mathbf{17.5\text{ g } MnO_2}$$

5-55. (a)

$$\text{mol S} = 2000\text{ g S} \times \left(\frac{1\text{ mol S}}{32.066\text{ g S}}\right) = 62.4\text{ mol S}$$

$$\text{mol } H_2S = 62.4\text{ mol S} \times \left(\frac{2\text{ mol } H_2S}{3\text{ mol S}}\right) = 41.6\text{ mol } H_2S$$

$$\text{Volume } H_2S \text{ at STP} = 41.6\text{ mol} \times 22.4\,\frac{\text{L}}{\text{mol}} = \mathbf{932\ L\ H_2S}$$

(b) Note that we have 2 mol H_2S for 1 mol SO_2 in the chemical reaction. By Avogadro's hypothesis, we have 2 L H_2S for 1 L SO_2. Therefore

$$V_{SO_2} = \frac{V_{H_2S}}{2} = \mathbf{466\ L\ SO_2}$$

$$m_{SO_2} = 41.6\text{ mol } H_2S \times \left(\frac{1\text{ mol } SO_2}{2\text{ mol } H_2S}\right) \times \left(\frac{64.065\text{ g } SO_2}{1\text{ mol } SO_2}\right)$$

$$= 1330\text{ g } SO_2 = \mathbf{1.33\ kg\ SO_2}.$$

5-57. In a combustion problem like this, the moles of H_2O and CO_2 permit the determination of the empirical formula (see problem 2-37).

For this problem:

$$\text{mol C} = 1.930\text{g } CO_2 \times \left(\frac{1\text{ mol } CO_2}{44.021\text{ g } CO_2}\right) \times \left(\frac{1\text{ mol C}}{1\text{ mol}CO_2}\right) = 0.0438\text{ mol C}$$

$$\text{mol H} = 1.054\text{ g } H_2O \times \left(\frac{1\text{ mol } H_2O}{18.015\text{ g } H_2O}\right) \times \left(\frac{2\text{ mol H}}{1\text{ mol } H_2O}\right) = 0.1170\text{ mol H}$$

(moles H : moles C) = (0.1170 : 0.0438) = (2.67 : 1) = ($^8/_3$: 1) = (8 : 3).

Therefore, the empirical formula is C_3H_8. The pressure, volume, and temperature data for the initial gas permit us to determine how many moles of C_xH_y we began with.

$$\text{mol } C_xH_y = \frac{PV}{RT} = \frac{(1.200\text{ atm}) \times (0.300\text{ L})}{\left(0.08206\,\frac{\text{L}-\text{atm}}{\text{mol}-\text{K}}\right) \times (300\text{ K})} = 0.0146\text{ mol.}$$

This many moles of C_xH_y yielded 0.0438 mol of CO_2. So there are $^{0.0438}/_{0.0146}$ = 3.00 mol of C per mole of C_xH_y. The molecular formula is $\mathbf{C_3H_8}$.

5-59. $P_{O_2} + P_{N_2} = P_{TOTAL}$

$$P_{N_2} = P_{TOTAL} - P_{O_2} = 2.43 \text{ atm} - 1.02 \text{ atm} = \mathbf{1.41 \text{ atm}}$$

$$X_{N_2} = \frac{P_{N_2}}{P_{TOTAL}} = \frac{1.41}{2.43} = \mathbf{0.580} \qquad X_{O_2} = \frac{P_{O_2}}{P_{TOTAL}} = \frac{1.02}{2.43} = \mathbf{0.420}$$

5-61. $$\text{mol } SO_2 = 263 \text{ g } SO_2 \times \left(\frac{1 \text{ mol } SO_2}{64.065 \text{ g } SO_2}\right) = 4.105 \text{ mol } SO_2$$

$$\text{mol } O_2 = 837 \text{ g } O_2 \times \left(\frac{1 \text{ mol } O_2}{31.9988 \text{ g } O_2}\right) = 26.157 \text{ mol } O_2$$

$$\text{mol } SO_3 = 179 \text{ g } SO_3 \times \left(\frac{1 \text{ mol } SO_3}{80.065 \text{ g } SO_3}\right) = 2.236 \text{ mol } SO_3$$

Total moles = 4.105 + 26.157 + 2.236 = 32.50 mol

$$X_{SO_3} = \frac{2.236 \text{ mol } SO_3}{32.50 \text{ mol total}} = \mathbf{0.0688}$$

$$P_{SO_3} = X_{SO_3} P_{TOTAL} = (0.0688) \times (0.950 \text{ atm}) = \mathbf{0.0654 \text{ atm}}$$

5-63. Gases can freely interpenetrate, so in fact the nitrogen in the Martian atmosphere has the entire volume of the atmosphere available to it. Nevertheless, it is often convenient to speak of volume fractions for gases. For an ideal gas, the volume fraction will be equal to the mole fraction.

$$X_{N_2} = \text{volume fraction} = 2.7\% = \mathbf{0.027}$$

$$P_{N_2} = X_{N_2} P_{TOTAL} = (0.027) \times (5.92 \times 10^{-3} \text{ atm}) = \mathbf{1.6 \times 10^{-4} \text{ atm}}$$

5-65. (a) $n_{total} = 10.0 \text{ mol} + 12.5 \text{ mol} = 22.5 \text{ mol} \quad \Rightarrow \quad X_{CO} = \frac{10.0}{22.5} = \mathbf{0.444}$

(b) 3 mol CO_2 is formed at the expense of *some* of the CO and O_2.

$$\text{mol } CO_{consumed} = 3 \text{ mol } CO_2 \times \left(\frac{1 \text{ mol CO}}{1 \text{ mol } CO_2}\right) = 3 \text{ mol } CO_{consumed}$$

$$\text{mol CO} = \text{mol } CO_{start} - \text{mol } CO_{consumed} = 10.0 - 3.0 = 7.0 \text{ mol CO}$$

$$\text{mol } O_{2\ consumed} = 3 \text{ mol } CO_2 \times \left(\frac{0.5 \text{ mol } O_2}{1 \text{ mol } CO_2}\right) = 1.5 \text{ mol } O_{2\ consumed}$$

$$\text{mol } O_2 = \text{mol } O_{2\ start} - \text{mol } O_{2\ consumed} = 12.5 - 1.5 = 11.0 \text{ mol } O_2$$

$$\text{mol}_{total} = 3.0 + 7.0 + 11.0 = 21 \text{ mol} \quad \Rightarrow \quad X_{CO} = \frac{7.0}{21} = \mathbf{0.33}$$

5-67. As in Example 5-12, a common $3RT$ term is present in both parts of this problem. R is used in units appropriate for a root-mean-squared speed problem.

$$3RT = 3 \times \left(8.3145 \frac{\text{kg}-\text{m}^2}{\text{s}^2-\text{mol-K}}\right) \times (300\text{ K}) = 7{,}480 \frac{\text{kg}-\text{m}^2}{\text{s}^2-\text{mol}}$$

(a) The molar mass of H_2 is 2.0159 g mol^{-1}, or 2.0159×10^{-3} kg mol^{-1}

$$u_{rms} = \sqrt{\frac{7{,}480 \frac{\text{kg}-\text{m}^2}{\text{s}^2-\text{mol}}}{2.0159 \times 10^{-3} \frac{\text{kg}}{\text{mol}}}} = \mathbf{1930 \frac{m}{s}}$$

(b) Molar mass of SF_6 is 146.05 g mol, or).14605 kg mol^{-1}

$$u_{rms}(SF_6) = \sqrt{\frac{7{,}480 \frac{\text{kg}-\text{m}^2}{\text{s}^2-\text{mol}}}{0.14605 \frac{\text{kg}}{\text{mol}}}} = \mathbf{226 \frac{m}{s}}$$

5-69. The molar mass of He is 4.0026×10^{-3} kg mol^{-1}

SUN: $$u_{rms}(\text{He}) = \sqrt{\frac{3 \times \left(8.3145 \frac{\text{kg}-\text{m}^2}{\text{s}^2\text{molK}}\right) \times 6000\text{K}}{4.0026 \times 10^{-3} \frac{\text{kg}}{\text{mol}}}} = \mathbf{6100 \frac{m}{sec}}$$

INTERSTELLAR CLOUD: $$u_{rms} = \sqrt{\frac{3 \times \left(8.3145 \frac{\text{kg}-\text{m}^2}{\text{s}^2\text{molK}}\right) \times 100\text{K}}{4.0026 \times 10^{-3} \frac{\text{kg}}{\text{mol}}}} = \mathbf{790 \frac{m}{sec}}$$

The ratio of speeds is about 8 times, which is reasonable because u_{rms} is proportional to $\sqrt{T}$.

5-71. An increase in temperature "shifts" the speed distribution to higher velocities. Therefore, the percentage of ClO_2 molecules with speeds in excess of 400 m sec^{-1} will *exceed* 35.0%.

5-73. The relative rate of effusion is proportional to reciprocal of the square root of the molecular mass, so the relative rate can be used to determine the unknown molar mass:

$$\sqrt{\frac{\mathcal{M}_{UNK}}{\mathcal{M}_{CH_4}}} = \frac{\text{rate of effusion of } CH_4}{\text{rate of effusion of UNK}}$$

$$\sqrt{\frac{\mathcal{M}_{UNK}}{16.0428 \text{ g mol}^{-1}}} = \frac{1.30 \times 10^{-8} \text{ mol s}^{-1}}{5.42 \times 10^{-9} \text{ mols}^{-1}} = 2.398$$

$$\frac{\mathcal{M}_{UNK}}{16.0428 \text{ g mol}^{-1}} = (2.398)^2 = 5.750$$

$$\mathcal{M}_{UNK} = 5.750 \times 16.0428 \text{ g mol}^{-1} = \mathbf{92.3\ g\ mol^{-1}}$$

5-75. The number of moles of oxygen in the cylinder is:

$$6.80 \text{ kg } O_2 \times \left(\frac{100 \text{ g } O_2}{1 \text{ kg } O_2}\right) \times \left(\frac{1 \text{ mol } O_2}{31.9988 \text{ g } O_2}\right) = 212.5 \text{ mol } O_2$$

Solving the van der Waal's equation for pressure gives:

$$P = \frac{nRT}{V - nb} - a\frac{n^2}{V^2}$$

$$P = \frac{(212.5 \text{ mol}) \times \left(0.08206 \frac{\text{L-atm}}{\text{mol-K}}\right) \times (293.15\text{K})}{28.0 \text{ L} - (212.5 \text{ mol}) \times \left(0.03183 \frac{\text{L}}{\text{mol}}\right)} - 1.360 \frac{\text{atm L}^2}{\text{mol}^2} \frac{(212.5 \text{ mol})^2}{(28.0 \text{ L})^2}$$

$$P = \frac{5111 \text{ L-atm}}{21.24 \text{ L}} - 78.3 \text{ atm} = 240.6 \text{ atm} - 78.3 \text{ atm} = 162.3 \text{ atm} = \mathbf{162\ atm}$$

This compares to a pressure of 182 atm calculated from the ideal gas equation--a 12% difference . The pressure in psi is: 162.3 atm x 14.7 psi atm^{-1} = **2390 psi**

5-77. (a) $$P = \frac{nRT}{V} = \frac{(0.7500 \text{ mol}) \times \left(0.08206 \frac{\text{L-atm}}{\text{mol-K}}\right)(240.0\text{K})}{1.000 \text{ L}} = \mathbf{14.77\ atm}$$

(b) $$P = \frac{nRT}{V - nb} - a\frac{n^2}{V^2}$$

$$= \frac{(0.7500 \text{ mol}) \times \left(0.08206 \frac{\text{L-atm}}{\text{mol-K}}\right)(240.0 \text{ K})}{1.000 \text{ L} - (0.7500 \text{ mol}) \times (0.04267 \text{ L mol}^{-1})} - 3.592 \frac{\text{atm L}^2}{\text{mol}^2} \frac{(0.7500 \text{ mol})^2}{(1.000 \text{ L})^2}$$

$$= \frac{14.771 \text{ L-atm}}{0.9680 \text{ L}} - 2.0205 \text{ atm} = \mathbf{13.24\ atm}$$

5-77. (continued)

(c) Neither the ideal gas law nor the van der Waal's equation is exact. The van der Waal's equation gives a pressure that is closer to the experimental pressure; it is a better approximation.

5-79. We will assume a worst-case scenario for the pressure difference: that the pressure of gravity acting on the 9.0 ft (=2.75 m) column of mud (density = 4.9 g cm^{-3} = 4.9 x 10^6 g m^{-3} = 4900 kg m^{-3}) is pressing fully against the basement wall. It will add to the 1 atm of pressure exerted by the earth's atmosphere. First, we determine the pressure of the mud:

$$P_{mud} = \left(4900\ \frac{kg}{m^3}\right) \times \left(9.807\ \frac{m}{s^2}\right) \times (2.75\ m)$$

$$= 132{,}000 \frac{kg}{m - s^2} = 132{,}000\ Pa$$

$$= (132{,}000\ Pa) \times \left(1 \frac{atm}{101{,}325\ Pa}\right) = 1.303\ atm$$

The air in the drained basement exerts standard atmospheric pressure on the inside of the walls also, so the pressure difference across the wall is:

$P_{outside} - P_{inside} = (P_{mud} + P_{air}) - P_{air} = P_{mud} =$ **1.30 atm.**

In units of psi: 1.303 atm x 14.696 psi atm^{-1} = **19.1 psi.**

5-81. Note that Table 5-2 lacks a direct conversion from bar to atm. So we must do two unit conversions, starting from 886 millibar = 0.886 bar:

$$0.886\ bar \times \left(\frac{10^5\ Pa}{bar}\right) \times \left(\frac{1\ atm}{101{,}325\ Pa}\right) = \mathbf{0.874\ atm}$$

5-83. The volume of the mixed gases is equal to the volume of the three flasks:

$$V_{total} = 5.00\ L + 4.00\ L + 3.00\ L = 12.00\ L$$

In this volume, there will be a pressure due the total number of moles of the gases. $n_{total} = n_{O_2} + n_{N_2} + n_{Ar}$

$$\frac{P_{total} V_{total}}{RT} = \frac{P_{N_2} V_{N_2}}{RT} + \frac{P_{O_2} V_{O_2}}{RT} + \frac{P_{Ar} V_{Ar}}{RT}$$

5-83. (continued) The RT factor will cancel and we will have:

$$P_{total}V_{total} = P_{N_2}V_{N_2} + P_{O_2}V_{O_2} + P_{Ar}V_{Ar}$$

$$P_{total} = \frac{P_{N_2}V_{N_2} + P_{O_2}V_{O_2} + P_{Ar}V_{Ar}}{V_{total}}$$

$$= \frac{(2.51\text{ atm} \times 5.00\text{ L}) + (0.792\text{ atm} \times 4.00\text{ L}) + (1.23\text{ atm} \times 3.00\text{ L})}{12.00\text{ L}}$$

$$= \mathbf{1.62\ atm.}$$

5-85. (a) The rule refers to *changes* in temperature and *changes* in pressure as if linear behavior applied:

$$\Delta P = C\,\Delta T, \text{ where } C = \frac{1\text{ psi}}{10\ ^{o}\text{F}} = 0.0680\ \frac{\text{atm}}{\text{K}}$$

This assumes several things, all incorrect and all leading to some error in the exactness of the rule:

(1) That $X\ (= \frac{nR}{V})$ doesn't vary with T or P. With a rubber tire, that is unlikely.

(2) That the gas is ideal. This is unlikely with a tire pressure of roughly 3 atm.

(3) That the *gauge* pressure (measured by the tire gauge) depends only on the pressure inside the tire. It does not. It really depends on the difference of pressure inside and outside, and the pressure outside--atmospheric pressure--is always nearly a constant 14.7 psi.

(b) The rule suggests $\Delta P = \left(\frac{1\text{ psi}}{10\ ^{o}\text{F}}\right) \times 50^{o}\text{F} = 5$ psi, so the Tire Council Rule suggests: $P = (28 - 5)\text{ psi} = \mathbf{23\ psi.}$

Now let's do it more rigorously. The interior pressure is 28 psi + 14.7 = 42.7 psi. The change in the pressure of an ideal gas can be obtained by a proportionality

$T_{initial} = 273.15 + \frac{5}{9}(70 - 32) = 294\text{ K}$ and $T_{final} = 273.15 + \frac{5}{9}(20 - 32) = 266\text{ K})$

$$\frac{P_{final}}{T_{final}} = \frac{P_{initial}}{T_{initial}} \Rightarrow P_{final} = \frac{T_{final}}{T_{initial}}P_{initial} = \left(\frac{266\text{ K}}{294\text{ K}}\right)(42.7\text{ psi}) = \mathbf{38.6\ psi}$$

$$P_{gauge} = P_{inside} - P_{outside} = 38.6 - 14.7 = \mathbf{24\ psi}$$

5-87. (a) We know the O_2 stoichiometry is indicated by the formula of the product, assuming Avogadro's hypothesis applies:

2 volumes CO_2 need 2 volumes O_2 4 volumes H_2O need 2 volumes O_2

2 volumes NO_2 need 2 volumes O_2

Therefore, **6 volumes** of O_2 are needed.

(b) The compound has a formula $C_xH_yN_z$, and the combustion reaction is:

$$6\ O_2 + C_xH_yN_z \rightarrow 2\ CO_2 + 4\ H_2O + 2\ NO_2$$

The C, H, and N on the right are all contained in the starting material:

2 CO_2 contain 2 C $\Rightarrow$ x=2 4 H_2O contain 8 H $\Rightarrow$ y = 8

2 NO_2 contain 2 N $\Rightarrow$ z = 2 The molecular formula is $\mathbf{C_2H_8N_2}$.

5-89. We know the decomposition of $CaCO_3$ proceeds: $CaCO_3 \rightarrow CO_2 + CaO$

Therefore mol CO_2 = mol CaO = mol $Ca(OH)_2$

$$\text{mol } Ca(OH)_2 = 8.47\text{ kg } Ca(OH)_2 \times \left(\frac{1000\text{ g}}{1\text{ kg}}\right) \times \left(\frac{1\text{ mol } Ca(OH)_2}{74.093\text{ g } Ca(OH)_2}\right)$$

$$= 114.3\text{ mol } Ca(OH)_2 = \text{mol } CO_2 = 114.3\text{ mol } CO_2$$

$$V_{CO_2} = \frac{nRT}{P} = \frac{(114.3\text{ mol}) \times \left(0.08206\ \frac{\text{L-atm}}{\text{mol-K}}\right) \times (950\text{ K})}{(0.976\text{ atm})} = \mathbf{9130\ L\ CO_2}$$

5-91. We use the final volume, pressure, and temperature of H_2 to determine moles of Na. Note that: $2.6\text{ ft}^3 \times \left(\frac{0.3048\text{ m}}{\text{ft}}\right)^3 \times \left(\frac{10\text{ dm}}{\text{m}}\right)^3 \times \left(\frac{1\text{ L}}{1\text{ dm}^3}\right) = 73.624\text{ L}$

$$\text{Then: mol } H_2 = \frac{PV}{RT} = \frac{(1.00\text{ atm})(73.62\text{ L})}{\left(.08206\frac{\text{L-atm}}{\text{mol-K}}\right) \times (273.15\text{ K})} = 3.285\text{ mol}$$

$$\text{mass Na} = 3.285\text{ mol } H_2 \times \left(\frac{2\text{ mol Na}}{1\text{ mol } H_2}\right) \times \left(\frac{22.9988\text{ g Na}}{1\text{ mol Na}}\right) = 151.1\text{ g Na}$$

$$\text{This is equal to } 151.1\text{ g} \times \frac{1\text{ lb}}{453.6\text{ g}} = 0.333\text{ lb Na}$$

$$\text{Mass \% Na} = \frac{0.333\text{ lb Na}}{1.0\text{ lb alloy}} \times 100 = 33.3\%$$

5-93. The balanced chemical reaction is:

$$CS_2\,(g) + 3\,O_2\,(g) \rightarrow CO_2\,(g) + 2\,SO_2\,(g).$$

We can use the stoichiometry to set up a changes table (these tables will be more common in Chapter 8). The first line shows the pressures *before* the reaction; the second line shows the *change* in the pressures in the course of the reaction, and the final line shows the pressures *after* the reaction. The relevant stoichiometric coefficients determine the relative magnitude of the changes. For example, a decrease of *x* atm in the partial pressure of CS_2 causes a decrease of *3x* atm in the partial pressure of O_2.

(all in atmospheres)	CS_2	O_2	CO_2	SO_2
Pressure Before	x	y	0	0
Pressure Change	$-x$	$-3x$	$+x$	$+2x$
Pressure After	0	$y - 3x$	x	$2x$

We know the total final pressure is 2.40 atm. We use Dalton's Law to determine *y* and *x*:

After the reaction:

$$P_{total} = P_{CS_2} + P_{O_2} + P_{CO_2} + P_{SO_2}$$

$$2.40 \text{ atm} = 0 + (y - 3x) + x + 2x = y$$

Before the reaction:

$$P_{total} = P_{CS_2} + P_{O_2} + P_{CO_2} + P_{SO_2}$$

$$3.00 \text{ atm} = x + y + 0 + 0 = x + y$$

$$x = 3.00 - y = 3.00 - 2.40 = 0.60 \text{ atm}$$

We now have the initial pressure of the CS_2 -- 0.60 atm. Then:

$$\text{mol } CS_2 = \frac{PV}{RT} = \frac{(0.60\,\text{atm}) \times (10.0\text{ L})}{\left(0.08206\,\dfrac{\text{L}-\text{atm}}{\text{mol}-\text{K}}\right) \times (373.15\text{ K})} = 0.1959 \text{ mol}$$

The mass is: $(0.1959 \text{ mol } CS_2) \times \left(\dfrac{76.14\,\text{g } CS_2}{1\text{mol } CS_2}\right) = \mathbf{15\,g\ CS_2}$

5-95. The pressure depends on the mass and the speed of the particles. Molecules of UF_6 may be heavier, but on average they move much more slowly. The two effects (mass and average velocity) cancel each other exactly in the ideal gas.

5-97. Separation by effusion requires that a molecule containing ^{235}U *never* have the same mass as a molecule containing ^{238}U. But with a ready supply of ^{20}F and ^{19}F, we could have some $^{235}U(^{20}F)_3(^{19}F)_3$ (molecular mass about 352) and $^{238}U(^{19}F)_6$ (molecular mass also about 352). These molecules would have very, very slightly different masses, on the order of 0.001%. But even then effusion would not separate these.

CHAPTER 6 - CONDENSED PHASES AND PHASE TRANSITIONS

6-1. The substance is most likely to be a gas; large compressibility and coefficients of thermal expansion are only found with non-condensed materials - gases.

6-3. (a) The density of the substance, in g cm^{-3}, is:

$$\left(\frac{2.71\ \text{kg}}{258\ \text{cm}^3}\right)\times\left(\frac{1000\ \text{g}}{1\ \text{kg}}\right) = 10.5\ \text{g cm}^{-3}$$

which is much denser than water (about 1 g cm^{-3}). The substance is either a liquid or a solid.

(b) The molar volume is: $\left(\frac{\text{cm}^3}{10.5\ \text{g}}\right)\times\left(\frac{108\ \text{g}}{1\ \text{mol}}\right) = \mathbf{10.3\ cm^3\ mol^{-1}}$.

Compare this to the STP molar volume of a gas, 22.4 L mol^{-1}, which is 22,400 cm^3 mol^{-1}.

6-5. This volume increase is just 0.3%, whereas (by the Charles' Law) a gas warming from 293 K to 313 K would expand 6.8%. Even a non-ideal gas would expand by a few percent with such a temperature change. The substance is condensed.

6-7. Ion-dipole forces arise from molecular properties that are always present, as in the interaction of the **permanent** ion charge on a potassium ion, K^+ and the **permanent** dipole on a water molecule. Ion-induced dipole forces arise when the charge on an ion induces a dipole on another molecule - a dipole that would not exist in the absence of the ion. An example is the interaction of the **fixed** ion charge on an iron ion with the **induced and transient** dipole on an oxygen molecule. Both interactions involve an ion, but the presence of a permanent dipole makes the ion-dipole interaction much stronger.

6-9. In *all* of the substances the dispersion force is present.

(a) KF – The K-F bond is strongly polar with **dominant ion-ion** interactions. KF will also have dipole-dipole interactions among KF molecules.

6-9. (continued)

(b) HI – Unlike HF or even HCl, there is little hydrogen bonding with iodine. Still, the molecule is strongly polar and **dipole-dipole interactions dominate.** Dispersion forces are also relatively strong in this case.

(c) CH_3OH – An O-H bond is present, so **hydrogen bonding will dominate** intermolecular interactions, along with some dipole-dipole interactions.

(d) Rn – The only interatomic force available to a noble gas is the **dispersion force.**

(e) N_2 is symmetric and, therefore, non-polar. The sole intermolecular force available is the **dispersion force.**

6-11. The three forces available are:

Na^+--- Br^-	ion-ion	*strongest*
Na^+---HBr	ion-dipole	*second strongest*
Na^+---Kr	ion-induced dipole	*least strong*

6-13. 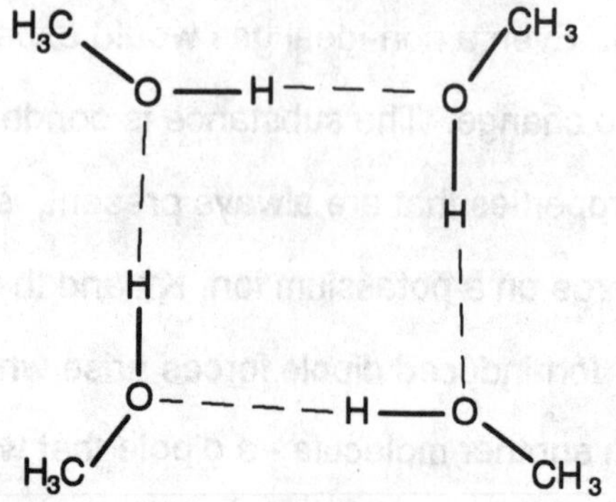

As discussed in the solution to problem 6-9c above, methanol will have hydrogen bonds as the dominant intermolecular interaction. It is reasonable to expect the tetramer to be held together by hydrogen bonds.

6-15. The problem requires that we know the number of water molecules in the flask:

$$1000\text{ g} \times \left(\frac{1\text{ mol}}{18.015\text{ g}}\right) \times \left(\frac{6.022 \times 10^{23}\text{ molecules}}{1\text{ mol}}\right) = 3.34 \times 10^{25}\text{ molecules}$$

Each molecule can accept two hydrogen bonds. So there are **6.7×10^{25} hydrogen bonds.**

6-17. The huge increase in volume is due to the conversion of water from a condensed phase to the gaseous phase (steam) at 100 °C.

6-19. Sodium chloride is an extended structure maintained by ion-ion interactions which are non-directional. Solid carbon tetrachloride, by contrast, is maintained as a solid by weak, dispersion forces that are most important for neutral, non-polar molecules like CCl_4. Sodium chloride should therefore be much harder.

6-21. The diffusion constant increases as it becomes easier for molecules to move around among the "cages" formed by their neighbors in a condensed phase -- a liquid or a solid. Compression should make these "cages" smaller and tighter, so compression should significantly decrease the diffusion constant of a liquid or a solid. The major determinants of the diffusion constant are the average speed and the rate of collision. The speed distribution will not be significantly affected by an increase in density. But the rate of collisions amongst gas molecules should increase dramatically when a gas is compressed. This will cause the diffusion constant of a gas to decrease when the density is increased.

6-23. By the ideal gas law, rearranged to yield volume:

$$V_{H_2} = \frac{n_{H_2}RT}{P} = \frac{(1.00\ \text{mol}\ H_2)\times\left(0.08206\dfrac{\text{L-atm}}{\text{mol-K}}\right)\times(16.0\ \text{K})}{(0.213\ \text{atm})} = \mathbf{6.16\ liters}$$

This is 27% of the volume of one mole of hydrogen gas at STP (22.4 liters).

6-25. This is really a problem in particles per unit volume. The ideal gas law permits the direct calculation of moles per liter;

$$\frac{n}{V} = \frac{P}{RT} = \frac{2.87\times10^{-6}\,\text{atm}}{\left(0.08206\dfrac{\text{L-atm}}{\text{mol-K}}\right)\times(300.15\text{K})} = 1.165\times10^{-7}\,\frac{\text{mol}}{\text{liter}}$$

Converting to atoms per cubic centimeter:

$$\left(1.165\times10^{-7}\,\frac{\text{mol}}{\text{liter}}\right)\times\left(\frac{6.0221\times10^{23}\,\text{atoms}}{1\,\text{mol}}\right)\times\left(\frac{1\,\text{liter}}{1000\,\text{cm}^3}\right) = \mathbf{7.02\times10^{13}\,\frac{atoms}{cm^3}}$$

6-27. The pressure of the hydrogen gas is only part of the total gas pressure; the pressure of the water vapor also contributes:

$$P_{water} + P_{C_2H_2} = P_{total}$$

$$P_{C_2H_2} = P_{total} - P_{water} = 0.9950 \text{ atm} - 0.0728 \text{ atm} = 0.9222 \text{ atm}$$

The ideal gas law, and the molar mass of acetylene (26.038 g mol^{-1}), then give the answer:

$$\frac{\text{grams}}{\text{liter}} = \left(\frac{\text{grams}}{\text{mol}}\right) \times \left(\frac{\text{mol}}{\text{liter}}\right) = \left(\frac{\text{grams}}{\text{mol}}\right) \times \left(\frac{P}{RT}\right)$$

$$= \left(\frac{26.038\,\text{grams}}{\text{mol}}\right) \times \left(\frac{0.9222 \text{ atm}}{0.08206\frac{\text{L-atm}}{\text{mol-K}} \times 313.15 \text{ K}}\right) = \mathbf{0.9345\frac{grams}{liter}}$$

6-29. The number of moles of $CaCO_3$ that react is equal to the number of moles of CO_2 formed. First we determine the partial pressure of the CO_2, then the number of moles.

$$P_{water} + P_{CO_2} = P_{total}$$

$$P_{CO_2} = P_{total} - P_{water} = 0.9963 \text{ atm} - 0.0231 \text{ atm} = 0.9732 \text{ atm}$$

$$\text{mol } CO_2 = \frac{PV}{RT} = \frac{(0.9732 \text{ atm}) \times (0.722\text{L})}{\left(0.08206\frac{\text{l-atm}}{\text{mol-K}}\right) \times (293.15\text{K})} = 0.0292 \text{ mol } CO_2$$

$$\text{mol } CaCO_3 = \text{mol } CO_2 = 0.0292 \text{ mol } CaCO_3$$

$$\text{mass } CaCO_3 = 0.0292 \text{ mol } CaCO_3 \times \left(\frac{100.09 \text{ g } CaCO_3}{1 \text{ mol } CaCO_3}\right) = \mathbf{2.92 \text{ g } CaCO_3}$$

6-31. The halogens are all neutral, non-polar diatomic molecules. Dispersion forces are the *only* important intermolecular force for them. Dispersion forces increase in strength with increasing number of electrons. The progression F_2 to Cl_2 to Br_2 to I_2 includes an increase in the number of electrons per "X_2" molecule, so the trend is well explained by and increase in the strength of the dispersion force.

6-33. Boiling point will increase as polarity does, because an increase in polarity will increase the magnitude of possible dipole-dipole interactions.

The trend in boiling point will then be: Br_2 < $SnBr_4$ < $SnBr_2$.

6-35. The vapor pressure of water at 90°C is approximately **0.70** atm from the figure (more precisely, it is **0.69 atm**). This indicates that the air pressure at this altitude is 0.69 atm and that only 69% of the earth's atmosphere is above the explorer. Fully 31% of the earth's atmosphere is below the explorer.

6-37. The trends in boiling and melting points indicate that the interatomic forces in iridium are much stronger than those of sodium. The surface tension of iridium will be higher than that of sodium.

6-39. A Lewis-dot structure of hydrazine indicates that each nitrogen has one lone pair of electrons: 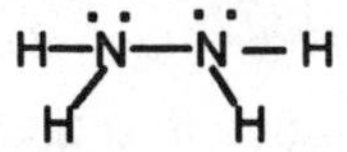 while the Lewis dot structure of ethylene has none: 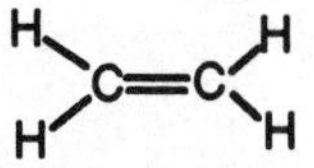 The presence of an asymmetric structure, N-H bonds, and lone pairs on the nitrogens suggest significant dipole-dipole and hydrogen bonding interactions in hydrazine, which should have much higher boiling and melting points than ethylene.

6-41. Compression will favor the denser phase, but the denser (liquid) phase is already present. The sample will remain liquid; no phase change will occur.

6-43.

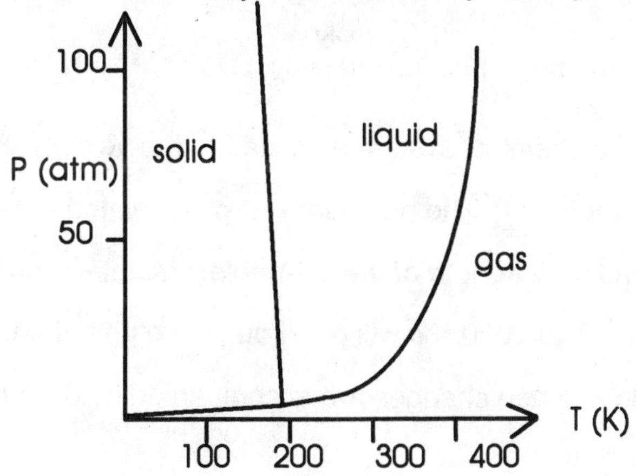

6-45. (a) liquid (b) gas

(c) solid (d) gas

6-47. (a) The temperature of the triple point must be above this; any point where liquid and gas are in equilibrium must always lie at a temperature equal to or higher than any point where the liquid and solid are in equilibrium.

(b) During this experiment, the temperature goes from well below to well above -84°C (= 189 K), where we know solid acetylene is in equilibrium with its vapor at a pressure of 1 atm. Therefore, the solid acetylene is sure to **sublime.**

6-49. The material in the tube will enter a "supercritical" phase beyond which there is no distinction between liquid and gas. This will be indicated by the disappearance of the meniscus between the liquid and gaseous phases. The pressure inside the tube will be very high.

6-51. They are both solids, because they are (relative to a gas) incompressible and do not flow readily (relative to a liquid or gas).

6-53. The dipoles on hydrogen chloride will line up with their positive ends (the H atoms) closest to a negatively charged ion (I) and their negative ends (the Cl atoms) closest to a positively charged ion (II).

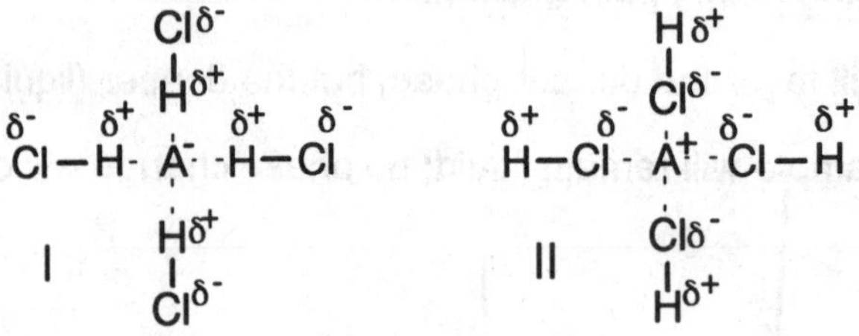

6-55. The internal kinetic energy of a chemical system is related to the velocity of the molecules (and also internal motions). The potential energy is related to relative positions of the molecules and the strength of the intermolecular interactions. As the sample is warmed from 10 K to 1000 K it will go through two phase changes, melting and vaporization. Both phase changes are accompanied by dramatic

6-55. (continued)

increases in kinetic energy and, because the molecules are interacting less strongly as they move about at higher speeds, dramatic **decreases in potential energy**. At temperatures where a phase change does not occur, more gradual increases in kinetic energy (and decreases in potential energy) will occur.

6-57. Convert the volume of the room to liters:

$$V = 110\ m^3 \times \left(\frac{10\,dm}{1\ m}\right)^3 = 110{,}000\ dm^3 = 110{,}000\ L$$

The chemical amount of water in the vapor phase will be determined by this volume and the vapor phase of water at this temperature.

$$mol\ H_2O = \frac{PV}{RT} = \frac{(0.03126\,atm) \times (110{,}000\ L)}{\left(0.08206\frac{L-atm}{mol-K}\right) \times (298.15K)} = 140.5\ mol$$

$$g\ H_2O = 140.5\ mol\ H_2O \times \left(\frac{18.0153\ g\ H_2O}{1\,mol\ H_2O}\right) = \mathbf{2530 g\ H_2O}$$

This is roughly 2.5 liters of liquid water, or almost 3 quarts.

6-59. After the can is sealed, the system is in a state where $P = 1$ atm and $T = 100^oC$ with no liquid water inside. As soon as the can begins to cool, liquid water will begin to condense. The system will remain at pressures and temperatures lying on the vapor-liquid coexistence curve. At room temperature the system will have a pressure of approximately 0.2 atm, we read from Fig. 6-28.

6-61. The spacecraft (and planets, and stars) *are* slowly losing mass to space. It is not boiling away, which refers to the case of liquid only. The spacecraft is a solid, to the loss of substances is by the process of sublimation. But that the equilibrium state of the spacecraft (and planets, and stars) is completely vaporized says *nothing* about the *rate* of sublimation, which is vanishingly small.

6-63. The temperature of the cooling bath cannot get below the sublimation temperature of CO_2 under 1 atm of pressure, which is -78.5°C. During the entire cooling process, CO_2 *(s)* will vaporize and cause the ethanol to cool. The ethanol will remain liquid throughout. When the preparation is done the cooling bath will consist of liquid ethanol with some solid CO_2 in it. Bubbles of subliming CO_2 *(g)* will appear continuously.

6-65

	a	*b*	T_c (K) Calc.	Obs'd.	P_c (atm) Calc.	Obs'd.	$(V/n)_c$ L mol^{-1}
O_2	1.360	0.03183	**154.3**	154.76	**49.72**	50.06	**0.09549**
CO_2	3.592	0.04267	**303.0**	304.20	**73.07**	72.86	**0.1280**
H_2O	5.464	0.03049	**647.1**	647.067	**217.7**	217.57	**0.09147**

The observed values for the critical temperature are taken from the experimental literature. The good agreement between calculated and observed values show the quality of the van der Waal's equation.

CHAPTER 7 - SOLUTIONS

7-1. We are told the mass of the components of the solution. We must convert these to moles to evaluate the mole fractions correctly.

$$\text{mol } H_2O = 143.2 \text{ g } H_2O \times \left(\frac{1 \text{ mol } H_2O}{18.0153 \text{ g } H_2O}\right) = 7.949 \text{ mol } H_2O$$

$$\text{mol } H_2O_2 = \quad 4.50 \text{ g} \times \left(\frac{1 \text{ mol } H_2O}{34.0147 \text{ g } H_2O}\right) = 0.1323 \text{ mol } H_2O_2$$

$$\text{weight \% } H_2O_2 = \quad 100 \times \left(\frac{4.50 \text{ g } H_2O_2}{143.2 \text{ g} + 4.50 \text{ g}}\right) = 3.05\%$$

$$\text{mole fraction } H_2O_2 = \left(\frac{0.1323 \text{ mol } H_2O_2}{7.949 \text{ mol} + 0.1323 \text{ mol}}\right) = \mathbf{0.0164}$$

7-3. Recall that there are 1×10^6 micrograms in one gram.

$$0.300 \ \mu\text{g Se} \times \left(\frac{1 \text{ g}}{1 \times 10^6 \ \mu\text{g}}\right) \times \left(\frac{1 \text{ mol Se}}{78.96 \text{ g Se}}\right) = 3.80 \times 10^{-9} \text{ mol Se}$$

$$\left(\frac{3.80 \times 10^{-9} \text{ mol}}{1 \text{ mL}}\right) \times \left(\frac{1000 \text{ mL}}{1 \text{ L}}\right) = 3.8 \times 10^{-6} \frac{\text{mol}}{\text{L}} = \mathbf{3.80 \times 10^{-6} \ M}$$

7-5. A hypothetical 100 g of solution will contain 38.0 g HCl and 62.0 g H_2O.

Then: $$\text{mol } H_2O = 62.00 \text{ g } H_2O \times \left(\frac{1 \text{ mol } H_2O}{18.0153 \text{ g } H_2O}\right) = 3.442 \text{ mol } H_2O$$

$$\text{mol HCl} = 38.00 \text{ g HCl} \times \left(\frac{1 \text{ mol HCl}}{36.4606 \text{ g HCl}}\right) = 1.0422 \text{ mol HCl}$$

$$\text{mol fraction HCl} = \frac{1.0422 \text{ mol}}{3.4415 \text{ mol} + 1.0422 \text{ mol}} = \mathbf{0.2324}$$

$$\text{molality HCl} = \left(\frac{1.042 \text{ mol}}{62.00 \text{ g } H_2O}\right) \times \left(\frac{1000 \text{ g } H_2O}{1 \text{ kg } H_2O}\right) = \mathbf{16.81 \frac{mol}{kg}}$$

7-7. Density is the bridge between the mass of the solution and the volume of solution.

$$\left(\frac{1.0422 \text{ mol HCl}}{100.0 \text{ g solution}}\right) \times \left(\frac{1.1886 \text{ g solution}}{1 \text{ cm}^3 \text{ solution}}\right) \times \left(\frac{1000 \text{ cm}^3 \text{ solution}}{1 \text{ L solution}}\right) = 12.39 \frac{\text{mol}}{\text{L}} = \mathbf{12.39 \ M}$$

7-9. The number of moles of N_2 is:

$$1.00 \text{ kg } N_2 \times \left(\frac{1000 \text{ g}}{1 \text{ kg}}\right) \times \left(\frac{1 \text{ mol } N_2}{28.0134 \text{ g } N_2}\right) = 35.70 \text{ mol } N_2$$

The number of moles of dissolved water is much smaller than the number of moles of N_2 solvent. Therefore:

$$\text{total moles} = \text{moles } (H_2O) + \text{moles } (N_2) \approx \text{moles } (N_2) = 35.70 \text{ mol}$$

The formula for mole fraction can be rearranged to solve for moles of H_2O:

$$\frac{\text{moles } (H_2O)}{\text{total moles}} = X_{H_2O}$$

$$\text{moles } (H_2O) = (\text{total moles}) \times \left(X_{H_2O}\right)$$

$$\approx 35.70 \times (1 \times 10^{-5}) = 3.57 \times 10^{-4} \text{ mol } H_2O$$

$$\text{grams } (H_2O) = 3.57 \times 10^{-4} \text{ mol } H_2O \times 18.0153 \text{ g mol}^{-1}$$

$$= \mathbf{0.00643 \text{ g } H_2O}$$

7-11. One liter of solution is equal to 1000 cm^3 of solution. It weighs:

$$1000 \text{ cm}^3 \times 1.33 \text{ g cm}^{-3} = 1330 \text{ g}$$

A liter of solution contains 12.2 mol H_3PO_4. This is equal to a mass of H_3PO_4:

$$\text{g } H_3PO_4 = (12.2 \text{ mol } H_3PO_4) \times \left(\frac{97.995 \text{ g } H_3PO_4}{1.0 \text{ mol } H_3PO_4}\right) = 1195.5 \text{ g } H_3PO_4$$

Therefore, the mass of water in 1 liter of solution is:

$$\text{mass } (H_3PO_4) + \text{mass } (H_2O) = \text{total mass}$$

$$\text{mass } H_2O = \text{total mass} - \text{mass } (H_3PO_4)$$

$$= 1330 \text{ g} - 1195.5 = 134.5 \text{ g } H_2O$$

We now obtain molality: $$\left(\frac{12.2 \text{ mol } H_3PO_4}{134.5 \text{ g } H_2O}\right) \times \left(\frac{1000 \text{ g } H_2O}{1 \text{ kg } H_2O}\right) = \mathbf{90.7 \frac{mol}{kg}}$$

7-13. The molality indicates $\frac{8.9660 \text{ mol acetic acid}}{1 \text{ kg } H_2O}$. Its reciprocal is:

$$\frac{1 \text{ kg } H_2O}{8.9660 \text{ mol acetic acid}} = \frac{0.11153 \text{ kg } H_2O}{1 \text{ mol acetic acid}} = \frac{111.53 \text{ g } H_2O}{\text{mol acetic acid}}$$

7-13. (continued)

One mol of acetic acid has a mass of 60.052 g. Therefore, *in this solution,* one mole of acetic acid is equivalent to

$$111.53 \text{ g } H_2O + 60.052 \text{ g } C_2H_4O_2 = \frac{171.582 \text{ g solution}}{1 \text{ mol } C_2H_4O_2}.$$

Multiply this factor by the molarity to determine the density:

$$\left(\frac{6.0835 \text{ mol } C_2H_4O_2}{1 \text{ L solution}}\right) \times \left(\frac{171.582 \text{ g solution}}{1 \text{ mol } C_2H_4O_2}\right) \times \left(\frac{1 \text{ L}}{1000 \text{ cm}^3}\right) = \mathbf{1.0438 \frac{g}{cm^3}}$$

7-15. (a) The 0.750 L solution we must prepare will contain:

$$\left(2.0 \times 10^{-5} \frac{\text{mol NaF}}{\text{L}}\right)(0.750 \text{ L}) = 1.5 \times 10^{-5} \text{ mol NaF.}$$

Of course, we need the *mass* of NaF in order to prepare the solution:

$$\text{mass NaF} = 1.5 \times 10^{-5} \text{ mol NaF} \times \left(\frac{41.9881 \text{ g NaF}}{1 \text{ mol NaF}}\right) = 6.30 \times 10^{-4} \text{ g NaF}$$

The solution can then be prepared by weighing **6.30 x 10^{-4} g** NaF into a flask, adding a small amount of water to dissolve it, and then adding water to make 0.750 L of total solution.

(b) Dilution problems follow the formula:

$$c_f V_f = c_i V_i; \qquad \text{where f = final, i = initial}$$

Here we need to determine the initial volume required:

$$V_f = \left(\frac{c_i}{c_f}\right) \times V_i = \left(\frac{2.0 \times 10^{-5} \text{ M}}{1.2 \times 10^{-5} \text{ M}}\right)(0.750 \text{ L}) = 0.125 \text{ L}$$

If we take **0.125 L** of the initial solution and add water to make a final volume of 1.25 L, we will then have the correct concentration.

7-17. We must keep track of moles of NaOH in this problem.

$$\text{mol NaOH added} = 25.0 \text{ g NaOH} \times \left(\frac{1 \text{ mol NaOH}}{39.997 \text{ g NaOH}}\right) = 0.625 \text{ mol NaOH}$$

$$\text{total NaOH} = 0.625 + 3.65 = 4.225 \text{ mol NaOH}$$

$$\text{Final molarity: } \frac{4.225 \text{ mol NaOH}}{4.0 \text{ L solution}} = 1.06 \frac{\text{mol}}{\text{L}} = \mathbf{1.06 \text{ M}}$$

7-19. The mass of the residue will be the mass of the contained salts, presuming that there are no hydrates that form.

(note: 100.0 mL = 0.1000 L)

$$\text{mass NaCl} = \left(\frac{0.556 \text{ mol NaCl}}{\text{L}}\right) \times (0.1000 \text{ L}) \times \left(\frac{58.4424 \text{g NaCl}}{1 \text{ mol NaCl}}\right) = 3.25 \text{ g NaCl}$$

$$\text{mass KCl} = \left(\frac{0.245 \text{ mol KCl}}{\text{L}}\right) \times (0.1000 \text{ L}) \times \left(\frac{74.551 \text{ g KCL}}{1 \text{ mol KCL}}\right) = 1.83 \text{ g KCl}$$

Total mass = 3.25 + 1.83 = **5.08 g residue**

7-21. First, how might the residue differ from the Na_2SO_4 added? It may contain waters of hydration. We can see if this makes sense by calculating the relative chemical amounts of the water and the sodium sulfate.

mass residue - mass Na_2SO_4 = 322.2 g - 142.04 g = 180.2 g

This is the mass of the water in the residue. In moles it equals

$$180.2 \text{ g } H_2O \times \left(\frac{1 \text{ mol } H_2O}{18.0153 \text{ g } H_2O}\right) = 10.00 \text{ mol } H_2O$$

Therefore, the residue has a formula **$Na_2SO_4 \cdot 10\ H_2O$.**

7-23. This is a stoichiometric calculation with the added feature that the amount of the key reactant is given as a volume

$$\text{Moles } OCl^- \text{ reacting} = 51.6 \text{ L} \times \frac{0.650 \text{ mol } OCl^-}{1 \text{ L}} = 33.5 \text{ mol } OCl^-$$

$$\text{mol } N_2H_4 = \text{mol } OCl^- = 33.5 \text{ mol } N_2H_4$$

$$33.5 \text{ mol } N_2H_4 \times \frac{32.045 \text{ g } N_2H_4}{1 \text{ mol } N_2H_4} = 1070 \text{ g } N_2H_4 = \mathbf{1.07 \text{ kg } N_2H_4}.$$

7-25. This is another stoichiometric calculation, with a volume of a reactant needed:

$$\text{mol } PbO_2 = 15.9 \text{ g} \times \left(\frac{1 \text{ mol } PbO_2}{239.20 \text{ g } PbO_2}\right) = 0.0665 \text{ mol } PbO_2$$

$$\text{mol } HNO_3 = (0.0665 \text{ mol } PbO_2) \times \left(\frac{4 \text{ mol } HNO_3}{2 \text{ mol } PbO_2}\right) = 0.133 \text{ mol } HNO_3$$

$$\text{volume } HNO_3 = 0.133 \text{ mol } HNO_3 \times \left(\frac{1 \text{ L}}{7.91 \text{ mol } HNO_3}\right) = \mathbf{0.0168 \text{ L } HNO_3}$$

This is equal to **16.8 mL** of the HNO_3 solution

7-27. Here we must also consider the amount of the reactant CO_2 as an ideal gas.

Note that T (K) = T (^oC) + 273.15 K, so 50^oC = 323.15 K

$$\text{mol } K_2CO_3 = 187 \text{ L} \times \left(\frac{1.36 \text{ mol } K_2CO_3}{1 \text{ L}}\right) = 254 \text{ mol } K_2CO_3$$

$$\text{mol } CO_2 = \text{mol } K_2CO_3 = 254 \text{ mol } CO_2$$

$$V_{CO_2} = \frac{nRT}{P} = \frac{(254 \text{ mol}) \times \left(0.8206 \frac{\text{L-atm}}{\text{mol-K}}\right) \times (323.15 \text{ K})}{1.00 \text{ atm}} = \mathbf{6740\ L\ CO_2}$$

7-29. (a) $PF_3 + 3\ H_2O \rightarrow H_3PO_3 + 3\ HF$

(b) Note that 25^oC = 298.15 K and 872 mL = 0.872 L

$$\text{mol } PF_3 = \frac{PV}{RT} = \frac{(0.970 \text{ atm}) \times (1.94 \text{ L } PF_3)}{\left(0.08206 \frac{\text{L-atm}}{\text{mol-K}}\right) \times (298.15 \text{ K})} = 0.0769 \text{ mol } PF_3$$

$$\text{mol } H_3PO_3 = \text{mol } PF_3 = 0.0769 \text{ mol } PF_3$$

$$\text{mol HF} = 3 \times \text{mol } PF_3 = 0.2307 \text{ mol HF}$$

$$[H_3PO_3] = \frac{0.0769 \text{ mol } H_3PO_3}{0.872 \text{ L}} = \mathbf{0.0882\ M\ H_3PO_3}$$

$$[HF] = \frac{2307 \text{ mol HF}}{0.872 \text{ L}} = \mathbf{0.265\ M\ HF}$$

7-31. In titration problems like this, one determines the chemical amount of one reactant and then calcluates how much of the other reactant "must have been there" to consume the known reactant. The concentration of the dichromate ion is equal to the concentration of the potassium dichromate salt.

$$[Cr_2O_7^{2-}] = \left(\frac{5.134 \text{ g } K_2Cr_2O_7}{1 \text{ L solution}}\right) \times \left(\frac{1 \text{ mol } K_2Cr_2O_7}{294.18 \text{ g } K_2Cr_2O_7}\right) = 0.01745\ \mathbf{M}$$

$$\text{mol } Cr_2O_7^{2-} = \left(\frac{0.01745 \text{ mol}}{\text{L}}\right) \times (34.26 \text{ mL}) \times \frac{1 \text{ L}}{1000 \text{ ml}}$$

$$= 5.979 \times 10^{-4} \text{ mol } Cr_2O_7^{2-}$$

$$\text{moles } Fe^{2+} = 6 \times \text{mol } Cr_2O_7^{2-} = 3.587 \times 10^{-3} \text{ mol } Fe^{2+}$$

$$[Fe^{2+}] = \frac{3.587 \ \times \text{mol } Fe^{2+}}{0.5000 \text{ L solution}} = \mathbf{0.007175\ M\ Fe^{2+}}$$

7-33. This acid-base titration involves a base that can accept one hydrogen ion and an acid that can donate one hydrogen ion Therefore, they react in a 1 : 1 ratio.

Note that 37.85 mL = 0.03785 L; 100.0 mL = 0.1000 L

$$\text{mol of OH}^- = \left(\frac{0.1279 \text{ mol OH}^-}{\text{L}}\right) \times (0.03785 \text{ L}) = 0.004841 \text{ mol OH}^-$$

$$\text{mol HNO}_3 = \text{mol OH}^- = 0.004841 \text{ mol HNO}_3$$

$$[\text{HNO}_3] = \left(\frac{0.004841 \text{ mol HNO}_3}{0.1000 \text{ L}}\right) = \mathbf{0.04841\ M\ HNO_3}$$

7-35. The mole fraction of the solute is determined using the known mass of the solvent and solute and computing their chemical amounts.

$$\text{mol C}_{13}\text{H}_{10}\text{O} = 15.0 \text{ g C}_{13}\text{H}_{10}\text{O} \times \left(\frac{1 \text{ mol C}_{13}\text{H}_{10}\text{O}}{182.22 \text{ g C}_{13}\text{H}_{10}\text{O}}\right) = 0.0823 \text{ mol}$$

$$\text{mol C}_3\text{H}_6\text{O} = 50.0 \text{ g C}_3\text{H}_6\text{O} \times \left(\frac{1 \text{ mol C}_3\text{H}_6\text{O}}{58.075 \text{ g C}_3\text{H}_6\text{O}}\right) = 0.861 \text{ mol C}_3\text{H}_6\text{O}$$

$$X_{\text{C}_3\text{H}_6\text{O}} = \frac{\text{mol}_{\text{C}_3\text{H}_6\text{O}}}{\text{mol}_{\text{C}_3\text{H}_6\text{O}} + \text{mol}_{\text{C}_{13}\text{H}_{10}\text{O}}} = \frac{0.861}{0.861 + 0.0823} = 0.913$$

$$P_{\text{C}_3\text{H}_6\text{O}} = X_{\text{C}_3\text{H}_6\text{O}} P^{\text{o}}_{\text{C}_3\text{H}_6\text{O}} = (0.913) \times (0.3720 \text{ atm}) = \mathbf{0.340\ atm}$$

7-37. The vapor pressure change is 0.411 - 0.437 = -0.026 atm.

Therefore: $-X_2 P_i^{\text{o}} = \Delta P_i^{\text{o}}$

$$X_2 = -\frac{\Delta P_i^{\text{o}}}{P_i^{\text{o}}} = -\frac{(-0.027 \text{ atm})}{0.437} = \mathbf{0.0595}$$

7-39. Note that 100.0 g toluene = 0.1000 kg toluene.

$$\text{molality C}_{14}\text{H}_{10} = \left(\frac{7.80 \text{ g C}_{14}\text{H}_{10}}{0.1000 \text{ kg toluene}}\right) \times \left(\frac{1 \text{ mol C}_{14}\text{H}_{10}}{178.23 \text{ g C}_{14}\text{H}_{10}}\right) = 0.4376 \frac{\text{mol}}{\text{kg}}$$

The boiling point elevation ΔT_b = 112.06 - 110.60 = 1.46 ^{o}C = 1.46 K (since a change of 1°C is equal to a change of 1K). Then:

$$K_b m = \Delta T_f$$

$$K_b = \frac{\Delta T_f}{m} = \frac{(1.46 \text{ K})}{0.4376 \frac{\text{mol}}{\text{kg}}} = \mathbf{3.34 \frac{K\text{-}kg}{mol}}$$

7-41. Molality of the sugar: $m = \dfrac{\Delta T_b}{K_b} = \dfrac{(0.30\text{ K})}{\left(0.512\dfrac{\text{K-kg}}{\text{mol}}\right)} = 0.586\text{ mol kg}^{-1}$

Moles of sugar in 200.0 g (= 0.2000 kg) H_2O:

$$\left(\frac{0.586\text{ mol sugar}}{1\text{ kg }H_2O}\right) \times (0.2000\text{ kg }H_2O) = 0.1172\text{ mol sugar}$$

Molar mass of sugar: $\mathcal{M} = \dfrac{39.8\text{ g}}{0.1172\text{ mol sugar}} = \dfrac{340\text{ g sugar}}{1\text{ mol sugar}} = \mathbf{340\text{ g mol}^{-1}}$.

7-43. $\Delta T_f = 178.4\ ^oC - 170.8\ ^oC = 7.6\ ^oC = 7.6\text{ K}$

$$\Delta T_f = K_f\, m$$

$$m = \frac{\Delta T_f}{K_f} = \frac{7.6\text{K}}{37.7\dfrac{\text{K-kg}}{\text{mol}}} = 0.202\frac{\text{mol}}{\text{kg}}$$

With 25.0 g (= 0.0250 kg) of solvent, the number of moles of the unknown is:

$$\text{moles unknown} = 0.202\frac{\text{mol}}{\text{kg}} \times 0.0250\text{ kg} = 0.00504\text{ mol unknown}$$

The molar mass of the unknown is: $\mathcal{M} = \dfrac{0.840\text{ g unknown}}{0.00504\text{ mol unknown}} = \mathbf{170\dfrac{g}{mol}}$

7-45. The substance which gives the largest number of moles of solute will give the lowest freezing point. This is the substance with the smallest molar mass-- N_2H_4.

7-47. Assume a 100 g sample, made of 34 g sucrose and 66 g (0.066 kg) water.

$$\text{Moles of sucrose} = \frac{34\text{ g}}{343.3\text{ g mol}^{-1}} = 0.099\text{ mol}$$

$$\text{Molality of sucrose} = \frac{0.099\text{ mol}}{0.066\text{ kg}} = 1.5\frac{\text{mol}}{\text{kg}}$$

$$\Delta T_f = -K_f\, m = -1.86\left(\frac{\text{kg-K}}{\text{mol}}\right) \times 1.5\left(\frac{\text{mol}}{\text{kg}}\right) = 2.79\text{ K}$$

$$T_f = 273.15\text{ K} - 2.79\text{ K} = 270.4\text{ K } (= \mathbf{-2.8\ ^oC})$$

The increasing concentration of sucrose will depress the freezing point further, until solid sucrose also begins to crystallize.

7-49. *If* it is true that acetone does not dissociate, then the freezing point depression would be equal to $K_f\, m$. Let us test that assumption against the experimental results. (Note: 50.00 g = 0.05000 kg):

$$\Delta T_f = -K_f\, m$$
$$= -1.86\left(\frac{\text{kg-K}}{\text{mol}}\right) \times \left(\frac{1.55 \text{ g acetone}}{0.0500 \text{ kg } H_2O}\right) \times \left(\frac{1 \text{ mol acetone}}{58.080 \text{ g acetone}}\right)$$
$$= -0.993 \text{ K} = -0.993^{o}\text{C}$$

This is very close to the observed freezing point. Acetone **does not** dissociate.

7-51. If a substance does dissociate, then the molality of all ions will be some multiple x of the listed molality. In this case, where x is the number of dissociated ions and m is the molality of the dissolved formula unit:

$$\Delta T_f = -K_f\, m\, x \quad \Rightarrow \quad x = \frac{-\Delta T_f}{K_f m} = \frac{-(-4.218 \text{ K})}{\left(1.86 \dfrac{\text{kg-K}}{\text{mol}}\right)\left(0.8402 \dfrac{\text{mol}}{\text{kg}}\right)} = 2.7$$

Na_2SO_4 dissociates into, effectively, **2.7 particles.**

7-53. The osmotic pressure permits us to determine the molarity of the unknown:

$$c = \frac{\pi}{RT} = \frac{0.0105 \text{ atm}}{\left(0.08206 \dfrac{\text{L-atm}}{\text{mol-K}}\right)(300 \text{ K})} = 4.265 \times 10^{-4} \text{ M}$$

The solution has a total volume of 25.0 cm^3 (25.0 mL, 0.0250 L). From this, we can get the number of moles of the unknown:

$$\text{moles unknown} = \left(4.265 \times 10^{-4} \frac{\text{mol}}{\text{L}}\right) \times (0.0250 \text{ L}) = 1.066 \times 10^{-5} \text{ moles}$$

The molar mass is then obtained: $\mathcal{M} = \dfrac{0.200 \text{ g}}{1.066 \times 10^{-5} \text{ moles}} = \mathbf{18{,}800 \dfrac{g}{mol}}$.

7-55. The pressure is expressed here as a height of water (15.2 cm = .152 m). Recall that this hydrostatic pressure is (see problem 5-9):

$$P = dgh = \left(1000\frac{kg}{m^3}\right) \times \left(9.80665\,\frac{m}{s^2}\right) \times (.0152\ m)$$

$$= 149.1\ \frac{kg}{m^2\text{-}s^2} = 149.1\ Pa$$

$$= 149.1\ Pa \times \left(\frac{1\ atm}{101.325\ Pa}\right) = 1.47 \times 10^{-3}\ atm$$

The concentration of the polymer is then

$$c = \frac{\pi}{RT} = \frac{1.47 \times 10^{-3}}{\left(0.08206\,\frac{L\text{-}atm}{mol\text{-}K}\right) \times (288.15\ K)} = 6.22 \times 10^{-5}\,\frac{mol}{L}$$

We are told that 1 L has 4.64 g of polymer. Therefore:

$$\mathcal{M} = \frac{4.64\ g}{6.22 \times 10^{-4}\ mol} = \mathbf{7{,}460\ \frac{g}{mol}}$$

7-57. (a) We will need to know the number of moles of water in 1 L of water, since Henry's law deals with mole fractions. We assume that 1 L of water has a density of 1.00 g cm^{-3} or 1,000 g L^{-1}. Then the number of moles of water is:

$$\frac{1{,}000}{18.015} = 55.5\ mol\ H_2O.$$

Henry's Law states: $P_{CO_2} = X_{CO_2} k_H$

$$X_{CO_2} = \frac{P_{CO_2}}{k_H} = \frac{5.0\ atm}{1.65 \times 10^3\ atm} = 3.03 \times 10^{-3}$$

The mole fraction of CO_2 is so much smaller than the mole fraction of water that we can approximate: $X_{CO_2} = \dfrac{mol\ CO_2}{mol\ H_2O}$

$$mol\ CO_2 = (X_{CO_2})(mol\ H_2O)$$

$$= (3.03 \times 10^{-3})\ (55.5) = \mathbf{0.17\ mol\ CO_2}$$

(b) On a microscopic level, the removal of the cap allows the reaction $CO_2\ (aq) \rightarrow CO_2\ (g)$ to shift from left to the right.

7-59. The methane evolved is equal to the number of moles of methane in 1.00 kg (= 1.00 L) water, which we know (see problem No. 57) contains 55.5 mol H_2O. Because 1.00 mol of an ideal gas occupies 22.4 L at STP, the number of moles of methane gas is: $\frac{3.01\ \text{L}}{22.4\ \text{L mol}^{-1}} = 0.134\ \text{mol}\ CH_4$

The Henry's Law constant is obtained by rearranging the basic equation:

$$P_{CH_4} = X_{CH_4} k_H$$

$$k_H = \frac{P_{CH_4}}{X_{CH_4}} = \frac{1.00\ \text{atm}}{(0.134\ \text{mol}/55.5\ \text{mol})} = \frac{55.5}{0.134}\ \text{atm} = \mathbf{414\ atm}$$

7-61. The mole fractions in the liquid phase are needed. Note that with equal chemical amounts $X_{toluene} = X_{benzene} = 0.50$

The partial pressures for each are estimated by Raoult's Law:

$$P_{benzene} = X_{benzene}\ P^{o}_{benzene} = (0.50)\ (0.0289\ \text{atm}) = 0.01445\ \text{atm}$$

The total pressure is 0.0494 + 0.01445 = 0.0638 atm. The mole fraction of benzene in the gas phase is obtained from the partial pressure:

$$X_{benzene} = \frac{P_{benzene}}{P_{total}} = \frac{0.0494}{0.0638} = \mathbf{0.774}$$

7-63. (a) Keeping track of all the variables requires a table:

compound	mass	molar mass	moles	mole fraction
CCl_4	30.0 g	$153.8\ \frac{g}{mol}$	0.195	$\frac{0.195}{0.195 + 0.202} = \mathbf{0.491}$
$C_2H_4Cl_2$	20.g	$98.96\ \frac{g}{mol}$	0.202	.509

(b) To get the total vapor pressure, we need the mole fraction of both substances. That for $C_2H_4Cl_2$ is given in the table, too.

7-63. (continued)

$$P_{TOTAL} = P_{CCl_4} + P_{C_2H_4Cl_2}$$
$$= \left(X_{CCl_4} \times P^o_{CCl_4}\right) + \left(X_{C_2H_4Cl_2} \times P^o_{C_2H_4Cl_2}\right)$$
$$= (0.491 \times 0.293 \text{ atm}) + (0.509 \times 0.209 \text{ atm})$$
$$= 0.1439 \text{ atm} + 0.1063 \text{ atm} = \mathbf{0.250\ atm}$$

(c) $X_{CCl_4} = P_{CCl_4} / P_{TOTAL} = 0.1439 / 0.250 = \mathbf{0.575}$

7-65. A solution is homogenous with all molecules (or atoms) completely separated. With a colloid, some or many of these -- especially atoms -- form clusters. A colloid can be generated by reacting $AuCl_4^-$ *(aq)* with Sn^{2+} *(aq)*, both as solutions. A product, Au, results with very small Au clusters. These are, though, too small to be separated, for example, by filtering.

7-67. The original solution contained: 57.6 g x 4.40% = 2.5344 g KI. The remaining mass, 57.6 - 2.53 = 55.07 g, was water (= 0.05507 kg).

The additional KI brought the mass of KI to 2.6914 g KI. This is equivalent to

$2.6914 \text{ g} \times (166.00 \text{ g mol}^{-1}) = 0.01621 \text{ mol KI}$. The final molality is:

$$\text{molality} = \frac{0.01621 \text{ mol KI}}{0.05507 \text{ kg } H_2O} = \mathbf{0.294\ \frac{mol}{kg}}.$$

7-69. (a) Most of the work in this problem is in converting mg (= 0.001 g) and dL (=0.1 L) to g and L:.

$$\left(214\,\frac{\text{mg}}{\text{dL}}\right) \times \left(\frac{1\text{ g}}{1000\text{ mg}}\right) \times \left(\frac{10\text{ dL}}{1\text{ L}}\right) \times \left(\frac{1\text{ mol}}{386.64\text{ g}}\right) = 5.53 \times 10^{-3}\ \frac{\text{mol}}{\text{L}}$$

(b) Assume that 1 kg of blood contains 1 kg of water. Then,

with $1.06 \text{ g m}^{-3} = 1.06 \text{ g mL}^{-1} = 1.06 \text{ kg L}^{-1}$:

$$m = \left(5.53 \times 10^{-3}\,\frac{\text{mol}}{\text{L}}\right) \times \left(\frac{1\text{ L}}{1.06\text{ kg}}\right) = 5.86 \times 10^{-3} \text{ mol kg}^{-1}$$

(c) $8.10 \text{ g cholesterol} \times \left(\frac{1 \text{ dL blood}}{0.214 \text{ g cholesterol}}\right) \times \left(\frac{1\text{ L}}{10\text{ dL}}\right) = \mathbf{3.78\ L\ blood}$

7-71. The same 0.154 mol of KNO_3 now occupies the larger volume of the heated solution, 1040.1 mL (= 1.0401 L). Therefore $M = \frac{0.154 \text{ mol}}{1.0401 \text{ L}} = \mathbf{0.148\ \frac{mol}{L}}$

7-73. For such a dilution problem, $V_2 = 87.4$ mL, $c_2 = 0.374$ M, and $c_1 = 5.37$ M. So here:

$$c_1V_1 = c_2V_2$$
$$V_1 = \left(\frac{c_2}{c_1}\right)V_2 = \left(\frac{0.374\text{ M}}{5.37\text{ M}}\right)(87.4\text{ mL}) = 6.09\text{ mL}$$

To prepare the solution, measure **6.09 mL** of the 5.37 M H_2SO_4 solution into a graduated cylinder. With good mixing, add water up to the 87.4 mL line.

7-75. One liter of this solution weighs 1,007 g. Of this, 1%, or **10.07 g**, is $AgNO_3$. The mass of Ag in this is 10.07 g $AgNO_3$ × $\left(\frac{107.87\text{ g Ag}}{169.875\text{ g AgNO}_3}\right)$

7-77. (a) The insoluble material here is $BaBr_2$. If we denote solvation by ammonia as *(am)*, then: $2\,Br^-\,(am) + Ba^{2+}\,(am) \rightarrow BaBr_2\,(s)$

(b) mol $Ba(NO_3)_2$ = (0.215 L) x (0.076 mol L^{-1}) = 0.01634 mol $Ba(NO_3)_2$

mol AgBr = 2 x mol $BaNO_3$ = 0.03268 mol AgBr

volume of AgBr solution = 0.03268 mol x $\left(\frac{1\text{ L}}{0.5\text{ mol}}\right)$ = 0.06536 L = **65.4 mL**

(c) g $BaBr_2$ = 0.01634 mol $BaBr_2$ x 297.135 g mol^{-1} = **4.86 g**

7-79. Note that 150 mL = 150 cm^3. Then :

g NaCl = (150 cm^3) x (1.0726 g cm^{-3}) x $\left(\frac{10\text{ g Na}}{100\text{ g solution}}\right)$ = 16.089 g NaCl

$$\text{moles of Cl atoms} = \frac{16.089\text{ g NaCl}}{58.442\text{ g mol}^{-1}} \times \frac{1\text{ Cl atom}}{1\text{ NaCl}} = 0.02753\text{ mol Cl}$$

This is transferred with no loss of Cl into the final solution. The number of moles of Cl is equal to the number of moles of HCl in the final 250 mL (= 0.250 L) solution: $\frac{0.2753\text{ mol HCl}}{0.250\text{ L}}$ = **1.10 M**

7-81. Percent "relative humidity" is relative the vapor pressure of water in air saturated with water vapor over pure H_2O. The lower vapor pressure above the salt solution is a result of vapor pressure depression.

7-83. For a sample with a total of one mole of NaI + H_2O, there are: 0.390 mol NaI and 0.610 mol H_2O. The mass of this amount of water is:

$$(0.610 \text{ mol}) \times (18.015 \text{ g mol}^{-1}) = 10.989 \text{ g } H_2O = 0.010989 \text{ kg}$$

The molality *of all ions* is: $\dfrac{0.780 \text{ mol ions}}{0.010989 \text{ kg}} = 70.1 \dfrac{\text{mol}}{\text{kg}}$

$$\Delta T_b = K_b m = \left(0.512 \frac{\text{kg-K}}{\text{mol}}\right)\left(70.1 \frac{\text{mol}}{\text{kg}}\right) = \mathbf{36.4\ K}$$

This is only 82.7% of the observed elevation, but the very high concentration NaI has, after all, made this solution very non-ideal.

7-85. The data can all be used independently to determine a value of K_f for each of the acids. The formula for K_f is $K_f = \left(\dfrac{-\Delta T_f}{0.050 \text{ mol kg}^{-1}}\right)$.

SOLUTE	T_f (°C)	ΔT_f (K)	K_f (observed)
HCl	-22.795	-0.330	6.60 K-kg-mol^{-1}
H_2SO_4	-22.788	-0.323	6.46 K-kg-mol^{-1}
$HClO_4$	-22.791	-0.326	6.52 K-kg-mol^{-1}
HNO_3	-22.632	-0.167	3.34 K-kg-mol^{-1}

The K_f value for nitric acid is much smaller than for the other acids. In fact, it's about one-half. This can be explained by suggesting that HNO_3 doesn't dissociate *at all* while the other acids all dissociate almost completely to one H^+ and one X^- ion. If so, then the concentration of solute in the HCl, H_2SO_4, and $HClO_4$ solutions would be 2 x 0.050 mol kg^{-1} = 0.100 mol kg^{-1}. The values for K_f (observed) in these solutions are then 3.30, 3.23, and 3.26 K-kg-mol^{-1}. The average value for K_f is then 2.28 K-kg-mol^{-1}should be only HNO_3 gives the "true" value for K_f

$$K_f = \mathbf{3.34} \frac{\text{K-kg}}{\text{mol}}$$

7-87. The high pressure inside the sealed bottle kept a fair amount of CO_2 dissolved in the water, enough to significantly lower the freezing point. When the pressure is released by opening the can, enough of the dissolved CO_2 escapes to lessen the freezing point lowering. This raised the freezing point *above* the actual temperature of the solution. The mixture freezes.

7-89. Consider the possible dissociation products per gallium:

$GaCl_2 \rightarrow Ga^{2+} + 2Cl^-$ 3 ions

$Ga(GaCl_4) \rightarrow Ga^+ + GaCl_4^-$ 2 ions

Because the different substances form different numbers of particles when they dissolve, any experiment that depends on a colligative property would work. The chapter has discused four -- vapor pressure depression, boiling point elevation, freezing point depression, and osmotic pressure. Let's tabulate the different effects of dissolving 0.100 mol of "$GaCl_2$" in 1.00 L of water. We will assume that the molarity is equal to the molality in such a dilute solution. The mole fraction of the "$GaCl_2$" unit then is 1.80×10^{-3}.

PROPERTY	CONDITIONS	FORMULA	EFFECT OF "$GaCl_2$"	EFFECT OF "$Ga(GaCl_4)$"
Vapor pressure depression	T = 30.0°C $P^o_{H_2O}$ = 0.04187 atm	$\Delta P_{H_2O} = -X_{\text{all ions}} P^o_{H_2O}$	ΔP (atm) = -2.3×10^{-4}	ΔP (atm) = -1.5×10^{-4}
Boiling point elevation	K_b (H_2O) = 0.512 K kg mol^{-1}	$\Delta T_b = K_b m$	ΔT_b = 0.15 K	ΔT_b = 0.10 K
Freezing point depression	K_f (H_2O) = 1.86 K kg mol^{-1}	$\Delta T_f = -K_f m$	ΔT_f = - 0.56 K	ΔT_f = -0.37 K
Osmotic pressure	T = 300 K	$\pi = cRT$	π = 7.38 atm	π = 4.92 atm

7-91. We assume that $M_{NaCl} = c_{erythrocyte}$, where

$c_{erythrocyte}$= concentration of all dissolved species.

Re-arranging the freezing point depression and osmotic pressure equations

$$\pi = cRT \sim M\,RT \qquad \text{and} \qquad -K_f m = \Delta T_f \Rightarrow m = -\frac{\Delta T_f}{K_f}$$

$$\pi = -\frac{\Delta T_f}{K_f}RT = -\frac{(-0.406)}{(1.86)}(0.08206)(298) = \mathbf{5.34}\text{ atm}$$

7-93. In water: $$X_{N_2} = \frac{P_{N_2}}{K_{H,water}} = \frac{5.0\text{ atm}}{8.57 \times 10^4\text{ atm}} = \mathbf{5.83 \times 10^{-5}}$$

In CCl_4: $$X_{N_2} = \frac{P_{N_2}}{K_{H,water}} = \frac{5.0\text{ atm}}{3.52 \times 10^9\text{ atm}} = \mathbf{1.42 \times 10^{-9}}$$

7-95. (a) If we expand the Raoult's Law terms in the total vapor pressure, we obtain (with $X_{MB} + X_{EA} = 1$) data for the mole fractions in the solution phase:

$$X_{MB}P^o_{MB} + X_{EA}P^o_{EA} = P_{total}$$

$$(1 - X_{EA})P^o_{MB} + X_{EA}P^o_{EA} = P_{total}$$

$$X_{EA}^{solution} = \frac{P_{total} - P^o_{MB}}{P^o_{EA} - P^o_{MB}} = \frac{0.2400 - 0.1443}{0.3713 - 0.1443} = \mathbf{0.421}$$

(b) For the mole fraction in the *vapor* phase:

$$X_{EA}^{vap} = \frac{P_{EA}}{P_{total}} = \frac{X_{EA}^{sol'n}P^o_{EA}}{P_{total}} = \frac{(0.421)(0.3713\text{ atm})}{(0.240\text{ atm})} = \mathbf{0.651}$$

7-97. When the equimolar mixture is boiled, the first vapor produced will be richer in HCl. This will cause the mole fraction of HCl in the remaining solution to drop moving the composition across the diagram towards pure H_2O at the left. Eventually, at the azeotropic composition, the composition of the vapor will exactly equal the composition of the solution.

CHAPTER 8 - CHEMICAL EQUILIBRIUM

8-1. (a) $K = \dfrac{(P_{H_2O})^2}{(P_{H_2})^2(P_{O_2})}$ (b) $K = \dfrac{(P_{XeF_6})}{(P_{F_2})^3(P_{Xe})}$

(c) $K = \dfrac{(P_{CO_2})^{12}(P_{H_2O})^6}{(P_{C_6H_6})^2(P_{O_2})^{15}}$

8-3. Chemical equation: $P_4\ (g) + 2\ O_2\ (g) + 6\ Cl_2\ (g) \rightarrow 4\ POCl_3\ (g)$

$$K = \frac{(P_{POCl_3})^4}{(P_{P_4})(P_{O_2})^2(P_{Cl_2})^6}$$

8-5. We must indicate the equilibrium expression before inserting the numbers. In this problem, we will do this *with the* P_{ref} *terms included* to emphasize the convention followed in the textbook and this manual. This also renders the equilbrium constant as a dimensionless number. In all subsequent problems, division by P_{ref} = 1 atm is assumed.

$$K = \frac{\left(\dfrac{P_{Al_3Cl_9}}{P_{ref}}\right)^2}{\left(\dfrac{P_{Al_2Cl_6}}{P_{ref}}\right)^3} = \frac{\left(\dfrac{1.02\times10^{-2}\text{ atm}}{1\text{ atm}}\right)^2}{\left(\dfrac{1.00\text{ atm}}{1\text{ atm}}\right)^3} = \mathbf{1.04\times10^{-4}}$$

8-7. The equilibrium expression is $K = \dfrac{P_{boat}}{P_{chair}}$. It does not matter what the units are for pressure , because all we need to know is the *ratio* of the two pressures -- and by Dalton's Law for gases the pressure ratio is equal to the ratio of the mole fractions or mole percentages. Since 6.42% of the molecules are in the chair form, there must be 93.58% of the molecules in the boat form.

Therefore: $$\frac{P_{boat}}{P_{chair}} = \frac{X_{boat}P_{total}}{X_{chair}P_{total}} = \frac{X_{boat}}{X_{chair}} = \frac{93.58}{6.42} = \mathbf{14.6}$$

8-9. To keep track of the partial pressures, it is important to lay out the relationships among the amounts of substances before, during, and after the reaction. This is cleanly done by a table of changes listing initial pressures, the change in pressures on the way to equilbrium, and the equilibrium pressures. The changes in pressure during the reaction are proportional to the stoichiometric coefficients for the substances. A negative change in pressure appears for the reactants, for they are being consumed. A positive change in pressure appears for the products, for they are being generated.

(all P in atm)	H_2	I_2	HI
Initial Pressure	5.73	5.73	0.00
Change in Pressure	$-x$	$-x$	$+2x$
Equilibrium Pressure	$5.73-x$	$5.73-x$	$2x$

These pressures all share a common variable x, which we can obtain in this case because we know the pressure of HI at the end of the reaction:

$$P_{HI} = 9.00 = 2x, \text{ so } x = 4.50 \text{ atm}$$

and:

$$P_{I_2} = P_{H_2} = 5.73 - x = 5.73 - 4.50 = 1.23 \text{ atm}$$

These values are the equilibrium pressures, and they are used to determine the magnitude of the equilibrium constant:

$$K = \frac{(P_{HI})^2}{(P_{H_2})(P_{I_2})} = \frac{(9.00)^2}{(1.23)\times(1.23)} = \mathbf{53.5}$$

8-11. (a) The question tells the amount of SO_2Cl_2 added as a liquid. This will completely vaporize as the system is warmed to the reaction temperature. We must use the ideal gas law to determine the pressure of the SO_2Cl_2 at the start of the reaction.

8-11. (continued)

Rather than calculate the number of moles of SO_2Cl_2 in a separate step, we can use the relation $n = \frac{m}{\mathcal{M}}$ in the ideal gas law, where

m = mass of SO_2Cl_2 and $\mathcal{M}$ = molar mass of SO_2Cl_2.

$$P = \frac{mRT}{\mathcal{M}V} = \frac{(3.174\text{ g}) \times \left(0.08206 \frac{\text{L-atm}}{\text{mol-K}}\right) \times (373.15\text{ K})}{\left(134.97 \frac{\text{g}}{\text{mol}}\right) \times (1.000\text{ L})} = 0.7200\text{ atm}$$

(all P in atm)	SO_2Cl_2	SO_2	Cl_2
Initial Pressure	0.7200	0.00	0.00
Change in Pressure	$-x$	$+x$	$+x$
Equilibrium Pressure	$0.7200 - x$	x	x

We get x by noting that the equilibrium pressures are the partial pressures at the end of the reaction. Then:

$$P_{total} = P_{SO_2Cl_2} + P_{SO_2} + P_{Cl_2}$$

$$1.30\text{ atm} = (0.7200 - x) + x + x = 0.7200 + x$$

$$1.30 - 0.72 = 0.58\text{ atm} = x$$

$$P_{SO_2Cl_2} = 0.7200 - x = 0.7200 - 0.58 = \mathbf{0.14\text{ atm}}$$

$$P_{Cl_2} = P_{SO_2} = \mathbf{0.58\text{ atm}}$$

(b) The values calculated in part (a) are put into the expression for K:

$$K = \frac{(P_{SO_2})(P_{Cl_2})}{(P_{SO_2Cl_2})} = \frac{(0.58) \times (0.58)}{(0.14)} = \mathbf{2.40}.$$

8-13. The equilibrium expression for the first equation is:

$$K_1 = \frac{(P_{CO_2})(P_{SO_2})^2}{(P_{CS_2})(P_{O_2})^3} = \left[\frac{(P_{CO_2})^{\frac{1}{3}}(P_{SO_2})^{\frac{2}{3}}}{(P_{CS_2})^{\frac{1}{3}}(P_{O_2})}\right]^3$$

While that for the second equation is: $K_2 = \dfrac{(P_{CO_2})^{\frac{1}{3}}(P_{SO_2})^{\frac{2}{3}}}{(P_{CS_2})^{\frac{1}{3}}(P_{O_2})}$.

The first equilibrium constant is the cube of the second: $\boldsymbol{K_1 = K_2^3}$.

8-15. The third reaction has XeO_4 *(g)* as a reactant; this also occurs as a reactant in the second reaction. The third reaction has 2 HF *(g)* as a reactant, while the first reaction has it as product.

Therefore, we can try to obtain the third reaction by taking the second reaction and adding it to the *reverse* of the first reaction:

$$XeO_4\,(g) + XeF_6\,(g) \rightleftarrows XeOF_4\,(g) + XeO_3F_2\,(g) \qquad K = K_2$$

$$XeOF_4\,(g) + 2\,HF\,(g) \rightleftarrows XeF_6\,(g) + H_2O\,(g) \qquad K = \frac{1}{K_1}$$

$$XeO_4\,(g) + 2\,HF\,(g) \rightleftarrows XeO_3F_2\,(g) + H_2O\,(g) \qquad K = \frac{K_2}{K_1}$$

8-17. The equilbrium expression is: $K = \dfrac{(P_{NOBr})^2}{(P_{Br_2})(P_{NO})^2}$. The values for the initial partial pressures, when input into the same expression, give us the reaction quotient *Q*. If *Q* > *K*, then the reaction will go to the *left*. If the *Q* < *K*, then the reaction will proceed to the *right*.

(a) $Q = \dfrac{(0.969)^2}{(0.400)(0.105)^2}$ = **213 >** *K*; reaction proceeds ***right* to *left*.**

(b) $Q = \dfrac{(0.969)^2}{(0.105)(0.400)^2}$ = **55.9 <** *K*; reaction proceeds ***left* to *right*.**

(c) $Q = \dfrac{(1.94)^2}{(0.800)(0.210)^2}$ = **107 <** *K*; reaction proceeds ***left* to *right*.**

8-19. (a) The reaction quotient is determined by putting the actual pressures into the equilibrium expression. In this case:

$$Q = \frac{\left(P_{Al_3Cl_9}\right)^2}{\left(P_{Al_2Cl_6}\right)^3} = \frac{\left(1.02 \times 10^{-2}\right)^2}{(0.473)^3} = \mathbf{9.83 \times 10^{-4}}$$

(b) From Problem 5, K = 1.04 × 10^{-4}. Since $Q > K$, the reaction will go *right to left* and there will be net **consumption** of Al_3Cl_9.

8-21. The observations indicate that the reaction proceeds with consumption of Br_2. This means that the initial reaction mixture had a reaction quotient *Q* that was *less* than *K*: $Q < K$.

The value of *K* cannot be obtained from this data, but we can get a limit for it.

$$K > Q = \frac{\left(P_{HBr}\right)^2}{\left(P_{H_2}\right) \times \left(P_{Br_2}\right)} = \frac{(0.90)^2}{(0.40) \times (0.40)} = 5.0625.$$

$K > 5.1$

8-23. The partial pressure of phosgene is one component of the equilibrium

expression: $K = \dfrac{\left(P_{COCl_2}\right)}{\left(P_{CO}\right) \times \left(P_{Cl_2}\right)}$;

Rearranging: $P_{COCl_2} = K \times \left(P_{CO}\right) \times \left(P_{Cl_2}\right)$

$= 0.20 \times 0.025 \times 0.0035 = \mathbf{1.8 \times 10^{-5}}$ **atm.**

8-25. The equilibrium expression is: $K = \dfrac{\left(P_{SO_2}\right)\left(P_{Cl_2}\right)}{\left(P_{SO_2Cl_2}\right)}$

(a) When the reaction begins, $P_{SO_2} = P_{Cl_2} = 0$, so $\mathbf{Q = 0} < K$ and the reaction will proceed to the *right*. Since two moles of gas are produced for every one mole of SO_2Cl_2 consumed, the total number of particles will increase as the reaction proceeds, and so the **pressure will increase**, too.

8-25. (continued)

(b)

(all P in atm)	SO_2Cl_2	SO_2	Cl_2
Initial Pressure	1.50	0.00	0.00
Change in Pressure	$-x$	$+x$	$+x$
Equilibrium Pressure	$1.50 - x$	x	x

At equilbrium: $K = \dfrac{x^2}{1.50 - x} = 2.40$

rearranging: $0 = x^2 + 2.40\,x - 3.60$

The values for x are determined by using the quadratic formula, with

$a = 1$, $b = 2.40$, and $c = -3.60$:

$$x = \frac{-b \pm \sqrt{b^2 - 4ac}}{2a} = \frac{-2.40 \pm \sqrt{(2.40)^2 - (4 \times 1 \times -3.60)}}{2 \times 1} = 1.045 \text{ or } -3.44$$

Note that $x = -3.44$ would mean a *negative* pressure for the products, so this root is rejected as not physically reasonable. The only suitable root is $x = 1.045$, and:

$P_{SO_2} = P_{Cl_2} =$ **1.04 atm**; $P_{SO_2Cl_2} = 1.50 - 1.04 =$ **0.46 atm**

8-27. (a) The pressure of the benzyl alcohol before the reaction proceeds can be calculated from the ideal gas equation:

$$P_{C_7H_8O} = \frac{mRT}{\mathcal{M}V} = \frac{(1.20\text{ g}) \times \left(0.08296 \dfrac{\text{L-atm}}{\text{mol-K}}\right) \times (523\text{K})}{\left(108.14 \dfrac{\text{g}}{\text{mol}}\right) \times (2.00\text{ L})} = 0.238\text{ atm}$$

(all P in atm)	C_7H_8O	C_7H_6O	H_2
Initial Pressure	0.238	0.00	0.00
Change in Pressure	$-x$	$+x$	$+x$
Equilibrium Pressure	$0.238 - x$	x	x

8-27. (continued)

At equilibrium: $K = \dfrac{x^2}{0.238 - x} = 0.558$

rearranging: $0 = x^2 + 0.558\,x - 0.1328$

The values for x are determined by using the quadratic equation,

with $a = 1$, $b = 0.558$, and $c = -0.1328$:

$$x = \frac{-b \pm \sqrt{b^2 - 4ac}}{2a} = \frac{-0.558 \pm \sqrt{(0.558)^2 - (4 \times 1 \times -0.1328)}}{2 \times 1} = 0.180 \text{ or } -0.737$$

The root $x = -0.737$ is rejected as unreasonable. The only suitable root is $x = 0.180$, so $P_{C_7H_6O} = x =$ **0.180 atm**

(b) The pressure of the benzyl alcohol decreases by 0.180 atm from the 0.238 atm at the start. This represents a fractional loss of $\dfrac{0.180}{0.238} =$ **0.756**.

8-29. For this problem, we are only told the total pressure of the $PCl_5 + PCl_3 + Cl_2$ mixture at equilibrium and the value of the equilibrium constant. But these facts are enough, given a knowledge of the reaction stoichiometry, to get an answer.

(all P in atm)	PCl_5	PCl_3	Cl_2
Initial Pressure	y	0.00	0.00
Change in Pressure	$-x$	$+x$	$+x$
Equilibrium Pressure	$y - x$	x	x

The total pressure is the sum of the partial pressures:

$$P_{total} = P_{PCl_5} + P_{PCl_3} + P_{Cl_2} = (y - x) + x + x = y + x$$

$$0.895 = y + x; \qquad y = 0.895 - x$$

$$P_{PCl_5} = y - x = (0.895 - x) - x = 0.895 - 2x; \quad P_{Cl_2} = P_{PCl_3} = x$$

We can get x from the expression for K and these partial pressures:

$$K = \frac{P_{PCl_3} \times P_{Cl_2}}{P_{PCl_5}} = \frac{x^2}{0.895 - 2x} = 2.15 \Rightarrow 0 = x^2 + 4.30\,x - 1.924$$

8-29. (continued)

The values for x are determined by using the quadratic equation:

$$x = \frac{-4.30 \pm \sqrt{(4.30)^2 - (4 \times 1 \times -1.924)}}{2 \times 1} = 0.4086; -4.70$$

The root x = -4.70 is rejected as unreasonable. The only suitable root is x = 0.4086, so: P_{PCl_5} = 0.895 - 2 x = 0.895 - 2 (0.4086) = **0.078 atm**

$P_{Cl_2} = P_{PCl_3} = x =$ **0.409 atm.**

8-31. This problem has two reactants, *both* present at the start of the reaction.

The table tracking their pressures from start to equlibrium is:

(all P in atm)	Br_2	I_2	IBr
Initial Pressure:	0.0500	0.0400	0.00
Change in Pressure:	-x	-x	+2x
Equilibrium Pressure:	0.0500 - x	0.0400 - x	2x

These final pressures go into the equilbrium expression:

$$K = 322 = \frac{(P_{IBr})^2}{(P_{Br_2}) \times (P_{I_2})} = \frac{(2x)^2}{(0.0500 - x) \times (0.0400 - x)}$$

Rearranging: $0 = 318\,x^2 - 28.98\,x + 0.644$

For the quadratic formula: a = 318; b = -28.98; c = +0.644.

$$x = \frac{-(-28.98) \pm \sqrt{(-28.98)^2 - (4 \times 318 \times 0.644)}}{2 \times 318} = 0.0527; 0.0384$$

Here, both roots are positive, but the first one, 0.0527, is greater than 0.0400 or 0.0500, the initial partial pressures of I_2 and Br_2. It would give *negative* pressures of both gases, which is physically unreasonable.

So: P_{I_2} = 0.0400 - x = 0.0400 - 0.0384 = **0.0016 atm**

P_{Br_2} = 0.0500 - x = 0.0500 - 0.0384 = **0.0116 atm**

P_{BrI} = 2 x = 2 (0.0384) = **0.0768 atm.**

8-33. Problem 8-17 refers to three different sets of initial partial pressures. All the gases are at the same temperature, 25°C (= 298.15 K), so the method used convert to concentration units is the same for each. Here is one example in detail-- the conditions for NO in part (a).

We begin with a P_{NO} = 0.105 atm. The ideal gas law can be rewritten to obtain the concentration, $\frac{n}{V}$:

$$[NO] = \frac{n}{V} = \frac{P_{NO}}{RT} = \frac{(0.105\ \text{atm})}{\left(0.08206\frac{\text{L-atm}}{\text{mol-K}}\right)(298.15\ \text{K})} = 4.29 \times 10^{-3}\ \text{mol L}^{-1}$$

The others are worked in turn. Mathematically, the conversion *in this case* is:

$[X] = 0.0408727\ P_X$. where the number refers to the $^1/_{RT}$ term.

	[NO]	$[Br_2]$	[NOBr]
(a)	4.29×10^{-3} M	1.63×10^{-2} M	3.96×10^{-2} M
(b)	1.63×10^{-2} M	4.29×10^{-3} M	3.96×10^{-2} M
(c)	8.58×10^{-3} M	3.27×10^{-2} M	7.93×10^{-2} M

8-35. The value of the equilibrium constant given in problem No. 23 is related to units of *atmospheres.* Here we need units of mol L^{-1}. In the chemical equation, two moles of gas are in the reactants and one mole is in the product, so the sum of the stoichiometric coefficients is: 2 - 1 = + 1.

For an equilibrium in units of mol L^{-1}:

$$\frac{[COCl_2]}{[CO]\times[Cl_2]} = K \times \left(\frac{RT}{P_{ref}}\right)^{+1} = 0.20 \times \left(\frac{\left(0.08206\frac{\text{L-atm}}{\text{mol-K}}\right)\times(873.15\ \text{K})}{1\ \text{atm}}\right) = 14.33\frac{\text{L}}{\text{mol}}$$

$$[COCl_2] = [CO]\times[Cl_2]\times 14.33\ \frac{\text{L}}{\text{mol}}$$

$$= \left(2.3\times10^{-4}\,\frac{\text{mol}}{\text{L}}\right)\times\left(1.7\times10^{-2}\,\frac{\text{mol}}{\text{L}}\right)\times\left(14.33\frac{\text{L}}{\text{mol}}\right) = \mathbf{5.6\times10^{-5}\frac{mol}{L}}$$

8-37. Two equilibrations occur in this experiment: the first as the reactant H_2 and I_2 equilibrate, and the second after the reduction of the partial pressure of the HI. The first equilibrium state is computed in a way similar to Problem No. 9, except here the value for *K*, 53.7, is slightly different.

For the first equilibration:

(all P in atm)	H_2	I_2	HI
Initial Pressure	5.73	5.73	0.00
Change in Pressure	-*x*	-*x*	+2*x*
Equilibrium Pressure	5.73-*x*	5.73-*x*	2*x*

$$K = \frac{(P_{HI})^2}{(P_{H_2})(P_{I_2})} = \frac{(2x)^2}{(5.73-x)^2} = 53.7$$

This problem does not in fact require the quadratic equation, for both the top and the bottom of the fraction are squares, so we can rewrite:

$$\frac{(2x)^2}{(5.73-x)^2} = \left[\frac{2x}{5.73-x}\right]^2 = 53.7 \Rightarrow \frac{2x}{5.73-x} = \sqrt{53.7} = 7.328$$

Rearranging: $x = 4.501$

$P_{HI} = 2x = 9.002$; $P_{I_2} = P_{H_2} = 5.73 - x = 5.73 - 4.501 = 1.229$ atm

For the second equilibration, the preceding partial pressures are altered by the removal of 2.00 atm of HI, so we must do a second calculation, starting with the pressures for H_2 and I_2 derived above and $P_{HI} = 7.002$ atm

(all P in atm)	H_2	I_2	HI
Initial Pressure	1.229	1.229	7.002
Change in Pressure	-*x*	-*x*	+2*x*
Equilibrium Pressure	1.229-*x*	1.229-*x*	7.002 +2*x*

8-37. (continued)

$$K = \frac{(P_{HI})^2}{(P_{H_2})(P_{I_2})} = \frac{(7.002 + 2x)^2}{(1.229 - x)^2} = \left[\frac{7.002 + 2x}{1.229 - x}\right]^2 = 53.7$$

$$\frac{7.002 + 2x}{1.229 - x} = \sqrt{53.7} = 7.328$$

$$x = 0.2148$$

So, at this point: $P_{HI} = 7.002 + 2x =$ **7.43 atm**

For completeness: $P_{I_2} = P_{H_2} = 1.229 - x = 1.01$ atm

This problem illustrates LeChatelier's principle: in response to the stress of removing product, the equilibrium responds by converting more of the reactants to product.

8-39. (a) The additional N_2O on the right of the equation will cause the equilibrium to shift from **right to left** - making more NO and consuming NO_2 and N_2O.

(b) When the volume of the system is reduced, the equilibrium concentrations will react to make *fewer* particles (think in terms of a reduction of crowding). In this system, there are more particles on the left than on the right, so the system will respond to a reduction in volume by moving from **left to right.**

(c) The reaction is exothermic, so heat appears as a "product." Removing heat by reducing the temperature is like removing a chemical product, so the reaction will proceed from **left to right**

(d) The Ar does not cause a reaction, but it does increase the total volume that reacting species have to move around in. This increase in volume will cause the equilibrium to shift to a state of *more* particles, which in this case is from **right to left.**

(e) A non-reactant such as Ar can never affect an equilibrium system, unless it induces a change in volume, which is not the case here. There will be **no effect.**

8-41. There will be different strategies for the different steps. For the first reaction, one should work at ***higher pressures*** (to take advantage of the decrease in the number of gaseous particles) and at ***lower temperatures*** (to remove the heat evolved). For the second reaction, one should work at ***lower pressures*** (because there are more moles of gas among the products) and at ***higher temperatures*** (to give the reaction the heat it requires).

8-43. (a) A reaction that is driven by cooling - removing heat - is one that gives off heat as it proceeds. The reaction is **exothermic.**

(b) A reaction that is driven by decreasing the volume (and thereby increasing the total pressure) must have more gas molecules in the reactants. There is a net **decrease** in the number of gas molecules.

8-45. (a) $K = \dfrac{(P_{H_2S})^8}{(P_{H_2})^8}$ (b) $K = \dfrac{(P_{H_2})(P_{COCl_2})}{(P_{Cl_2})}$ (c) $K = P_{CO_2}$ (d) $K = \dfrac{1}{(P_{C_2H_2})^3}$

8-47. (a) $K = \dfrac{[Zn^{2+}]}{[Ag^+]^2}$ (b) $K = \dfrac{[VO_3(OH)^{2-}][OH^-]}{[VO_4^{3-}]}$ (c) $K = \dfrac{[HCO_3^-]^6}{(P_{CO_2})^6[As(OH)_6^{3-}]^2}$

8-49.

$[N_2O_4]$	$[NO_2]^2$	$K = \dfrac{[NO_2]^2}{[N_2O_4]}$
0.190×10^{-3}	0.784×10^{-5}	0.0412
0.686×10^{-3}	2.70×10^{-5}	0.0393
1.54×10^{-3}	5.27×10^{-5}	0.0342
2.55×10^{-3}	10.8×10^{-5}	0.0423
3.75×10^{-3}	13.7×10^{-5}	0.0363
7.86×10^{-3}	29.9×10^{-5}	0.0380
11.9×10^{-3}	44.1×10^{-5}	0.0370

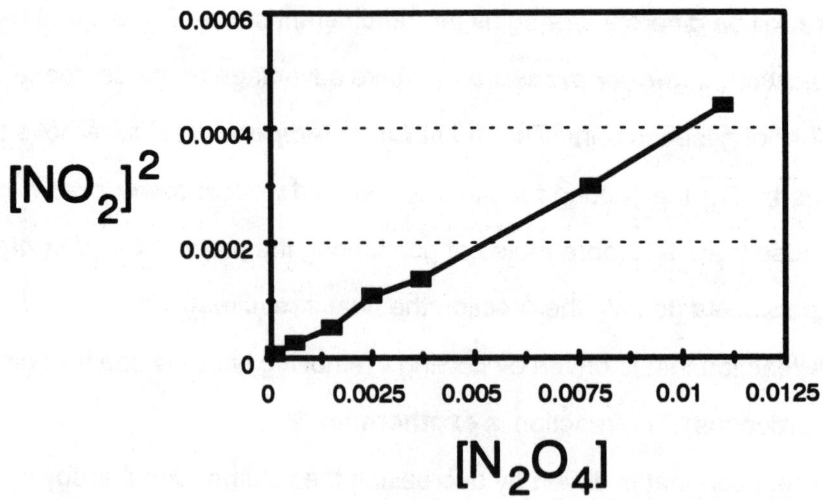

(b) The average value for the *K*'s calculated at the different points is **0.0383**.

8-51. The equilibrium expression for this reaction is: $K = \frac{(P_{H_2})(P_{CO})}{(P_{H_2O})}$

Evaluating *Q* by putting the listed values of the pressures into this equation, we obtain:

(a) $Q = \mathbf{2.05} < K \Rightarrow$ reaction will go to **left to right**.

(b) $Q = \mathbf{3.27} > K \Rightarrow$ reaction will go **right to left**.

8-53. (a) The pressure in the reaction flask is due to build up of the NH_3 *(g)* and the H_2Se *(g)*, which will have equal partial pressures.

$$P_{total} = P_{NH_3} + P_{H_2Se} = 2x$$

$$x = \frac{P_{total}}{2} = \frac{0.0184}{2} = 0.0092 \text{ atm}$$

For this reaction, we have: $K = P_{NH_3}P_{H_2Se} = (0.0092)^2 = 8.46\times 10^{-5}$.

(b) Rearranging the equilibrium expression:

$$P_{H_2Se} = \frac{K}{P_{NH_3}} = \frac{8.46\times 10^{-5}}{0.0252} = 0.00336 \text{atm}$$

8-55. The table of changes relating the starting and final pressures is:

all P in atm	CO_2	H_2	CO
Initial pressure	x	x	0
Change in pressure	$-y$	$-y$	$+y$
Equilibrium pressure	$x-y=$ $x-0.100$	$x-y=$ $x-0.100$	$y=0.100$

We solve for x in the equilibrium expression:

$$K=\frac{(P_{CO})}{(P_{CO_2})(P_{H_2})}=\frac{(0.100)}{(x-0.100)(x-0.100)}=\frac{0.100}{(x-0.100)^2}$$

There is no need to work this problem as a quadratic formula (see also problem No. 37). Taking a square root of both sides and rearranging:

$$(x-0.100)^2=(P_{H_2})^2=\frac{0.100}{K}$$

$$P_{H_2}=\sqrt{\frac{0.100}{K}}=\sqrt{\frac{0.100}{3.22\times10^{-4}}}=\sqrt{310.6}=17.62$$

$$P_{CO_2}=P_{H_2}=\mathbf{17.6\ atm}$$

8-57. A critical piece of information here is that the volumes of the water and the organic solvent are *equal.* Their values are not given, but that is OK. We still know that a decrease in the concentration of iodine in the water by x mol L^{-1} will be matched by an *increase* in the concentration of iodine in the organic layer by the same amount x. In this case, the change in the concentration of the iodine in the water layer is (1.00×10^{-2} M) - (1.30×10^{-4}) = .00987 M.

Therefore: $$K=\frac{[I_2]_{CCl_4}}{[I_2]_{H_2O}}=\frac{0.00987}{0.00013}=76$$

8-59. (a) First reaction: $K_1=[C_6H_5COOH]_{aq}=\left(2.00\frac{g}{L}\right)\times\left(\frac{1\ mol}{122.1\ g}\right)=0.0164$

Second reaction: $K_2=[C_6H_5COOH]_{ether}=\left(660\frac{g}{L}\right)\times\left(\frac{1\ mol}{122.1\ g}\right)=5.41$

8-59. (continued)

The partition reaction is obtained by combining the two solubility equilibria :

$$C_6H_5COOH\ (s) \rightleftharpoons C_6H_5COOH\ (ether) \qquad K_2$$
$$C_6H_5COOH\ (aq) \rightleftharpoons C_6H_5COOH\ (s) \qquad \frac{1}{K_1}$$

$$C_6H_5COOH\ (aq) \rightleftharpoons C_6H_5COOH\ (ether) \qquad K_3 = \frac{K_2}{K_1} = \frac{5.41}{0.0164} = \mathbf{330}$$

8-61. Relative chemical amounts are directly proportional to the mole fractions, so we can say:

$$P_{BCl_3} = \frac{90}{805}P_{total} \qquad P_{BF_3} = \frac{470}{805}P_{total}$$
$$P_{BF_2Cl} = \frac{200}{805}P_{total} \qquad P_{BFCl_2} = \frac{45}{805}P_{total}$$

In the equilbrium expression, the $\frac{P_{total}}{805}$ terms cancel cancel:

$$K_1 = \frac{\left(P_{BFCl_2}\right)^3}{\left(P_{BCl_3}\right)^2\left(P_{BF_3}\right)} = \frac{\left(45\frac{P_{total}}{805}\right)^3}{\left(90\frac{P_{total}}{805}\right)^2\left(470\frac{P_{total}}{805}\right)} = \frac{(45)^3}{(90)^2(470)} = \mathbf{0.024}$$

A similar calculation for the second reaction yields $K_2 = \frac{(45)^3}{(90)^2(470)}$ = **0.40**

(b) The value of the equilibrium constant can be obtained for the third reaction directly from the partial pressures:

$$K_3 = \frac{\left(P_{BFCl_2}\right)\left(P_{BF_2Cl}\right)}{\left(P_{BCl_3}\right)\left(P_{BF_3}\right)} = \frac{\left(45\frac{P_{total}}{805}\right)\left(200\frac{P_{total}}{805}\right)}{\left(90\frac{P_{total}}{805}\right)\left(470\frac{P_{total}}{805}\right)} = \frac{(45)(200)}{(90)(470)} = \mathbf{0.21}$$

However, this third reaction is just a combination of the first two, so we could have obtained K_3 from them.

8-63. (a) The relative concentrations [*cis*] and [*trans*] are a fraction of the total,

$$[cis] + [trans] = [\text{total}]:$$

$$[trans] = 0.736\ [\text{total}] = 0.736\ \frac{(P_{total})}{RT} \qquad [cis] = 0.264\ [\text{total}] = 0.264\ \frac{(P_{total})}{RT}$$

The fact that the concentration P_{total} isn't known doesn't matter in the actual

equilibrium calculation: $K = \dfrac{P_{cis}}{P_{trans}} = \dfrac{0.736\dfrac{(P_{total})}{RT}}{0.264\dfrac{(P_{total})}{RT}} = \dfrac{0.736}{0.264} = \mathbf{2.79}$

(b) The initial pressure for the *cis* compound is, by the ideal gas law (and noting that 426.6°C = 699.75 K):

$$P_{cis(initial)} = \frac{nRT}{V} = \frac{(0.525) \times \left(0.08206 \frac{\text{L-atm}}{\text{mol-K}}\right) \times (699.75\ \text{K})}{15.00\ \text{L}} = 2.010\ \text{atm}$$

All P in atm	P_{cis}	P_{trans}
Initial pressure	2.007	0
Change in pressure	$-x$	$+x$
Equilibrium pressure	$2.007 - x$	x

Then: $K = \dfrac{P_{trans}}{P_{cis}} = \dfrac{x}{2.010 - x} = 2.79 \quad \Rightarrow \quad x = 1.48$

$P_{cis} = 2.007 - 0.529 = \mathbf{0.53\ atm}$ $\qquad$ $P_{trans} = \mathbf{1.48\ atm.}$

8-65. (a) The tabular format works perfectly well even when the system starts with all possible chemical substances present. First, we note that looking at Q will tell us the direction of the approach to equilibrium:

$$Q = \frac{(P_{IBr})^2}{(P_{Br_2})(P_{I_2})} = \frac{(3.00)^2}{(2.00)(4.00)} = 1.125 < K = \mathbf{131}.$$

The reaction will proceed left to *right*, with loss of Br_2 and I_2 and gain of IBr.

8-65. (continued)

(all P in atm)	Br_2	I_2	IBr
Initial pressure:	4.00	2.00	3.00
Change in pressure:	-*x*	-*x*	+2*x*
Equilibrium pressure:	4.00 - *x*	2.00 - *x*	3.00+2*x*

$$K = \frac{(P_{IBr})^2}{(P_{Br_2})(P_{I_2})} = \frac{(3.00+2x)^2}{(4.00-x)(2.00-x)} = \frac{9.00+12.00x+4x^2}{8.00-6x+x^2}$$

For the purposes of clean algebraic manipulation, it is wise to rearrange to the quadratic formula with *K* as a symbol:

$$K\left(8.00-6x+x^2\right) = 9.00+12.00x+4x^2$$

$$0 = (4-K)x^2+(6K+12)x+(9-8K)$$

For the quadratic formula: $a = 4 - K = 4 - 131 = -127$

$b = 6K + 12 = 6(131) + 12 = 798$

$c = 9 - 8K = 9 - 8(131) = -1039$

Processing through the quadratic formula (not shown here) gives two roots:

$x = 1.84$ $\qquad$ $x = 4.44$

The second root is physically unreasonable, since it would give negative equilibrium pressures for Br_2 and I_2. But the first root is reasonable, so then we will have: $P_{Br_2} = 4.00 - 1.84 =$ **2.16 atm**

$P_{I_2} = 2.00 - 1.84 =$ **0.16 atm**

$P_{IBr} = 3.00 + 2(1.84) =$ **6.68 atm.**

8-67. $$Q = \frac{\left(P_{C_6H_{12}}\right)}{\left(P_{C_6H_6}\right)\left(P_{H_2}\right)^3}$$

$$Q = \frac{\left(\frac{n_{C_6H_{12}}RT}{V}\right)}{\left(\frac{n_{C_6H_6}RT}{V}\right)\left(\frac{n_{H_2}RT}{V}\right)^3} = \left(\frac{\left(n_{C_6H_{12}}\right)}{\left(n_{C_6H_6}\right)\left(n_{H_2}\right)^3}\right) \times \left(\frac{V}{RT}\right)^3$$

(a) If we begin with chemical amounts such that $Q = K$, then the addition of H_2 will cause Q to **decrease** to a value less than K. The reaction will go to the **right** in returning to equilibrium.

(b) A decrease in volume will **decrease** Q to a value less than K. The reaction will go to the **left** in returning to equilibrium.

8-69. For reaction 1, the value for $[Cl_2]$ to use in the equilibrium expression is $[Cl_2]$, corrected for the reaction to give HOCl and Cl^-:

$$Cl_2\ (g) \rightleftarrows Cl_2\ (aq) \qquad K_1 = \frac{[Cl_2]}{P_{Cl_2}} = \frac{0.061}{1.00} = \mathbf{0.061}$$

Reaction 2 forms aqueous chloride, hypochlorous acid, and hydrogen ion. Their concentrations will be equal, so $[H^+] = 0.030$ M. The equilibrium constant then becomes:

$$K_2 = \frac{[H^+][HOCl][Cl^-]}{[Cl_2]} = \frac{(0.030)^3}{(0.061)} = \mathbf{4.43 \times 10^{-4}}$$

8-71. (a) The decomposition reaction is:

$$NH_4HS\ (s) \rightleftarrows NH_3\ (g) + H_2S\ (g) \qquad K = \left(P_{NH_3}\right)\left(P_{H_2S}\right)$$

For the first equilibration, the only source of either NH_3 or H_2S is the decomposition reaction. Therefore, the final pressure is equal to twice the pressure of each of them. That is, before the addition of extra NH_3 *(g)*, $P_{NH_3} = P_{H_2S} = 0.659/2 = 0.3295$ atm and $K = (0.3295)^2 = \mathbf{0.1086}$.

(b) The system is then changed by increasing P_{NH_3} by some amount *x*. But rather than carefully tracking pressure changes with *x*'s and *y*'s, we just need to

8-71. (continued)

realize that the equilibrium partial pressure of H_2S will be at a value determined by the equilibrium partial pressure of NH_3 -- *which we are given.*

We are told that at the end $P_{NH_3} = 0.750$ atm

Substituting: $K = (P_{NH_3})(P_{H_2S})$

$$P_{H_2S} = \frac{K}{P_{NH_3}} = \frac{0.1086}{0.750} = \mathbf{0.145\ atm}$$

8-73. We have two equations to work with, and two unknown pressures.

$$P_{total} = P_{CO_2} + P_{CO} \quad \Rightarrow \quad P_{CO_2} = P_{total} - P_{CO}$$

$$K = \frac{P_{CO_2}}{P_{CO}} = \frac{P_{total} - P_{CO}}{P_{CO}} \quad \Rightarrow \quad P_{CO} = \frac{P_{total}}{K+1} = \frac{2.50}{256.4} = \mathbf{0.00975\ atm}$$

$$P_{CO_2} = 2.50 - 0.00975 = \mathbf{2.49\ atm}$$

8-75. We have two equations to work with, and two unknowns. For simplicity:

$[C_{17}H_{35}COOH]$ = [monomer] $\qquad$ $[(C_{17}H_{35}COOH)_2]$ = [dimer]

The initial concentration of the monomer is:

$$[\text{monomer}]_o = \left(\frac{15.0\ \text{g}}{284.48\ \text{g mol}^{-1}}\right) \times \left(\frac{1}{1.250\ \text{L}}\right) = 0.0422\ \text{M}$$

All concentrations in M	[monomer]	[dimer]
Initial concentration:	0.0422	0.00
Change in concentration:	$-2x$	$+x$
Equilibrium concentration	$0.0422-2x$	x

$$K = \frac{[\text{dimer}]}{[\text{monomer}]^2} = \frac{x}{(0.0422 - 2x)^2} = \frac{x}{0.00178 - 0.1688x + 4x^2}$$

$$0 = 4Kx^2 + (-1 - 0.1688K)x + 0.00178K$$

$a = 4K = 160 \qquad b = -1 - 0.1688K = -7.752 \qquad c = 0.00178K = 0.0712$

Use of the quadratic formula yields the roots $x = 0.0123$ and 0.6361. Only the first is physically reasonable. Then:

[monomer] $= 0.0422 - 2x = 0.0176$ M $\qquad$ [dimer] $= x = 0.0123$ M

8-77. This problem does *not* entail an equilibrium *between* PCB-2 and PCB-11. We are merely concerned with the how much they will, relative to one another, partition between octanol and water. Let's assume they both start off with a concentration x in the octanol layer. Then the table of changes becomes:

	$[PCB\text{-}2]_o$	$[PCB\text{-}2]_w$	$[PCB\text{-}11]_o$	$[PCB\text{-}11]_w$
Initial concentration:	x	0	x	0
Change in concentration:	$-y$	$+y$	$-z$	$+z$
Equilibrium concentration	$x - y$	y	$x - z$	z

The equilibrium expressions are the only data we have. We can rearrange each separately to get x:

For PCB-2	$K(2) = \dfrac{x-y}{y}$	$y \times K(2) = x - y$	$\mathbf{[K(2) + 1]y = x}$
For PCB-11	$K(11) = \dfrac{x-z}{z}$	$z \times K(11) = x - z$	$\mathbf{[K(11) + 1]z = x}$

The expressions in bold give a link between y and z.

$$[K(2) + 1]y = [K(11) + 1]z$$

$$\frac{y}{z} = \frac{K(11)+1}{K(2)+1}$$

$$\frac{[PCB\text{-}2]_w}{[PCB\text{-}11]_w} = \frac{126{,}001}{39{,}801} = \mathbf{3.16}$$

This result indicates that the more PCB-2 is left in the water layer; PCB-11 is removed from the water much better than the PCB-2.

8-79. This interesting separation problem is complicated by the fact that there are *unequal volumes of the organic and the water layer.* This means we must keep track of the number of **moles** of I_2 in each layer, not the concentrations. (which was done in Example 8-12). The table of changes in this case is constructed of

8-79. (continued)

amounts of moles, and the last line is a return to concentration units. Moles of I_2 at the start: 0.100 L × 0.002 mol L^{-1} = 0.00020 mol

All concentrations in M	moles I_2 (H_2O)	moles I_2 (CCl_4)
Initial No. of moles	0.0002	0
Change in No. of moles in layer	$-x$	$+x$
Equilibrium No. of moles	$0.0002 - x$	x
Volume of layer (liters)	0.100	0.025
Equilibrium concentration	$\frac{0.0002-x}{0.100}$	$\frac{x}{0.025}$

The last line contains the values needed for the partition equilibrium expression:

$$K = \frac{[I_2\ (CCl_4)]}{[I_2\ (aq)]} = \frac{\left(\frac{x}{0.025}\right)}{\left(\frac{0.0002-x}{0.100}\right)} = \left(\frac{x}{0.0002-x}\right)\left(\frac{0.100}{0.025}\right)$$

$$85 = 4\left(\frac{x}{0.0002-x}\right)$$

Rearranging: $x = 1.9 \times 10^{-4}$; so: $[I_2\ (H_2O)] = 9 \times 10^{-5}$ M

This means that 9×10^{-6} moles of I_2 remaining in the aqueous layer. This is $9 \times 10^{-6} / 2 \times 10^{-4}$ = **0.045** = **4.5%** of the original I_2.

(b) The result from the first part of the problem -- that the 9×10^{-6} mol of I_2 remain in the aqueous phase -- is used in a new separation calculation, with fresh CCl_4. The table is set up as in part (a), except for the different initial value for the moles of I_2 in the aqueous phase.

The equilibrium concentrations are then:

$$[I_2\ (H_2O)] = \frac{9 \times 10^{-6} - x}{0.100} \quad \text{and } [I_2\ (CCl_4)] = \frac{x}{0.025}.$$

8-79. (continued)

These are put into the expression for *K* and the result is solved for *x*:

$$x = 8.6 \times 10^{-6} \text{ mol.}$$

Then the number of moles remaining in the water is

$$I_2\ (H_2O) = 9.0 \times 10^{-6} - 8.4 \times 10^{-6} = 4 \times 10^{-7}.$$

The is a fraction $4 \times 10^{-7} / 2 \times 10^{-4}$ = **0.002** = **0.2%** of the original value.

(c) The single 50.0 mL extraction left 2.3% of the I_2 behind in the aqueous layer. This is more than *ten times* the amount left behind after two 25.0 mL extractions. Smaller separate extractions are much more efficient.

CHAPTER 9 - ACID-BASE EQUILIBRIA

9-1. For this sample, pH = - $\log_{10}[H_3O^+]$ = - $\log_{10}(2.0 \times 10^{-4})$ = +3.70.

Just as there is a mathematical relationship between $[H_3O^+]$, $[OH^-]$ and K_w, where we know $[H_3O^+] \times [OH^-] = K_w$, so there is a very useful relationship between pH, pOH, and pK_w. As discussed in the chapter:

$$pH + pOH = pK_w$$

At 25°C, $K_w = 1.0 \times 10^{-14}$, so we then have:

$$pH + pOH = 14.00$$

$$pOH = 14.00 - pH$$

Here: $pOH = 14.00 - 3.70 = 10.30$.

An important point concerns **significant figures and the pH (or pOH) function.** Consider a number $x = y \times 10^z$. The digit or digits *before* the decimal point in the pH are determined by the exponent *z*. The digits *after* the decimal point are determined by the pre-exponential factor *y*. Any variation in the accuracy or precision of a measurement will be found in the pre-exponential factor *y*. Therefore, in pH, pOH, or pK_a the number of digits after the decimal point is determined by the number of digits in the pre-exponential part of *x*. Conversely, when we go from pH or pOH to the number *x*, the number of digits after the decimal place indicates the number of significant figures that should present in *y*.

9-3.

	Lower pH level	Upper pH level
pH	5.5	6.5
pOH = 14.0 - pH	8.5	7.5
$[H_3O^+] = 10^{(-pH)}$	3×10^{-6}	3×10^{-7}
$[OH^-] = 10^{(-pOH)}$	3×10^{-9}	3×10^{-8}

9-3. (continued)

Note that the pH and pOH values have one digit after the decimal place. Therefore, the pre-exponential factor is determined to *one* significant digit, too.

9-5. **Since nitric acid is a strong acid, the major source of H_3O^+ is nitric acid; the pH represents the concentration of all the moles of hydronium ions that could form.**

In concentration units: $[H_3O^+] = 10^{(-pH)} = 4.79 \times 10^{-3}$ M = $c_{initial}$

The problem is then a dilution problem, where the unknown is c_{final}.

$$c_{final} \times V_{final} = c_{initial} \times V_{initial}$$

$$c_{final} = c_{initial} \times \frac{V_{initial}}{V_{final}} = (4.79 \times 10^{-3} M) \times \frac{1}{8} = 5.99 \times 10^{-5} M$$

$$pH_{final} = -\log_{10}(5.99 \times 10^{-5}) = 3.22$$

$$pOH = 14.00 - pH = 14.00 - 3.22 = 10.78$$

$$[OH^-] = 10^{(-10.78)} = \mathbf{1.7 \times 10^{-11}\ M}$$

9-7. In the seawater $[H_3O^+] = 10^{(-8.00)} = 1.00 \times 10^{-8}$ M

$$pH + pOH = pK_w$$

$$pOH = pK_w - pH = 13.776 - 8.00$$

$$= 5.776$$

$$[OH^-] = 10^{(-5.776)} = \mathbf{1.7 \times 10^{-6}\ M.}$$

9-9. A neutralization reaction will occur, to the extent of the limiting reactant:

$$H_3O^+\ (aq) + OH^-\ (aq) \rightarrow 2\ H_2O\ (l)$$

Note that the acid volume is 11.74 mL = 0.01174 L and the base volume is 15.78 mL = 0.01578 L.

Number of moles of OH^-: 0.01174 L × 0.071 mol L^{-1} = 8.34 × 10^{-4} mol

Number of moles of H_3O^+: 0.01578 L × 0.094 mol L^{-1} = 1.48 × 10^{-3} mol

The OH^- is the limiting reactant. The number of moles of excess H_3O^+ is:

1.48 × 10^{-3} mol - 8.3 × 10^{-4} mol = 6.5 × 10^{-4} mol H_3O^+

9-9. (continued)

This amount of hydronium ion is now present in a total water volume of 0.01578 + 0.01174 = 0.02752 L, so the concentration of hydronium ion is

$$[H_3O^+] = 6.5 \times 10^{-4} \text{ mol } H_3O^+ / 0.02752 = 0.0236 \text{ M}$$

$$pH = -\log_{10}(0.0236) = \mathbf{1.63}$$

9-11. A smaller acid ionization constant means the concentration of hydronium ion is smaller and an acid is weaker. In this pair, benzoic acid is weaker.

9-13. (a) We don't need to know anything but that the compound, in acting as a base, can accept a hydrogen ion from water:

$$C_{10}H_{15}ON\ (aq) + H_2O\ (l) \rightarrow C_{10}H_{15}ONH^+\ (aq) + OH^-\ (aq)$$

(b) The general equation is $K_a \times K_b = K_w$, so $K_b = K_w / K_a$

assuming we are working in water at 25°C (where $K_a = 1 \times 10^{-14}$), we know:

$$K_a = 1.0 \times 10^{-14} / 1.4 \times 10^{-4} = \mathbf{7.1 \times 10^{-11}}$$

(c) Ammonium ion has $K_a = 5.6 \times 10^{-10}$. which makes it a stronger acid than $C_{10}H_{15}ONH^+$. Therefore, $C_{10}H_{15}ON$ is a **stronger** base than ammonia.

9-15. (a) $OCl^-\ (aq) + H_2O\ (l) \rightarrow ClOH\ (aq) + H_3O^+\ (aq)$

(b) The reaction is the hydrolysis of the conjugate base to HOCl.

The acid HOCl has $K_a = 3.0 \times 10^{-8}$.

Therefore: $K_b = 1.0 \times 10^{-14} / 3.0 \times 10^{-8} = \mathbf{3.3 \times 10^{-7}}$

9-17. (a) The conjugate base of phenol is $C_6H_5O^-$. Note that the hydrogen ion leaves the oxygen atom in phenol.

(b) The K_a of phenol is relatively small; phenol is a weak acid. Phenolate ion must therefore be a weak base.

(c) $C_6H_5O^-\ (aq) + H_2O\ (l) \rightleftharpoons C_6H_5OH\ (aq) + OH^-\ (aq)$

9-19. The new equilbrium reaction must be constructed from two other equilibria. Notice that in the reaction written, nitrite ion, NO_2^- *(aq)* is acting as a base while chlorous acid is acting as an acid. These facts suggest we combine the acid equilbrum equation for $HClO_2$ and another reaction where NO_2^- reacts with H_3O^+ to give H_2O and HNO_2 -- the *reverse* of the acid ionization equilibrium for nitrous acid.

$$HClO_2\,(aq) + H_2O\,(l) \rightleftarrows ClO_2^-\,(aq) + H_3O^+\,(aq) \qquad K_a(HClO_2) = 1.1 \times 10^{-2}$$

$$NO_2^-\,(aq) + H_3O^+\,(aq) \rightleftarrows HNO_2\,(aq) + H_2O\,(l) \qquad \frac{1}{K_a(HNO_2)} = \frac{1}{4.6 \times 10^{-4}}$$

$$HClO_2\,(aq) + NO_2^-\,(aq) \rightleftarrows HNO_2\,(aq) + ClO_2^-\,(aq) \qquad K = \frac{1.1 \times 10^{-2}}{4.6 \times 10^{-4}} = \mathbf{24}$$

9-21. (a) The figure shows that the color change for methyl orange occurs at lower pH (range: 3.2-4.4) than the change for bromocresol green (range: 3.8-5.4). The acid form of methyl orange must lose a hydrogen ion more easily than the acid form of bromocresol green. Therefore, the acid form of methyl orange is the stronger acid.

(b) This observation defines a narrow range: around pH 3.8-4.4.

9-23. The chemical amount of the aspirin is $0.65\ g/180.16\ g\ mol^{-1} = 3.6 \times 10^{-3}$ mol. This is used in preparing a 50 mL (0.050 L) solution, so the initial concentration of aspirin is $3.6 \times 10^{-3}\ mol/0.050\ L = 7.22 \times 10^{-2}$ M.

The calculation of a weak acid (or a weak base) equilibrium is best done with the appropriate table of changes:

(all concentrations in M)	$[HC_9H_7O_4]$	$[H_3O^+]$	$[C_9H_7O_4^-]$
Initial concentration :	7.22×10^{-2}	0.00	0.00
Change in concentration:	$-y$	$+y$	$+y$
Equilibrium concentration:	$7.22 \times 10^{-2} - y$	y	y

9-23. (continued)

Note that y is conveniently set equal to the most important chemical quantity, $[H_3O^+]$. The equilibrium concentrations are then put into the acid ionization equilibrium expression for $HC_9H_7O_4$:

$$K_a = \frac{[C_9H_7O_4^-][H_3O^+]}{[HC_9H_7O_4]} = \frac{y^2}{7.22 \times 10^{-2} - y} = 3.0 \times 10^{-4}$$

Rearranging: $0 = y^2 + (3.0 \times 10^{-4})y - 2.166 \times 10^{-5}$

Substitution in the quadratic formula gives $y = 4.5 \times 10^{-3}$ and -4.8×10^{-3}. Only the positive root has physical meaning (the negative root implies a negative $[H_3O^+]$). So $[H_3O^+] = 4.5\times 10^{-3}$ M and **pH = 2.35.**

9-25. The K_a for propionic acid (C_2H_5COOH) is 1.34×10^{-5}. This is relatively small, and the initial concentration is relatively large, so we will try to solve the system without the quadratic formula. The table of changes is still set up as before:

(all concentrations in M)	$[C_2H_5COOH]$	$[H_3O^+]$	$[C_2H_5COO^-]$
Initial concentration :	0.35	0.00	0.00
Change in concentration:	$-y$	$+y$	$+y$
Equilibrium concentration:	$0.35 - y$	y	y

$$K_a = \frac{y^2}{0.35 - y} \approx \frac{y^2}{0.35} = 1.34 \times 10^{-5} \Rightarrow y = \sqrt{(0.35)(1.34 \times 10^{-5})} = 0.00217$$

Assumptions to neglect y in pH calculations like this are justified if y (= $[H_3O^+]$) is less than 5% of the final value of $[H_3O^+]$. Here y is much less than 5% of 0.35. so our assumption to neglect y is justified and $[H_3O^+] = 0.00217$ M; **pH = 2.66.**

(b) Formic acid is only slightly stronger that propionic acid. We can therefore assume that the solution required to generate a pH = 2.66 will be relatively concentrated. In that case, we can take the general equation for $[H_3O^+]$ ("y" in part a) and solve for $[HCOOH]_o$, the initial acid concentration.

9-25. (continued)

$$K_a \approx \frac{[H_3O^+]^2}{[HCOOH]_0} = 1.77 \times 10^{-4}$$

$$[HCOOH]_0 \approx \frac{(0.00217)^2}{1.77 \times 10^{-4}} = \mathbf{0.026\ moles\ per\ liter}$$

9-27. The wording of the question indicates that the quadratic formula is required.

(all concentrations in M)	$[HIO_3]$	$[H_3O^+]$	$[IO_3^-]$
Initial concentration :	0.100	0.00	0.00
Change in concentration:	$-y$	$+y$	$+y$
Equilibrium concentration:	$0.100 - y$	y	y

$$K_a = \frac{[IO_3^-][H_3O^+]}{[HIO_3]} = \frac{y^2}{0.100 - y} = 0.16$$

Rearranging: $0 = y^2 + (0.16)y - 0.016$

Substitution in the quadratic formula gives only one positive (and therefore physically reasonable) root: $y = 0.0697 = [H_3O^+]$. Then **pH = 1.16.**

9-29. The problem gives us the pH (3.31, which means $[H_3O^+] = 4.89 \times 10^{-4}$ M) and intitial acid concentration, 0.205 M. A weak acid at relatively high concentration means we can assume (see problem No. 25):

$$K_a \approx \frac{[H_3O^+]^2}{[papH^+]_o} = \frac{(4.89 \times 10^{-4})^2}{0.205} = \mathbf{1.2 \times 10^{-6}}$$

9-31. The strategy for handling weak bases is similar to weak acids. The starting concentration of the morphine ("morph") is 0.0400 mol / 0.600 mol = 0.0667 M.

(all concentrations in M)	morph	OH^-	$morphH^+$
Initial concentration :	0.0667	0.00	0.00
Change in concentration:	$-y$	$+y$	$+y$
Equilibrium concentration:	$0.0667 - y$	y	y

9-31. (continued) $K_b = \dfrac{y^2}{0.0667 - y} \approx \dfrac{y^2}{0.0667} = 8 \times 10^{-7}$

$$y = \sqrt{(0.0667)(8 \times 10^{-7})} = 0.000230 \ (<< 0.0667)$$

$[OH^-] = 2.3 \times 10^{-4}$ M; pOH = 3.6

pH = 14.00 - pOH = 10.4

9-33. This problem requires that we recognize that the fractional ionization of nitrous acid will indicate the ratio of $[NO_2^-]/[HNO_2] = 4.5\%/95.5\% = 0.0471$

Then we will have: $K_a = \dfrac{[H_3O^+][NO_2^-]}{[HNO_2]} = 0.0471\ [H_3O^+] = 4.6 \times 10^{-4}$

$$[H_3O^+] = 4.6 \times 10^{-4} / 0.0471 = 0.00976 \text{ M}$$

The actual determination of the nitrous acid concentration is done as in the last part of problem 9-25: $[HNO_2] \approx \dfrac{(0.00976)^2}{4.6 \times 10^{-4}} = \mathbf{0.207\ M}$

9-35. (a) basic - CN^-, cyanide, is the conjugate base to HCN, a weak acid.

(b) acidic - Br^- is the conjugate base to HBr, a strong acid; it will have no effect on the pH. The transition metal ion imparts acidity through hydrolysis.

(c) neutral - ClO_4^- is the conjugate base to $HClO_4$, a strong acid; it won't affect the pH. Rb^+, an alkali metal cation, won't hydrolyze to any appreciable extent.

(d) acidic - NO_3^- is the conjugate base to HNO_3, a strong acid, so it will have no affect on the pH. The ion Mg^{2+} will cause acidity through hydrolysis.

9-37. Since the solution as a whole is acidic, the acidity of the $Co(H_2O)_6^{2+}$ cation must be greater than the basicity of acetate. In terms of the equilibrium constants,

$$K_a\,(Co(H_2O)_6^{2+}) > K_b\,(CH_3COO^-)$$

9-39. *K* can be determined from the respective acid ionization equilibria (see No. 19):

$NH_4^+\ (aq) + H_2O\ (l) \rightleftarrows NH_3\ (aq) + H_3O^+\ (aq)$ $\quad K_a(NH_4^+) = 5.6 \times 10^{-10}$

$CN^-\ (aq) + H_3O^+\ (aq) \rightleftarrows HCN\ (aq) + H_2O\ (l)$ $\quad \dfrac{1}{K_a(HCN)} = \dfrac{1}{6.12 \times 10^{-10}}$

$NH_4^+\ (aq) + CN^-\ (aq) \rightleftarrows NH_3\ (aq) + HCN\ (aq)$ $\quad K = \dfrac{5.6 \times 10^{-10}}{6.12 \times 10^{-10}} = \mathbf{0.91}$

9-41. The equation for reaction of equal chemical amounts of acetic acid and hydroxide ion is:

$$CH_3COOH\ (aq) + OH^-\ (aq) \rightarrow H_2O\ (l) + CH_3COOO^-\ (aq)$$

The resulting solution will have an appreciable amount of acetate, CH_3COOO^-, which is itself a weak base. It will hydrolyze to make a basic solution (pH > 7).

9-43. Formic acid is a weak acid, and therefore a mixture of a substantial amount of formic acid and its conjugate base, the formate ion, generates a buffer solution. The total volume is 500 mL, or 0.500 L, so 0.060 mol of formic acid will give [HCOOH] = 0.120 M and 0.045 mol of formate will give $[HCOO^-]$ = 0.090 M. This solution *starts* with these concentrations of formic acid and formate. In a table of changes, we allow the formic acid to dissociate to generate hydronium ion and additional formate ion:

(all concentrations in M)	[HCOOH]	$[H_3O^+]$	$[HCOO^-]$
Initial concentration :	0.120	0.000	0.090
Change in concentration:	$-y$	$+y$	$+y$
Equilibrium concentration:	$0.120 - y$	y	$0.090 + y$

With a buffer of a weak acid like formic acid the concentration of formic acid and formate will change very little from their initial values; this means *y* will be small. In this case:

$$[HCOOH] \approx 0.120\ M \qquad [HCOO^-] \approx 0.090\ M$$

Then: $$K_a = \frac{[HCOO^-][H_3O^+]}{[HCOOH]} \approx \frac{0.090 \times [H_3O^+]}{0.120}$$

$$[H_3O^+] = K_a \times 1.333 = 1.77 \times 10^{-4} \times 1.333 = 2.35 \times 10^{-4}\ M$$

pH = 3.62.

9-45. The 0.25 mol of HCl, a strong acid, will react with the 0.50 mol of tris according to the equation: $HCl\ (aq) + tris\ (aq) \rightarrow Cl^-\ (aq) + trisH^+\ (aq)$

9-45. (continued)

The HCl is the limiting reactant; after this reaction the solution will contain 0.25 mol of $trisH^+$ and 0.25 mol of tris. This is a mixture of a weak acid and its conjugate base, so a buffer exists. The concentration of each species in the 2.00 L of total solution will be: [tris] = 0.125 M and [$trisH^+$] = 0.125 M

We are given $pK_b = 5.92$. But $pK_b + pK_a = 14.00$, so pK_a ($trisH^+$) = 8.08.

The pH is found most directly through the Henderson-Hasselbalch equation, noting that the [tris] = [$trisH^+$] in this case:

$$pH = pK_a - \log_{10}\frac{[trisH^+]}{[tris]} = 8.08 - \log_{10}(1) = \mathbf{8.08}.$$

9-47. (a) This is similar to the situation encountered in problem No. 43. The concentration of acetic acid in the initial mixture (with a total volume of 0.500 L) is 0.10 M, and the concentration of acetate is 0.040 M. Then the hydronium ion concentration (given $K_a = 1.76 \times 10^{-5}$) is:

$$[H_3O^+] = K_a \times \frac{[CH_3COOH]}{[CH_3COO^-]} = (1.76 \times 10^{-5}) \times \left(\frac{0.10}{0.04}\right) = 4.40 \times 10^{-5}\ M$$

pH = 4.36

(b) The added hydroxide ion will react with some of the acetic acid, according to the following equation:

$$CH_3COOH\ (aq) + OH^-\ (aq) \rightarrow CH_3COOO^-\ (aq) + H_2O\ (l)$$

The limiting reactant is hydroxide ion, and after it is gone there will be 0.040 mol of acetic acid (0.080 M) and 0.030 mol of acetate (0.060 M).

The solution is still a buffer, because a significant amount of acetic acid and acetate are both still present. In this case,

$$[H_3O^+] = (1.76 \times 10^{-5}) \times \left(\frac{0.080}{0.060}\right) = 2.35 \times 10^{-5}\ M \quad \mathbf{pH = 4.63}$$

9-49. The optimal buffering species will have a K_a close to the desired $[H_3O^+]$. In this case, given pH = 3.82, $[H_3O^+] = 1.5 \times 10^{-4}$ M. The best acid will be ***m*-chlorobenzoic acid**, with $K_a = 1.04 \times 10^{-4}$.

9-51. One important preliminary calculation is that the total number of moles of OH^- is twice the number of moles of $Ba(OH)_2$:

$$\text{mole } OH^- = 2 \times 0.100 \text{ L} \times 0.375 \text{ mol L}^{-1} = 0.0750 \text{ mol } OH^-$$

i) At the start: The acid-base properties of the solution are determined by the initial concentration of OH^-, which is $\dfrac{0.0750 \text{ mol } OH^-}{0.1000 \text{ L}} = 0.750$ M OH^-

In that case, pOH = $\log_{10}(0.750)$ = 0.125 and **pH = 13.875.**

ii) The equivalence point will occur when the $HClO_4$ added is just sufficient to react with all the OH^- present, or when 0.0750 mol $HClO_4$ has been added. This volume required is: $\dfrac{0.0750 \text{ mol}}{0.4540 \text{ mol L}^{-1}} = 0.16520 \text{ L} = 165.20 \text{ mL}.$

For this part of the problem, we need 1.00 mL less than this amount, or 164.20 mL. Then the amount of $HClO_4$ added is:

$$(0.4540 \text{ mol L}^{-1}) \times (0.16420 \text{ L}) = 0.074546 \text{ mol}.$$

This will leave a small amount of hydroxide unreacted, specifically: 0.07500 - 0.074546 = 0.000454 mol. This will determine the acid-base properties of the solution. With a total volume of 0.1000 + 0.1642 = 0.2642 L, the solution now has a hydroxide concentration of:

$$[OH^-] = \frac{0.000454 \text{ mol}}{0.2642 \text{ L}} = 0.001718 \text{ M}$$

pOH = 2.765; **pH = 11.235**

iii) At the equivalence point of a strong acid-strong base titration, there is exact neutrality, since there are no acids or base present. Therefore, **pH = 7.00**.

iv) The volume of acid added is 0.1662 L, which contains a total of $0.1662 \text{ L} \times 0.4540 \text{ mol L}^{-1} = 0.0754548$ moles of $HClO_4$.

9-51. (continued)

The excess $HClO_4$ is 0.0754548 - 0.0750 = 0.0004548 mol $HClO_4$ which, because $HClO_4$ is a strong acid and the total solution volume is 0.2662 L, will give $[H_3O^+] = \dfrac{0.0004548}{0.2662} = 0.001708$ M, and **pH = 2.767.**

9-53. Preliminaries: HN_3 is a weak acid with $K_a = 1.9 \times 10^{-5}$ and $pK_a = 4.72$,

The number of moles of HN_3 is 0.05000 L × 0.1000 mol L^{-1} = 0.005000 mol at the start of the titration.

i) Before any OH^- added, all that is needed is a simple weak acid calculation:

$$K_a = \frac{y^2}{0.1000 - y} \approx \frac{y^2}{0.1000}; \; y = [H_3O^+]$$

$$y = \sqrt{K_a \times 0.1000} = \sqrt{1.9 \times 10^{-5} \times 0.1000}$$

$[H_3O^+] = 1.265 \times 10^{-3}$ M

pH = 2.89

ii) The number of moles of added OH^- is

0.02500 L × 0.1000 mol L^{-1} = 0.002500 mol.

This will react with an equal amount of HN_3, and the resulting solution will contain 0.002500 mol HN_3 and 0.002500 mol N_3^-, creating a buffer.

A buffer with an equal amount of a weak acid and its conjugate weak base will have (see problem No. 45) pH = pK_a and here, **pH = 4.72.**

iii) The number of moles of added OH^- is:

$$0.05000 \text{ L} \times 0.1000 \text{ mol L}^{-1} = 0.005000 \text{ mol}$$

This is equal to the number of moles of HN_3 in the initial solution. Hence, this is the equivalence point. The HN_3 is all used up, but the product N_3^- is a weak base, and will hydrolyze somewhat. In this experiment:

$$[N_3^-]_o = \frac{0.005000 \text{ mol}}{0.10000 \text{ L}} = 0.05000 \text{ M}$$

$$K_b = K_w / K_a = 1.00 \times 10^{-14} / 1.9 \times 10^{-5} = 5.263 \times 10^{-10}.$$

9-53. (continued)

$$K_b = \frac{[HN_3][OH^-]}{[N_3^-]} = \frac{y^2}{[N_3^-]_0 - y} \approx \frac{y^2}{[N_3^-]_0}; \text{ where } y = [OH^-]$$

$$y = \sqrt{K_b \times [N_3^-]_0} = \sqrt{5.263 \times 10^{-10} \times 0.05000} = 5.129 \times 10^{-6}$$

$[OH^-] = 5.129 \times 10^{-6}$ M; pOH = 5.29; **pH = 8.71.**

iv) The total number of moles of hydroxide ion added is

$$0.05100 \text{ L} \times 0.1000 \text{ mol L}^{-1} = 0.005100 \text{ mol}$$

This is a slight excess over the number of moles of HN_3 initially present. The excess OH^- is 0.005100 - 0.005000 = 1.00×10^{-4} mol. This will lead to total OH^- concentration of: $[OH^-] = 1.00 \times 10^{-14} / 0.10100 \text{ L} = 9.90 \times 10^{-4}$ M.

This is a much larger $[OH^-]$ than the N_3^- that is present could give, so we can neglect the hydrolysis of N_3^-. The pOH will be 3.00 and **pH = 11.00.**

9-55. The equivalence point is reached when the number of moles of added HCl (= 0.0750 mol L^{-1} × 0.01590 L = 0.0011925 mol) is equal to the number of moles of codeine. Thus, there were 0.0011925 mol of codeine in the initial solution. Its mass was 0.0011925 mol × 299.37 g mol^{-1} = **0.357 g.**

At the equivalence point, all of the codeine has been converted into its conjugate acid, $C_{18}H_{21}O_3NH^+$. The pH calculation required is for a weak acid solution. Note: The total volume of the solution is 115.90 mL (=0.11590 L).

$$K_a(C_{18}H_{21}O_3NH^+) = K_w / K_b = 1.00 \times 10^{-14} / 9.0 \times 10^{-7} = 1.11 \times 10^{-8}$$

$$K_b = \frac{[C_{18}H_{21}O_3N][H_3O^+]}{[C_{18}H_{21}O_3NH^+]} = \frac{y^2}{[C_{18}H_{21}O_3NH^+]_o - y} \approx \frac{y^2}{[C_{18}H_{21}O_3NH^+]_o}; \; y = [H_3O^+]$$

$$y = \sqrt{K_a \times [C_{18}H_{21}O_3NH^+]_0} = \sqrt{1.11 \times 10^{-8} \times 0.010289}$$

$$= 1.069 \times 10^{-5} \Rightarrow \quad [H_3O^+] = 1.069 \times 10^{-5} \text{ M}; \quad \textbf{pH = 4.97}$$

The ideal indicator has a transition in color near this pH. It would be **bromocresol green.**

9-57. The amount of hydroxide ion added at equivalence is:

$$0.02328 \text{ L} \times 0.2000 \text{ mol L}^{-1} = 0.004656 \text{ mol.}$$

This is the number of moles of cacodylic acid that was present in the initial solution, so the initial concentration was:

$$0.004656 \text{ mol} / 0.04000 \text{ L} = \mathbf{0.1164\ M}$$

At the half-equivalence point, half of the cacodylic acid had been converted into its conjugate base, cacodylate ion. Under these (buffering) conditions:

$$\text{pH} = \text{p}K_a = 6.19; \qquad K_a = 10^{-6.19} = \mathbf{6.5 \times 10^{-7}}$$

9-59. (a) The pH drops at the equivalence point from above pH = 10 to below pH = 4. This must be the titration of a base by added acid. Such a drop in pH, moreover, could only happen with the titration of RbOH by HBr. If NH_3 were present, we would expect a buffer to form around the pK_a of NH_4^+ -- 9.25.

(b) The transition in pH occurs across the pH range 10 to 4. Many indicators would work, including phenophthalein (transition in the range pH = 10 to 8.2), cresol red (pH = 8.8 to 7.0), bromothymol blue (pH = 7.6 to 6.0) and methyl red (6.0 to 4.8).

(c) The transition occurs after 31 mL (= 0.031 L) of acid have been added. This contains $0.031 \text{ L} \times 0.065 \text{ mol L}^{-1} = 2.015 \times 10^{-3}$ mol of acid. An equivalent amount of base must have been present, so the concentration of base in the original 100 mL (=0.100 L) of solution is:

$$[\text{NaOH}] = 2.015 \times 10^{-3} \text{ mol} / 0.100 \text{ L} = \mathbf{0.020\ M\ NaOH}$$

9-61. The data from Table 9-2 are:

$$H_3AsO_4\ (aq) + H_2O\ (l) \rightleftarrows H_2AsO_4^-\ (aq) + H_3O^+\ (aq) \quad K_{a1} = 5.0 \times 10^{-3}$$

$$H_2AsO_4^-\ (aq) + H_2O\ (l) \rightleftarrows HAsO_4^{2-}\ (aq) + H_3O^+\ (aq) \quad K_{a2} = 9.3 \times 10^{-8}$$

$$HAsO_4^{2-}\ (aq) + H_2O\ (l) \rightleftarrows AsO_4^{3-}\ (aq) + H_3O^+\ (aq) \quad K_{a3} = 3.4 \times 10^{-12}$$

Note that arsenic acid is a weak acid and dihydrogen arsenate ion and hydrogen

9-61. (continued)

arsenate ion are very weak acids. Assume that only the first ionization contributes significantly to $[H_3O^+]$, and that $[H_2AsO_4^-] = [H_3O^+]$. Then we calculate the concentration of hydrogen arsenate and arsenate from these values.

(all concentrations in M)	$[H_3AsO_4]$	$[H_3O^+]$	$[H_2AsO_4^-]$
Initial concentration :	0.100	0.000	0.000
Change in concentration:	$-y$	$+y$	$+y$
Equilibrium concentration:	$0.120 - y$	y	y

$$K_a = \frac{[H_2AsO_4^-][H_3O^+]}{[H_3AsO_4]} = \frac{y^2}{0.100 - y} = 5.0 \times 10^{-3}$$

Rearranging: $0 = y^2 + (5.0 \times 10^{-3})y - 5.0 \times 10^{-4}$

Substitution in the quadratic formula gives:

$$y = \frac{-5.0\times10^{-3} \pm \sqrt{(5.0\times10^{-3})^2 - 4(1)(-5.0\times10^{-4})}}{2(1)} = 0.020 \text{ and } -0.025$$

Only the positive root has physical meaning. So:

$[H_3O^+]$ **= 0.020 M,** $[H_2AsO_4^-]$ **= 0.020 M,** $[H_3AsO_4]$ **= 0.080 M**

We know from the small value for K_{a2} that very little of the $H_2AsO_4^-$ ionizes, so that the value of $[H_3O^+]$ and $[H_2AsO_4^-]$ are set by the first ionization.

Then: $$K_a = \frac{[HAsO_4^{2-}][H_3O^+]}{[H_2AsO_4^-]} = \frac{[HAsO_4^{2-}]\times 0.020}{0.020} = 9.3\times10^{-8}$$

$[HAsO_4^{2-}]$ **= 9.3 × 10⁻⁸ M.**

For the third ionization, we proceed as for the second:

$$K_a = \frac{[AsO_4^{3-}][H_3O^+]}{[HAsO_4^{2-}]} = \frac{[AsO_4^{3-}]\times 0.020}{9.3\times10^{-8}} = 3.0\times10^{-12}$$

$[AsO_4^{3-}]$ **= 1.40 × 10^{-17} M.**

9-63. The initial solution is prepared with a base, the phosphate ion. We are much better off working with the K_b's that go with the three species:

$$PO_4^{3-}\ (aq) + H_2O\ (l) \rightleftarrows HPO_4^{2-}\ (aq) + OH^-\ (aq) \qquad K_{b1} = 4.5 \times 10^{-2}$$

$$HPO_4^{2-}\ (aq) + H_2O\ (l) \rightleftarrows H_2PO_4^-\ (aq) + OH^-\ (aq) \qquad K_{b2} = 1.605 \times 10^{-7}$$

$$H_2PO_4^-\ (aq) + H_2O\ (l) \rightleftarrows H_3PO_4\ (aq) + OH^-\ (aq) \qquad K_{b3} = 1.33 \times 10^{-12}$$

For the calculation, we assume that only the first reaction contributes significantly to the acid-base properties of the solution.

Then: $$K_{b1} = \frac{[HPO_4^{2-}][OH^-]}{[PO_4^{3-}]} = \frac{y^2}{0.050 - y} = 0.045$$

$$0 = 0.00225 - 0.045\,y - y^2$$

The only reasonable root is $y = 0.030$ M, so $[OH^-] = 0.030$ M, $[HPO_4^{2-}] = 0.030$ M, and $[PO_4^{3-}] =$ **0.020 M.**

For the second equilibrium reaction, we use $[OH^-]$ and $[HPO_4^{2-}]$ from the first::

$$K_{b2} = \frac{[H_2PO_4^-][OH^-]}{[HPO_4^{2-}]} = \frac{[H_2PO_4^-](0.030)}{0.030} = 1.61 \times 10^{-7}$$

$[H_2PO_4^-] =$ **1.61×10^{-7}**

For the third equilibrium reaction:

$$K_{b3} = \frac{[H_3PO_4][OH^-]}{[H_2PO_4^-]} = \frac{[H_3PO_4](0.030)}{1.605 \times 10^{-7}} = 1.33 \times 10^{-12}$$

$[H_3PO_4] =$ **7.12×10^{-18}**

9-65. The layout of this problem is identical to that for example 9-13; only the pH is different and here we are told the total concentration of carbonates. The procedure is again to determine the *fraction* of each form of the carbonate, and then to multiply by the concentration of total carbonate. At pH = 5.6, $[H_3O^+] = 2.5\times 10^{-6}$ and The ratios of the various forms are determined by $[H_3O^+]$.

9-65. (continued)

$$\frac{[HCO_3^-]}{[H_2CO_3]} = \frac{K_{a1}}{[H_3O^+]} = \frac{4.3\times10^{-7}}{2.5\times10^{-6}} = 0.172$$

$$\frac{[CO_3^{2-}]}{[HCO_3^-]} = \frac{K_{a2}}{[H_3O^+]} = \frac{4.8\times10^{-11}}{2.5\times10^{-6}} = 1.92\times10^{-5}$$

$$\text{fraction } HCO_3^- = \frac{[HCO_3^-]}{[H_2CO_3]+[HCO_3^-]+[CO_3^{2-}]}$$

This can be solved by dividing through by $[HCO_3^-]$

$$\text{fraction } HCO_3^- = \frac{1}{\frac{[H_2CO_3]}{[HCO_3^-]}+1+\frac{[CO_3^{2-}]}{[HCO_3^-]}} = \frac{1}{\frac{1}{.172}+1+(1.92\times10^{-5})} = 0.14676$$

$$\text{fraction } H_2CO_3 = \frac{\frac{[H_2CO_3]}{[HCO_3^-]}}{\frac{[H_2CO_3]}{[HCO_3^-]}+1+\frac{[CO_3^{2-}]}{[HCO_3^-]}} = \frac{\frac{1}{.172}}{\frac{1}{.172}+1+(1.92\times10^{-5})} = 0.85324$$

$[H_2CO_3]$ = total carbonate × fraction H_2CO_3

= 1.0×10^{-5} M × 0.85324 = **8.5×10^{-6} M**

$[HCO_3^-]$ = total carbonate × fraction HCO_3^-

= 1.0×10^{-5} M × 0.14676 = **1.5×10^{-6} M**

The value for $[CO_3^{2-}]$ will be very small. It is best to determine it from the ratio of hydrogen carbonate to carbonate we calculated above.

$[CO_3^{2-}] = [HCO_3^-]\times1.92\times10^{-5}$

$= 1.47\times10^{-6}\times1.92\times10^{-5}$ = **2.8×10^{-11} M.**

9-67.

	(a) Orange juice	(b) Tomato juice	(c) Milk	(d) Borax	(e) Ammonia
pH	2.8	3.9	4.1	8.5	11.9
pOH	11.2	10.1	9.9	5.5	2.1
$[H_3O^+]$ (M)	1.6×10^{-3}	5.0×10^{-4}	7.9×10^{-5}	3.2×10^{-9}	1.3×10^{-12}
$[OH^-]$ (M)	6.3×10^{-12}	2.0×10^{-11}	1.3×10^{-10}	3.1×10^{-6}	7.9×10^{-3}

9-69. This problem cannot be solved by averaging the pH values for the two solutions because the pH is a logarithmic function. One can average the hydroxide ion concentrations, but only because equal volumes of the solutions are used. The general way to work such mixing experiments is to determine the total number of moles of OH^-, then the final concentration:

Solution #1: $1.00 \text{ L} \times 1.00 \times 10^{-5} \text{ mol L}^{-1} = 1.00 \times 10^{-5} \text{ mol}$

Solution #2: $1.00 \text{ L} \times 1.00 \times 10^{-6} \text{ mol L}^{-1} = 1.00 \times 10^{-6} \text{ mol}$

Total OH^-: 1.10×10^{-5} mol Final volume: 2.00 L

Final $[OH^-]$: 5.50×10^{-6} M Final pOH: 5.26 **Final pH: 8.74**

9-71. Hydronium ion, H_3O^+, is present on the same side of the reaction as Cl^-. So increasing $[H_3O^+]$ will drive the reaction away from Cl^- and toward Cl_2. The conditions should be acidic to ensure experimental success.

9-73. As was done at 25 °C, $[H_3O^+] = \sqrt{K_w(60^oC)} = \sqrt{9.61 \times 10^{-14}} = \mathbf{3.1 \times 10^{-7}}$

9-75. (a) This problem requires the same methodology as No. 39.

$$H_2SO_3\,(aq) + H_2O\,(l) \leftrightarrows HSO_3^-\,(aq) + H_3O^+\,(aq) \quad K_a(H_2SO_3) = 1.54 \times 10^{-2}$$

$$CH_3COO^-\,(aq) + H_3O^+\,(aq) \leftrightarrows CH_3COOH\,(aq) + H_2O\,(l) \quad \frac{1}{K_a(CH_3COOH)} = 5.68 \times 10^{4}$$

$$H_2SO_3(aq) + CH_3COO^-(aq) \leftrightarrows HSO_3^-(aq) + CH_3COOH(aq)$$

$$K = \frac{1.54 \times 10^{-2}}{5.68 \times 10^{-4}} = \mathbf{8.70 \times 10^{2}}$$

The reaction written is **spontaneous**.

9-75. (continued)

(b) A more general approach to all of these is to note that there are two reactions -- one an acid ionization reaction of acid 1, the other the opposite of an acid ionization reaction, or acid 2. Therefore, the equilibrium constant for the combined reaction will be $K = K_a(1)\dfrac{1}{K_a(2)} = \dfrac{K_a(1)}{K_a(2)}$

For this part: $K = \dfrac{K_a(\text{HF})}{K_a(\text{CH}_2\text{ClCOOH})} = \dfrac{6.6\times10^{-4}}{1.4\times10^{-3}} = 0.47$ **-- not spontaneous**

(c) $K = \dfrac{K_a(\text{HCN})}{K_a(\text{HNO}_2)} = \dfrac{4.93\times10^{-10}}{6.6\times10^{-4}} = 1.3\times10^{-6}$ **-- not spontaneous.**

9-77. The Ka of urea acidium ion, $H_2NCONH_3^+$, is given as 0.66 in Table 9-2. This is *not* an acid that only ionizes to a small degree!

(all concentrations in M)	$H_2NCONH_3^+$	H_3O^+	H_2NCONH_2
Initial concentration :	0.15	0.00	0.00
Change in concentration:	$-y$	$+y$	$+y$
Equilibrium concentration:	$0.15 - y$	y	y

$$Ka = \frac{[\text{H}_2\text{NCONH}_2][\text{H}_3\text{O}^+]}{[\text{H}_2\text{NCONH}_3^+]} = \frac{y^2}{0.15 - y} = 0.66 \quad\Rightarrow\quad 0 = y^2 + 0.66y - 0.099$$

The only reasonable root obtained from the quadratic formula is $y = 0.125$,so **[urea] = 0.125 M**, which means $[H_3O^+] = 0.125$ M and **pH = 0.90.**

9-79. (a) Yes, this procedure works. Equal concentrations of CH_3COOH and CH_3COO^- exist in the solution, and with pKa = 4.75, this solution buffer solution will have a pH of 4.75.

(b) Yes, this procedure works. The sodium hydroxide is present in one-half the chemical amount of acetic acid, so one-half of the acetic acid will be converted into acetate. Again equal concentrations of CH_3COOH and CH_3COO^- exist and pH = 4.75.

9-79. (continued)

(c) Yes, this procedure works. The strong base will react with some of the acetic acid to generate an acetic acid/acetate buffer. We know that there must be a substantial amount of both acetic acid and acetate if the pH will be 4.75.

(d) No, this procedure does not work. Hydrochloric acid is a strong acid. It cannot form a buffer at pH = 4.75.

(e) Yes, this procedure works. The excess reagent here is acetate; it will react with all the HCl. The final solution will have equal concentrations of CH_3COOH and CH_3COO^- and pH = 4.75.

9-81. The initial concentrations of the substances will be:

$[C_6F_5COOH]$: 0.025 M $[C_6F_5COO^-]$: 0.030 M

In this buffer, we cannot assume that only a negligible amount of the acid will ionize. Thus, methods that work for much weaker acids, such as the Henderson-Hasselbalch equation, cannot be used. We must calculate the ionization explicitly.

(all concentrations in M)	$[C_6F_5COOH]$	$[H_3O^+]$	$[C_6F_5COO^-]$
Initial concentration :	0.025	0.000	0.030
Change in concentration:	$-y$	$+y$	$+y$
Equilibrium concentration:	$0.025 - y$	y	$0.030 + y$

Then, in this buffer: $K_a = \dfrac{[H_3O^+][C_6F_5COO^-]}{[C_6F_5COOH]} = \dfrac{y(0.030 + y)}{0.025 - y} = 0.033$

$$0 = y^2 + 0.063\,y - 0.000825$$

The only reasonable root is $y = 0.011$, so $[H_3O^+] = 0.011$ M and **pH = 1.95.**

9-83. Moles of OH^- = 0.2023 L × 0.451 mol L^{-1} = 0.09125 mol

Moles of H_2SO_4 = 0.1594 L × 0.251 mol L^{-1} = 0.04001 mol

Since H_2SO_4 is diprotic, it will react with 2 × 0.4001 mol = 0.08001 mol OH^- and 0.09125 - 0.08001 = 0.01123 mol of OH^- will remain in the total volume, 0.362 L. Therefore, $[OH^-] = {}^{0.01123}/_{0.362}$ = 0.031 M and pOH = 1.73; **pH = 12.27.**

9-85. The experiment involves addition of HCl to a solution of benzoate, to give a solution of unreacted (excess) HCl + benzoic acid. Upon addition of the hydroxide, the *HCl will react first*, and the benzoic acid will react second. Thus, the first equivalence point indicates the complete consumption of the unreacted HCl. At this point, the amount of NaOH added was 0.04650 L × 0.393 mol L^{-1} = 0.018275 mol OH^-, so the amount of excess HCl added was 0.018275 mol. The second equivalence point is reached when all of the benzoic acid was used up. The volume of NaOH used to neutralized the benzoic acid was (0.06391 L - 0.04650 L) = 0.01711 L. The number of moles of NaOH in this volume was 0.01711 L × 0.393 mol L^{-1} = 0.006725 mol OH^-. This is equal to the number of moles of benzoic acid, and to the number of moles of benzoate in the original sample. Therefore, the mass of the benzoate in the original sample is 0.006725 mol × 144.105 g mol^{-1} = **0.969g sodium benzoate.**

We can check the titration results by noting that the number of moles of benzoic acid and excess HCl must equal the number of moles of HCl added to the salt mixture. In this case, that is:

moles HCl + moles benzoic acid = moles HCl_{added}

0.018275 mol + 0.006725 mol = 0.500 mol L^{-1} × 0.0500 L

0.025000 mol = 0.02500

9-87. (a) $HCO_3^- (aq) + HC_3H_5O_3 (aq) \rightarrow H_2CO_3 (aq) + C_3H_5O_3^- (aq)$

$$H_2CO_3 (aq) \rightarrow CO_2 (g) + H_2O (l)$$

Overall: $HCO_3^- (aq) + HC_3H_5O_3 (aq) \rightarrow CO_2 (g) + H_2O (l) + C_3H_5O_3^- (aq)$

(b) $236.6 \text{ mL} / 48 \text{ tsp} = 4.93 \text{mL} / 1 \text{ tsp} = 4.93 \text{cm}^3 / 1 \text{ tsp}$

$$\text{g baking soda} = 0.5 \text{ tsp} \times \left(\frac{4.93 \text{cm}^3}{1 \text{ tsp}}\right) \times \left(\frac{2.16 \text{ g}}{\text{cm}^3}\right) = 5.325 \text{ g}$$

$$\text{mol } NaHCO_3 = \text{mol } HC_3H_5O_3 = \frac{5.325 \text{ g}}{84.01 \text{ g mol}^{-1}} = 0.0634 \text{ mol}$$

volume of milk = 1 cup = 0.2366 L

$$[HC_3H_5O_3] = \frac{0.0634 \text{ mol}}{0.2366 \text{ L}} = \mathbf{0.27 \text{ M}}$$

(c) We calculated that 0.5 tsp of baking soda contains 0.0634 mol of $NaHCO_3$. This will yield an equivalent number of moles of CO_2, and at 177 °C = 450 K the CO_2 will occupy a volume of:

$$V = \frac{nRT}{P} = \frac{(0.0634 \text{ mol}) \times (0.08206 \frac{\text{L-atm}}{\text{mol-K}}) \times (450 \text{ K})}{1 \text{ atm}}$$

$$= \mathbf{2.34 \text{ L}}$$

9-89. For the sake of compactness, phosphonocarboxylic acid will be abbreviated "H_3PC". The three ionization equilbria are:

$$H_3PC (aq) + H_2O (l) \rightleftarrows H_2PC^- (aq) + H_3O^+ \qquad K_{a1} = \frac{[H_3O^+][H_2PC^-]}{[H_3PC]}$$

$$H_2PC^- (aq) + H_2O (l) \rightleftarrows HPC^{2-} (aq) + H_3O^+ \qquad K_{a2} = \frac{[H_3O^+][HPC^{2-}]}{[H_2PC^-]}$$

$$HPC^{2-} (aq) + H_2O (l) \rightleftarrows PC^{3-} (aq) + H_3O^+ \qquad K_{a3} = \frac{[H_3O^+][PC^{3-}]}{[HPC^{2-}]}$$

9-89. (continued)

The ratios of the various species is set by the pH of the blood, 7.40 ($[H_3O^+] = 3.981 \times 10^{-8}$ M). This will not vary.

$$\frac{[H_2PC^-]}{[H_3PC]} = \frac{K_{a1}}{[H_3O^+]} = \frac{0.01}{3.981 \times 10^{-8}} = 2.512 \times 10^5$$

$$\frac{[HPC^{2-}]}{[H_2PC^-]} = \frac{K_{a2}}{[H_3O^+]} = \frac{7.8 \times 10^{-6}}{3.981 \times 10^{-8}} = 195.9$$

$$\frac{[PC^{3-}]}{[HPC^{2-}]} = \frac{K_{a3}}{[H_3O^+]} = \frac{2.0 \times 10^{-9}}{3.981 \times 10^{-8}} = 0.0502$$

These will all contribute to the fractional amount of each species. For the calculations, though, it helps to have all species as a ratio to just one of them - here chosen to be $[H_3PC]$:

$$\frac{[HPC^{2-}]}{[H_3PC]} = \frac{[HPC^{2-}]}{[H_2PC^-]} \times \frac{[H_2PC^-]}{[H_3PC]} = 195.9 \times 2.513 \times 10^5 = 4.921 \times 10^7$$

$$\frac{[PC^{3-}]}{[H_3PC]} = \frac{[PC^{3-}]}{[HPC^{2-}]} \times \frac{[HPC^{2-}]}{[H_3PC]} = 0.0502 \times 4.921 \times 10^7 = 2.47 \times 10^6$$

Before determining the actual concentrations , we should determine the fractional amounts of each of the species.

$$\text{fraction } H_3PC = \frac{[H_3PC]}{[H_3PC]+[H_2PC^-]+[HPC^{2-}]+[PC^{3-}]};$$

Divide top and bottom by $[H_3PC]$:

$$= \frac{1}{1+\frac{[H_2PC^-]}{[H_3PC]}+\frac{[HPC^{2-}]}{[H_3PC]}+\frac{[PC^{3-}]}{[H_3PC]}}$$

$$= \frac{1}{1+2.512 \times 10^5 + 4.921 \times 10^7 \times 2.47 \times 10^6} = 1.93 \times 10^{-8}$$

$$\text{fraction } H_2PC^- = \frac{[H_2PC^-]}{[H_3PC]+[H_2PC^-]+[HPC^{2-}]+[PC^{3-}]};$$

9-89. (continued)

Divide top and bottom by $[H_3PC]$:

$$= \frac{\dfrac{[H_2PC^-]}{[H_3PC]}}{1+\dfrac{[H_2PC^-]}{[H_3PC]}+\dfrac{[HPC^{2-}]}{[H_3PC]}+\dfrac{[PC^{3-}]}{[H_3PC]}}$$

$$\text{fraction } H_2PC^- = \frac{2.513\times10^5}{1+2.512\times10^5+4.921\times10^7\times2.47\times10^6} = 4.84\times10^{-3}$$

$$\text{fraction } HPC^{2-} = \frac{[HPC^{2-}]}{[H_3PC]+[H_2PC^-]+[HPC^{2-}]+[PC^{3-}]};$$

Divide top and bottom by $[H_3PC]$:

$$= \frac{\dfrac{[HPC^{2-}]}{[H_3PC]}}{1+\dfrac{[H_2PC^-]}{[H_3PC]}+\dfrac{[HPC^{2-}]}{[H_3PC]}+\dfrac{[PC^{3-}]}{[H_3PC]}}$$

$$= \frac{4.923\times10^7}{1+2.512\times10^5+4.921\times10^7\times2.47\times10^6} = 0.9476$$

The fractional amount of PC^{3-} is obtained by difference:

fraction PC^{3-} = $1.00 - 1.92\times10^{-8} - 4.84\times10^{-3} - 0.9476 = 0.04756$

These fractional values permit the determination of absolute concentatrations, given a total concentration of all species of 1.0×10^{-5} M:

$$[H_3PC] = (1.93\times10^{-8})(1.0\times10^{-5}\ \text{M}) = 1.9\times10^{-13}\ \text{M}$$

Similarly: $[H_2PC^-] = 4.8\times10^{-8}$ M; $[HP^{2-}] = 9.5\times10^{-6}$ M; $[P^{3-}] = 4.7\times10^{-7}$ M

CHAPTER 10 - DISSOLUTION AND PRECIPITATION EQUILIBRIA

10-1. The mass of one mole of $CuSeO_4$ is 206.50 g and the mass of five moles of H_2O is 90.08 g. Therefore, the fraction of mass due to $CuSeO_4 \cdot 5H_2O$ is:

$$\frac{206.50 \text{ g } CuSeO_4}{(206.50 + 90.08) \text{ g } CuSeO_4 \cdot 5H_2O} = 0.6963$$

We assume that above 150° C all of the water will be driven off, leaving only the mass of the copper (II) selenate that was in the initial sample:

64.8 g x 0.6963 = **45.1 g solid**

10-3. The mass of the water of cystallization in this sample is 38.4 - 21.2 = 17.2 g H_2O. This corresponds to $\frac{17.2 \text{ g}}{18.0153 \text{ g mol}^{-1}} = 0.9547 \text{ mol } H_2O$.

This was combined with 21.2 g $CoSO_4$, which corresponds to

$$\frac{21.2 \text{ g}}{155.00 \text{ g mol}^{-1}} = 0.1368 \text{ mol } CoSO_4.$$

Thus the molar ratio of water to cobalt is $\frac{0.9547 \text{ mol}}{0.1368 \text{ mol}} = 6.98 \sim 7.00 \frac{\text{mol } H_2O}{\text{mol } CoSO_4}$

The formula for bieberite is **$CoSO_4 \cdot 7H_2O$.**

10-5. The temperature where 80 g of KBr will dissolve is at about **47-48 °C**.

10-7. Endothermic reactions proceed more to the right with increased temperature. Thus, the solubility of NH_4Cl will **increase**.

10-9. (a) Molarity $SrBr_2 = \frac{0.156 \text{ mol } SrBr_2}{4.15 \text{ L solution}} =$ **0.0376 M $SrBr_2$**

(b) $\left(0.0376 \frac{\text{mol } SrBr_2}{\text{L}}\right) \times \left(\frac{2 \text{ mol } Br^-}{1 \text{ mol } SrBr_2}\right) =$ **0.0752 M Br^-**

10-11. (a) $SrI_2 (s) \rightleftarrows Sr^{2+} (aq) + 2 I^- (aq)$ $K_{sp} = [Sr^{2+}][I^-]^2$

(b) $I_2 (s) \rightleftarrows I_2 (aq)$ $K_{sp} = [I_2]$

(c) $Ca_3(PO_4)_2\ (s) \leftrightarrows 3\ Ca^{2+}\ (aq) + 2\ PO_4^{3-}\ (aq)$ $K_{sp} = [Ca^{2+}]^3\ [PO_4^{3-}]^2$

(d) $BaCrO_4\ (s) \leftrightarrows Ba^{2+}\ (aq) + CrO_4^{2-}\ (aq)$ $K_{sp} = [Ba^{2+}]\ [CrO_4^{2-}]$

10-13. $Fe_2(SO_4)_3 \leftrightarrows 2\ Fe^{3+}\ (aq) + 3\ SO_4^{2-}\ (aq)$ $K_{sp} = [Fe^{3+}]^2\ [SO_4^{2-}]^3$

10-15. For this: $K_{sp} = [Hg_2^{2+}]\ [I^-]^2$; The table of changes is:

(All concentrations in M)	$[Hg_2^{2+}]$	$[I^-]$
Initial Concentration	0.0	0.0
Change in Concentration	$+x$	$+2x$
Equilibrium Concentration	x	$2x$

Here, $[Hg_2^{2+}] = x$ and $[I^-] = 2x$. Therefore:

$$K_{sp} = (x)\ (2x)^2 = 4x^3$$

$$x = \sqrt[3]{\frac{K_{sp}}{4}} = \sqrt[3]{\frac{1.2 \times 10^{-28}}{4}} = \sqrt[3]{3.0 \times 10^{-29}} = 3.1 \times 10^{-10}$$

$[Hg_2^{2+}] = 3.1 \times 10^{-10}$ M **$[I^-] = 6.2 \times 10^{-10}$ M**

10-17. It is best to determine solubilities in mol L^{-1}, then convert to the final volume (here 100.0 mL = 0.100 L). For the general case for $TlIO_3$:

(All concentrations in M)	$[Tl^+]$	$[IO_3^-]$
Initial Concentration	0.0	0.0
Change in Concentration	$+x$	$+x$
Equilibrium Concentration	x	x

$$K_{sp} = [Tl^+]\ [IO_3^-] = x^2$$

$$x = \sqrt{K_{sp}} = \sqrt{3.07 \times 10^{-5}} = 1.752 \times 10^{-3}$$

The solubility of $TlIO_3$ is equal to the concentration of Tl^+ present at equilibrium, 1.75×10^{-3} M. In 100.0 mL of water, so little $TlIO_3$ will dissolve that we can assume the total solution volume is 100.0 mL (= 0.1000 L). For this solution (note that molar mass of $TlIO_3$ is 379.29 g mol^{-1}):

$$1.752 \times 10^{-3}\ \frac{\text{mol } TlIO_3}{L} \times (0.100\ L) \times \frac{379.29\ \text{g } TlIO_3}{1\ \text{mol } TlIO_3} = \mathbf{0.0665\ g\ TlIO_3}$$

10-19.

(All concentrations in M)	$[K^+]$	$[ClO_4^-]$
Initial Concentration	0.0	0.0
Change in Concentration	+x	+x
Equilibrium Concentration	x	x

$K_{sp} = x^2 \quad \Rightarrow \quad x = \sqrt{K_{sp}} = \sqrt{1.07 \times 10^{-2}} = 0.1034$

$[KClO_4] = 0.1034$ mol L^{-1}

grams = $(0.1034 \text{ mol } L^{-1}) \times (138.55 \text{ g mol}^{-1}) = \mathbf{14.3 \text{ g } L^{-1}}$

10-21. Another layout used to computer the solubility of salts in **pure water** is to write the relative equilibrium concentrations under the reaction:

$Ag_2CrO_4\ (s) \rightleftarrows 2\ Ag^+\ (aq) + CrO_4^{2-}\ (aq)$

at equilibrium: $2x$ $\quad x$

Given the solubility of 0.0129 g in 500 mL of H_2O, the solubility in mol L^{-1} is:

$$\frac{0.0129 \text{ g } Ag_2CrO_4}{500 \text{ mL}} \times \frac{500 \text{ mL}}{0.5 \text{ L}} \times \frac{1 \text{ mol } Ag_2CrO_4}{331.73 \text{ g } Ag_2CrO_4} = 7.78 \times 10^{-5} \frac{\text{mol } Ag_2CrO_4}{\text{L}}$$

This value, 7.78×10^{-5} M, is "x" above. Thus:

$K_{sp} = [Ag^+]^2 [CrO_4^{2-}]$

$= (2x)^2 (x) = 4x^3 = 4 (7.78 \times 10^{-5})^3 = \mathbf{1.9 \times 10^{-12}}$

10-23. The reaction is: $AgCl\ (s) \rightleftarrows Ag^+\ (aq) + Cl^-\ (aq)$

At equilibrium: $x \quad x$

Solubility in M: $\dfrac{1.8 \times 10^{-2} \text{ g } L^{-1}}{143.32 \text{ g mol}^{-1}} = 1.256 \times 10^{-4} \text{ M} = x$

$K_{sp} = x^2 = \mathbf{1.6 \times 10^{-8}}$

10-25. We answer this by determining the value of the reaction quotient Q generated by the high temperature equilibrium:

$[Ba^{2+}] = [CrO_4^{2-}] = \dfrac{6.3 \times 10^{-3} \text{ g } L^{-1}}{253.32 \text{ g mol}^{-1}} = 2.49 \times 10^{-5}$ M

$Q = [Ba^{2+}] [CrO_4^{2-}] = (2.49 \times 10^{-5})^2 = \mathbf{6.2 \times 10^{-10}}$

10-25. (continued)

At 25 °C, $K_{sp} = 2.1 \times 10^{-10}$ (from Table 10-1). Since $Q > K_{sp}$, **precipitation will occur** upon cooling.

10-27. We are only concerned with $[Ce^{3+}]$ and $[IO_3^-]$. They are the species that enter into the solubility product constant. The solubility equilibrium is:

$Ce(IO_3)_3\ (s) \rightleftarrows Ce^{3+}\ (aq) + 3\ IO_3^-\ (aq)$ $\quad Q = [Ce^{3+}]\,[IO_3]^3$

The relevant concentrations are due to the added Ce^{3+} and IO_3^-. Both will be diluted from their initial concentrations, because the final solution has a larger volume (400.0 mL) due to mixing. The general equation for a concentration C_{final} after dilution is:

$$C_{final} = C_{initial} \times \left(\frac{V_{initial}}{V_{final}}\right)$$

$$[Ce^{3+}] = (2.0 \times 10^{-3}\text{ M}) \times \left(\frac{250.0\text{ mL}}{400.0\text{ mL}}\right) = 1.25 \times 10^{-3}\text{ M}$$

$$[IO_3^-] = (1.0 \times 10^{-2}\text{ M}) \times \left(\frac{150\text{ mL}}{400.0\text{ mL}}\right) = 3.75 \times 10^{-3}\text{ M}$$

We put these concentrations into the expression for Q:

$Q = (1.25 \times 10^{-3})\,(3.75 \times 10^{-3})^3 = 6.6 \times 10^{-11} < K_{sp}$

No precipitate will form.

10-29. This sort of problem is worked in more detail in No. 27. Note that the volume of NaF solution is 1000 mL - 140 mL = 860 mL. Then:

moles F^- added = 0.860 L × 0.0050 mol L^{-1} = 4.3×10^{-3} moles

$[Sr^{2+}] = 1.4 \times 10^{-4}$ M $\qquad [F^-] = 4.3 \times 10^{-3}$ M

$Q = [Sr^{2+}]\,[F^-]^2 = (1.4 \times 10^{-4})(4.3 \times 10^{-3})^2 = \mathbf{2.6 \times 10^{-9} < K_{sp}}$

No precipitate will form

10-31. The wording of the problem indicates that a precipitation will occur, so we can skip a calculation of Q. The initial concentrations of Pb^{2+} and IO_3^- *are* required for the equilibrium calculation. The volume of the solution after mixing will be 90.0 mL.

10-31. (continued)

$$[Pb^{2+}]_{initial} = [Pb^{2+}]_{stock} \times \left(\frac{V_{stock}}{V_{initial}}\right) = 0.0500\ \text{M} \times \left(\frac{50\ \text{mL}}{90\ \text{mL}}\right) = 0.0278\ \text{M}$$

$$[IO_3^-]_{initial} = [IO_3^-]_{stock} \times \left(\frac{V_{stock}}{V_{initial}}\right) = 0.200\ \text{M} \times \left(\frac{40\ \text{mL}}{90\ \text{mL}}\right) = 0.0889\ \text{M}$$

Before continuing, we note that this reaction will go essentially to completion, and that Pb^{2+} is a limiting reactant. This key insight leads to the most convenient way to work the calculation: **(i)** assume that all the Pb^{2+} will precipitate, along with a stoichiometric amount of IO_3^-. Then **(ii)** determine how much Pb^{2+} is soluble in the presence of the unreacted IO_3^-.

Here, the moles of IO_3^- that will precipitate is twice the number of moles of Pb^{2+}, 2×0.0278 moles $L^{-1} = 0.0556$ mol L^{-1}. The remaining IO_3^- will be

$[IO_3^-] = (0.0889\ \text{mol L}^{-1}) - (0.0556\ \text{mol L}^{-1}) = 0.0333\ \text{M}$.

If we assume x moles of $Pb(IO_3)_2$ dissolves in the presence of 0.0333 M, then:

$$K_{sp} = [Pb^{2+}]\,[IO_3^-]^2$$

$$[Pb^{2+}] = \frac{K_{sp}}{[IO_3^-]^2} = \frac{2.6 \times 10^{-13}}{(0.0333)^2} = \mathbf{2.3 \times 10^{-10}\ M}$$

10-33. As in No. 31: Volume of final solution: 80.0 mL = 0.0800 L

moles of Ag^+: $0.0500\ \text{L} \times 0.100\ \text{mol L}^{-1} = 5 \times 10^{-3}$ mol

moles of CrO_4^{2-}: $0.0300\ \text{L} \times (0.0600\ \text{mol L}^{-1}) = 1.8 \times 10^{-3}$ mol

The CrO_4^{2-} is the limiting reactant, and the moles of Ag^+ that remain in solution (note that 2 Ag^+ precipitate for 1 CrO_4^{2-}) is:

$(5 \times 10^{-3}\ \text{mol}) - (2 \times 1.8 \times 10^{-3}\ \text{mol}) = 1.4 \times 10^{-3}$ mol Ag^+

The silver concentration will be: $[Ag^+] = \dfrac{1.4 \times 10^{-3}\ \text{mol Ag}^+}{0.080\ \text{L solution}} = \mathbf{0.018\ M.}$

In the solubility product equilibrium:

$$K_{sp} = [Ag^+]\,[CrO_4^{2-}]$$

$$[CrO_4^{2-}] = \frac{K_{sp}}{[Ag^+]^2} = \frac{1.9 \times 10^{-12}}{(0.0175)^2} = \mathbf{6.2 \times 10^{-9}\ M}$$

10-35. The solubility of the salt will equal the concentration of Ca^{2+}. K_{sp} is taken from Table 10-1.

$$K_{sp} = [Ca^{2+}]\,[F^-]^2$$

$$[Ca^{2+}] = \frac{K_{sp}}{[F^-]^2} = \frac{3.9 \times 10^{-11}}{(0.040)^2} = \mathbf{2.4 \times 10^{-8}\ M}$$

10-37. (a) If we set $[Ni^{2+}] = x$, then

$[OH^-] = 2x$ (neglecting the autoionization of water) and:

$$K_{sp} = [Ni^{2+}]\,[OH^-]^2 = 4x^3$$

$$x = \sqrt[3]{\frac{K_{sp}}{4}} = \sqrt[3]{\frac{1.6 \times 10^{-16}}{4}} = 3.4 \times 10^{-6}$$

Solubility = $[Ni^{2+}]$ = $\mathbf{3.4 \times 10^{-6}\ mol\ L^{-1}}$

(b) In this case, $[OH^-]$ is set by [NaOH], just like any common ion problem:

$$K_{sp} = [Ni^{2+}]\,[OH^-]^2$$

$$[Ni^{2+}] = \frac{K_{sp}}{[OH^-]^2} = \frac{1.6 \times 10^{-16}}{(0.100)^2} = 1.6 \times 10^{-14}\ M$$

Solubility = $[Ni^{2+}]$ = $\mathbf{1.6 \times 10^{-14}\ mol\ L^{-1}}$

10-39. If we set $[Ag^+] = x$, then in the *absence of other acid-base effects* such as buffering, $[OH^-] = x$. K_{sp} is taken from Table 10-1. Then:

$$K_{sp} = x^2 \quad \Rightarrow \quad x = \sqrt{K_{sp}} = \sqrt{1.5 \times 10^{-8}} = 1.2 \times 10^{-4}$$

$[Ag^+]$ = $\mathbf{1.2 \times 10^{-4}\ mol\ L^{-1}}$

When buffered at pH = 7, $[OH^-]$ will be a constant 10^{-7} M:

$$K_{sp} = [Ag^+]\,[OH^-] \qquad [Ag^+] = \frac{1.5 \times 10^{-8}}{1 \times 10^{-7}} = \mathbf{0.15\ M}$$

The solubility is over 1000 times higher at a buffered *p*H = 7.

10-41. If the solubility of the salt is 0.001 mol L^{-1}, then $[Fe^{2+}] = 0.001$ mol L^{-1}, and we can solve for $[OH^-]$. K_{sp} is taken from Table 10-1.

$$K_{sp} = [Fe^{2+}]\,[OH^-]^2 \Rightarrow [OH^-] = \sqrt{\frac{K_{sp}}{[Fe^{2+}]}} = \sqrt{\frac{1.6 \times 10^{-14}}{0.001}} = 4 \times 10^{-6}\ M$$

pOH = 5.4 ; **pH = 8.6**

10-43. (a) From Table 10-1:

K_{sp} (MgC_2O_4) = 8.6×10^{-5} K_{sp} (PbC_2O_4) = 2.7×10^{-11}

Both are 1 : 1 salts, so we are tell from the smaller K_{sp} for PbC_2O_4 that it is less soluble and Pb^{2+} will be present in the solid. To answer the first part of the question, we must determine the concentration of $C_2O_4{}^{2-}$ that will just cause the precipitation of magnesium oxalate:

$[Mg^{2+}]\ [C_2O_4{}^{2-}] = K_{sp}.$

$$[C_2O_4{}^{2-}] = \frac{K_{sp}}{[Mg^{2+}]} = \frac{8.6 \times 10^{-5}}{0.10} = \mathbf{8.6 \times 10^{-4}\ M}$$

(b) If we have $[C_2O_4{}^{2-}] = 8.6 \times 10^{-4}$ M, then what is $[Pb^{2+}]$?

$[Pb^{2+}]\ [C_2O_4{}^{2-}] = K_{sp}\ (PbC_2O_4)$

$$[Pb^{2+}] = \frac{K_{sp}}{[C_2O_4{}^{2-}]} = \frac{2.7 \times 10^{-11}}{8.6 \times 10^{-4}} = 3.1 \times 10^{-8}\ M$$

Since we started with 0.1 M Pb^{2+}, the remaining fraction is:

$$\frac{3.1 \times 10^{-8}}{0.1} = \mathbf{0.00000071}$$, **or 7.1 parts of every 10 million.**

10-45. As in example 10-8, we can manipulate the equilibria to get

$$\frac{[H_3O^+]\ [HS^-]}{[H_2S]} = 9.1 \times 10^{-8}$$

$$[HS^-] = 9.1 \times 10^{-8}\ \frac{[H_2S]}{[H_3O^+]} = 9.1 \times 10^{-8} \times \left(\frac{0.10}{1.0 \times 10^{-5}}\right) = 9.1 \times 10^{-4}\ M$$

Note also that at $[H_3O^+] = 1.0 \times 10^{-5}$ then $[OH^-] = 1.0 \times 10^{-9}$

$K(ZnS) = [Zn^{2+}]\ [OH^-]\ [HS^-]$

$$[Zn^{2+}] = \frac{K(ZnS)}{[OH^-][HS^-]} = \frac{2 \times 10^{-25}}{(1.0 \times 10^{-9})(9.1 \times 10^{-4})} = \mathbf{2 \times 10^{-13}\ M}$$

10-47. The concentration of HS^- is most important here. As in 10-45:

$$[HS^-] = 9.1 \times 10^{-8}\ \frac{[H_2S]}{[H_3O^+]} = 9.1 \times 10^{-8} \left(\frac{0.10}{1.0 \times 10^{-1}}\right) = 9.1 \times 10^{-8}\ M$$

$K(SnS) = 9 \times 10^{-27} = [Sn^{2+}]\ [OH^-]\ [HS^-]$

10-47. (continued)

Note that $[Sn^{2+}]$ will equal the molar solubility of SnS. But OH^- and SH^- are set by the pH. Here, pOH = 14.0 - pH = 13.0, so $[OH^-] = 1.0 \times 10^{-13}$ M.

Rearranging: $$[Sn^{2+}] = \frac{9 \times 10^{-27}}{[OH^-][HS]} = \frac{9 \times 10^{-27}}{(1.0 \times 10^{-13})(9.1 \times 10^{-8})} = \mathbf{1 \times 10^{-6}\ M.}$$

10-49. The condition that must be met concerns a given concentration of Fe^{2+} (0.10 M) and H_2S (0.10 M). The pH, and therefore the $[H_3O^+]$, $[OH^-]$, and $[HS^-]$ are determined by the pH. We will calculate the condition when $Q = K$ exactly for the given $[Fe^{2+}]$ and $[H_2S]$.

The equilibrium expression is:

$$K(\text{FeS}) = [Fe^{2+}]\,[HS^-]\,[OH^-] = 5 \times 10^{-19}$$

We know $[HS^-] = 9.1 \times 10^{-8} \dfrac{[H_2S]}{[H_3O^+]}$ and $[OH^-] = \dfrac{1.0 \times 10^{-14}}{[H_3O^+]}$

Then: $$K(\text{FeS}) = [Fe^{2+}] \times \left(9.1 \times 10^{-8}\ \frac{[H_2S]}{[H_3O^+]}\right) \times \frac{1.0 \times 10^{-14}}{[H_3O^+]}$$

$$K(\text{FeS}) = 9.1 \times 10^{-22} \times \frac{[Fe^{2+}][HS^-]}{[H_3O^+]^2}$$

Rearranging: $$[H_3O^+]^2 = \frac{9.1 \times 10^{-22} \times [Fe^{2+}]\,[H_2S]}{K(\text{FeS})}$$

$$= \frac{9.1 \times 10^{-22} \times 0.10 \times 0.10}{5 \times 10^{-19}} = 1.82 \times 10^{-5}$$

$$[H_3O^+] = \sqrt{1.82 \times 10^{-5}} = 4.3 \times 10^{-3}\ \text{M} \qquad \mathbf{pH = 2.4}$$

This represents the minimum pH compatible with all the Fe^{2+} remaining in solution. We must now determine how much Pb^{2+} will dissolve at this pH. We will still have $[H_2S] = 0.1$ M

$$K(\text{PbS}) = 9.1 \times 10^{-22} \times \frac{[Pb^{2+}][HS^-]}{[H_3O^+]^2}$$

$$[Pb^{2+}] = \frac{K(\text{PbS}) \times [H_3O^+]^2}{[H_2S] \times (9.1 \times 10^{-22})} = \frac{(3 \times 10^{-28}) \times (4.3 \times 10^{-3})^2}{(0.1) \times (9.1 \times 10^{-22})} = \mathbf{6 \times 10^{-11}\,M}$$

10-51. Exercise 10-9 has the following data:

$K_1 = 1 \times 10^4$, $K_2 = 2 \times 10^3$, $K_3 = 5 \times 10^2$, $K_4 = 9 \times 10^1$.

Since we are only interested in the $[Cu^{2+}]$, $[NH_3]$, and $[Cu(NH_3)_4{}^{2+}]$, we should combine these:

$K_f = K_1 \times K_2 \times K_3 \times K_4 = 9 \times 10^{11}$ where K_f refers to the reaction:

$$Cu^{2+}\,(aq) + 4NH_3\,(aq) \rightleftarrows Cu(NH_3)_4{}^{2+}\,(aq)$$

Note that K_f is very large. We may work the problem by assuming the reaction goes all the way to completion and then allowing some $Cu(NH_3)_4{}^{2+}$ to dissociate. In one liter, before any complexation, there is 0.10 mol of Cu^{2+} and 1.5 mol NH_3. The Cu^{2+} is the limiting reactant for the formation of $Cu(NH_3)^{2+}$. It will give rise to:

$$Cu(NH_3)_4{}^{2+} \sim 1.5 \text{ mol } NH_3 - \frac{4 \text{ mol } NH_3}{1 \text{ mol } Cu(NH_3)_4{}^{2+}} \times 0.10 \text{ mol } Cu(NH_3)_4{}^{2+}$$

$$\sim 1.1 \text{ mol } Cu(NH_3)_4{}^{2+}$$

Note that we must use the fact that four moles of NH_3 go into making one mole of $Cu(NH_3)_4{}^{2+}$. The calculations we have to start the equilibrium calculation are: $[Cu^{2+}] = 0.00$ M $[Cu(NH_3)_4{}^{2+}] = 0.10$ M $[NH_3] = 1.1$ M

These are used in the table of changes.

(All concentrations in M)	$[Cu(NH_3)_4{}^{2+}]$	$[Cu^{2+}]$	$[NH_3]$
Initial Concentration	0.10	0.00	1.1
Change in Concentration	$-x$	$+x$	$+4x$
Equilibrium Concentration	$0.1 - x$	x	$1.1 + 4x$

The appropriate equilibrium expression is:

$$K = \frac{[Cu(NH_3)_4{}^{2+}]}{[Cu^{2+}][NH_3]^4} = \frac{0.1 - x}{(x)(1.1 + x)^4}$$

If you multiplied this out, you would get a *fifth order* polynomial, which is impossible to solve analytically.

10-51. (continued)

A good compromise is to observe that very little $Cu(NH_3)_4^{2+}$ will dissociate, so x will be small. Then: $1.1 + 4x \approx 1.1$ and $0.1 - x \approx 0.1$

We will then have: $$K = \frac{0.1}{(1.1)^4 x} = \frac{0.0683}{x}$$

$$x = \frac{0.0683}{K} = \frac{0.083}{9 \times 10^{11}} = 7 \times 10^{-14}$$

Then $[Cu^{2+}]$ = **7×10^{-14} M**; $[Cu(NH_3)_4^{2+}]$ = **0.10 M**

10-53. The reason for the acidity is the hydrolysis of the aquo complex of Cu^{2+}:

$$Cu^{2+}\ (aq) + 2H_2O\ (l) \rightleftarrows CuOH^+\ (aq) + H_3O^+\ (aq)$$

10-55. We can treat $Co(H_2O)_6{}^{2+}$ as any other weak acid. Under such conditions -- concentration much larger than K -- we can avoid a quadratic:

$$[H_3O^+] \approx \sqrt{K[Co(H_2O)_6{}^{2+}]} = \sqrt{3 \times 10^{-10} \times 0.10} = 5.5 \times 10^{-6}\ ;\ \mathbf{pH = 5.3}$$

10-57. We assume the $Pt(NH_3)_4{}^{2+}$ generates hydronium ion by the reaction:

$$Pt(NH_3)_4{}^{2+}\ (aq) + H_2O\ (l) \rightleftarrows Pt(NH_3)_3(NH_2)^+\ (aq) + H_3O^+\ (aq)$$

Assuming the acid is very weak (and note $[H_3O^+] = 10^{-4.92} = 1.20 \times 10^{-5}$)

$$Ka \approx \frac{[H_3O^+]^2}{[Pt(NH_3)_4{}^{2+}]} = \frac{\left(1.20 \times 10^{-5}\right)^2}{0.15} = \mathbf{9.6 \times 10^{-10}}$$

10-59. The "best" separation will have $[I^-]$ just at the value where $Q(PbI_2) = K_{sp}(PbI_2)$

This requires: $[Pb^{2+}][I^-]^2 = 1.4 \times 10^{-8}$

$$[I^-] = \sqrt{1.4 \times 10^{-8} / 0.0500} = \mathbf{5.3 \times 10^{-4}\ M}$$

This iodide concentration will strongly suppress the solubility of Hg_2I_2.

10-61. We should perform a qualitative analysis for Ba^{2+}. This ion is in Group 4. As noted in the text, if the pH is set to 9.5 and $(NH_4)_2CO_3$ is added, $BaCO_3$ will precipitate; Cs_2CO_3 will not. A precipitate indicates Ba^{2+} is present. No precipitate (in this experiment) indicates Cs^+. Also barium gives a green flame test, Cesium gives a blue flame test.

10-63. We can test in the order of the groups:

First, is Hg^{2+}, from Group 2, present? The solution is made to a pH of 0.5 and H_2S is added. A precipitate indicates Hg^{2+}.

Second, is Ni^{2+}, from Group 3, present? Any precipitate is removed. The solution is made basic (pH = 9) by the addition of ammonia, which will react with the acid to give a buffer. A precipitate indicates Ni^{2+} is present.

If these tests are negative, we can conclude only Sr^{2+} is present. But to be sure, and in the event either Hg^{2+} or Ni^{2+} was found, then after removal of any precipitates, and H_2S (by acidification and heating), a test solution at pH = 9.5 is treated with $(NH_4)_2CO_3$. A precipitate indicates Sr^{2+}.

10-65. We can only say Group 1 is absent and ions from Group 2 or 3 are present. The treatment to precipitate Group 3 (basic sulfide) will *also* precipitate Group 2. The test does not tell us anything about Groups 4 and 5.

10-67. We know we have a Group 1 ion. It is lead, by the yellow precipitate with chromate. Note also that complete dissolution in hot water also indicates the absence of Ag^+ or Hg_2^{2+}.

10-69. The equation can be converted to yield X_{KNO_3} directly (T =25°C = 298.15 K):

$$X_{KNO_3} = 10^{[A + \frac{B}{T} + C\log(T)]}$$

$$X_{KNO_3} = 10^{[59.93 + \left(\frac{-3821.88}{298.15}\right) + (-19.5236)\log(298.15)]} = 10^{-1.199} = \mathbf{0.0633}$$

A similar calculation for T = 90°C = 363.15 K yields X_{KNO_3} = **0.265.**

The solubility increases with temperature, so the reaction must be **endothermic.**

We now want to convert the mole fraction of KNO_3 into grams KNO_3 per 1000 g H_2O. To do this, we first solve the mole fraction equation for moles KNO_3 per 55.5 mol H_2O.

10-69. (continued)

The number of moles of water is $\dfrac{1000\text{ g}}{18.015\text{ g mol}^{-1}}$ = 55.5 mol H_2O.

$$\frac{n_{KNO_3}}{n_{KNO_3} + n_{H_2O}} = X_{KNO_3}$$

$$n_{KNO_3} = X_{KNO_3} n_{KNO_3} + X_{KNO_3} n_{H_2O}$$

$$n_{KNO_3}\left(1 - X_{KNO_3}\right) = X_{KNO_3} n_{H_2O}$$

$$n_{KNO_3} = \frac{X_{KNO_3}}{1 - X_{KNO_3}} n_{H_2O}$$

At 25°C $\quad n_{KNO_3} = \dfrac{0.0633}{(1-0.0633)}(55.5) = 3.75 \text{ mol } KNO_3$

mass KNO_3 = 3.75 mol × 101.10 g mol^{-1} = **379 g KNO_3**

At 90° $\quad n_{KNO_3} = \dfrac{0.265}{(1-0.265)}(55.5) = 20.0 \text{ mol } KNO_3$

mass KNO_3 = 20.0 mol × 101.10 g mol^{-1} = **2020 g KNO_3**

10-71. $$Hg_2I_2\ (s) \rightleftarrows Hg_2^{2+}\ (aq) + 2\ I^-\ (aq)$$

$$K_{sp} = [Hg_2^{2+}][I^-]^2$$

10-73. Given K_{sp} ($BaSO_4$) = 1.1×10^{-10} and setting $[Ba^{2+}] = [SO_4^{2-}] = x$

$$x^2 = 1.1 \times 10^{-10}$$

$$x = \sqrt{1.1 \times 10^{-10}} = 1.05 \times 10^{-5}$$

$$[Ba^{2+}] = 1.05 \times 10^{-5}\ \text{M}$$

10-75. (a) $\quad CaCO_3$: $\dfrac{14 \times 10^{-3}\text{ g L}^{-1}}{100.09\text{ g mol}^{-1}} = 1.4 \times 10^{-5}\text{ mol L}^{-1}$

$SrCO_3$: $\dfrac{10 \times 10^{-3}\text{ g L}^{-1}}{147.63\text{ g mol}^{-1}} = 6.7 \times 10^{-5}\text{ mol L}^{-1}$

$BaCO_3$: $\dfrac{17 \times 10^{-3}\text{ g L}^{-1}}{197.34\text{ g mol}^{-1}} = 8.6 \times 10^{-5}\text{ mol L}^{-1}$

The molar solubility increases down the group.

10-75. (continued)

(b) In pure water with no side-reactions, $[M^{2+}] = [CO_3^{2-}]$ = molar solubility

K_{sp} = (molar solubility)^2 $K_{sp}(CaCO_3)$ = **2.0×10^{-10}**

$K_{sp}(SrCO_3)$ = **4.5×10^{-9}** $K_{sp}(BaCO_3)$ = **7.4×10^{-9}**

The K_{sp}'s here are for 20 °C. Table 10-1 refers to data at 25 °C. More importantly, there *are* side reactions, especially of carbonate, that make the dissolution reaction more complicated than we have considered.

10-77. (a) We set $[K^+] = [ClO_4^-] = x$ = molar solubility

$$x^2 = K_{sp}\,; \qquad x = \sqrt{K_{sp}} = \sqrt{0.0107} = \mathbf{0.103\ M}$$

(b) With such a large K_{sp}, we cannot neglect the amount of $KClO_4$ that will dissolve in the presence of a common ion. The table of changes becomes (for 0.075 M K_2SO_4, $[K^+]$ = 0.15 M):

(All concentrations in M)	$[K^+]$	$[ClO_4^-]$
Initial Concentration	0.15	0.0
Change in Concentration	$+x$	$+x$
Equilibrium Concentration	$0.15 + x$	x

Then: $(0.15 + x)(x) = K_{sp}\,;$ $x^2 + 0.15x - K_{sp} = 0$

The only reasonable root is x = 0.053, so the solubility is **0.053 M.**

(c) Here, the common ion is ClO_4^-, at $[ClO_4^-]$ = 0.075 M

(All concentrations in M)	$[K^+]$	$[ClO_4^-]$
Initial Concentration	0.0	0.075
Change in Concentration	$+x$	$+x$
Equilibrium Concentration	x	$0.075 + x$

Then: $(x)(0.075 + x) = K_{sp}\,;$ $x^2 + 0.075x - K_{sp} = 0$

The only reasonable root is x = 0.072, so the solubility is **0.072 M.**

10-79. We need a ratio of concentrations not an absolute value. We take the ratio of the K_{sp}'s: $\dfrac{[Cu^+][Br^-]}{[Ag^+][Br^-]} = \dfrac{K_{sp}(CuBr)}{K_{sp}(AgBr)}$

The $[Br^-]$ is unknown and, in this case, *irrelevant*, because it is in the numerator and the denominator.

$$\frac{[Cu^+]}{[Ag^+]} = \frac{K_{sp}(CuBr)}{K_{sp}(AgBr)} = \frac{4.2 \times 10^{-8}}{7.7 \times 10^{-13}} = \mathbf{55{,}000.}$$

10-81. Note that the different stoichiometries for the silver in the two salts means we must explicitly calculate which salt will precipitate first.

Ignoring dilution effects since we assume only a very small amount of Ag^+ is required to start precipitating something, we can ask what $[Ag^+]$ must be to start precipitation of both salts, which will occur when Q just equals K_{sp}.

For AgCl: $[Ag^+][Cl^-] > K_{sp}(AgCl)$

$$[Ag^+] > \frac{K_{sp}}{[Cl^-]} = \frac{1.6 \times 10^{-10}}{0.100} = 1.6 \times 10^{-9}$$

For Ag_2CrO_4, a similar calculation shows $[Ag^+]$ would have to exceed 2.8×10^{-5} M for a precipitation of Ag_2CrO_4. So we conclude that **AgCl will precipitate first.** The concentration of Ag^+ must be higher than this value for Ag_2CrO_4 to precipitate. The value of $[Ag^+]$ to cause Ag_2CrO_4 to precipitate can be determined after we consider that the added Ag^+ solution will *dilute* the CrO_4^{2-}. Let's assume very nearly all the Cl^- has precipitated at that point.

The number of moles of Cl^- present (if the solution was a volume V) was 0.100 V mol. This will require V liters of $AgNO_3$ solution, so the total solution volume is 2.00 V. The concentration of chromate present to complete the titration is now 0.00125 M CrO_4^{2-}, half of its initial concentration.

10-81. (continued)

The Ag^+ concentration that will cause precipitation is, if we set $[Ag^+] = x$:

$$x^2[CrO_4^{2-}] = K_{sp}\,(Ag_2CrO_4)$$

$$x = \sqrt{\frac{K_{sp}}{[CrO_4^{2-}]}} = \sqrt{\frac{1.9 \times 10^{-12}}{0.00125}} = 3.9 \times 10^{-5}$$

The $[Cl^-]$ in equilibrium with this is, if $[Cl^-] = x$:

$$[Ag^+]\,x = K_{sp}\,(AgCl)$$

$$x = \frac{K_{sp}}{[Ag^+]} = \frac{1.6 \times 10^{-10}}{3.9 \times 10^{-5}} = 4.1 \times 10^{-6}\ \text{M}$$

The number of *moles* of Cl^- in *this* 2.00 V L solution is:

$$4.1 \times 10^{-6}\ \text{mol L}^{-1} \times 2.00\ V\ \text{L} = 8.1 \times 10^{-6}\ V\ \text{mol Cl}^-$$

This compares to the initial 0.100 mol:

$$\text{fraction Cl}^- = \frac{8.1 \times 10^{-6} V}{0.100\ V} = 0.00008 = \mathbf{0.008\ \%}.$$

10-83. The "tiny" change in the solution is quite large from the point of view of a silver ion. The 0.10 mol of ammonia is a massive excess for complexation of silver according to the reaction:

$$Ag^+\,(aq) + 2NH_3\,(aq) \rightleftarrows Ag(NH_3)_2^+\,(aq) \qquad K = 1.7 \times 10^7$$

We can combine this with the solubility equilibrium for AgBr:

$$AgBr\,(s) \rightleftarrows Ag^+\,(aq) + Br^-\,(aq) \qquad K_{sp} = 7.7 \times 10^{-13}$$

Together these give us a solubility/complexation equilibrium:

$$AgBr\,(s) + 2NH_3\,(aq) \rightleftarrows Ag(NH_3)_2^+ + Br^- \qquad K = 1.3 \times 10^{-5}$$

This is still small, but it is *much* larger then K_{sp} (AgBr). The ammonia complex of silver ion is a very different substance than aqueous silver ion alone. It "pulls" the silver into solution.

10-85. The equilibrium for the potassium complexation by 18-crown-6 (abbreviated "18-C-6" here) :

$$K^+ \ (aq) + \text{18-C-6} \ (aq) \rightleftarrows K(\text{18-C-6})^+ \ (aq) \qquad K = 6.6$$

This is *not* a large equilibrium constant, and we must avoid any assumptions if possible. One operation that is *not* an assumption is to set up the table of changes so that the all of the potassium and 18-crown-6 are initially complexed.

(All concentrations in M)	$[K^+]$	[18-C-6]	$[K(\text{18-C-6})^+]$
Initial Concentration	0.0	0.0	0.0080
Change in Concentration	$+x$	$+x$	$-x$
Equilibrium Concentration	x	x	$0.0080 - x$

The appropriate equilibrium expression is:

$$K = \frac{[K(18\text{-}C\text{-}6)^+]}{[K^+][18-C-6]} = \frac{0.00800 - x}{x^2}$$

Rearranging: $0 = Kx^2 + x - 0.00800 = 6.6\,x^2 + x - 0.00800$

Use of the quadratic formula for this yields two roots:

$$x = +0.00762 \text{ and } x = -0.159$$

Only the positive root is reasonable, so

[18-C-6] = $[K^+]$ = 0.0076 M and $[K(\text{18-C-6})^+]$ = 0.0004 M

For sodium, we have the same conditions, except there is a different equilibrium constant. Then: $0 = Kx^2 + x - 0.00800 = 111.6\,x^2 + x - 0.00800$

Use of the quadratic formula for this yields two roots:

$$x = +0.00510 \text{ and } x = -0.014$$

Only the positive root is reasonable, so

[18-C-6] = $[Na^+]$ = 0.0051 M and $[K(\text{18-C-6})^+]$ = 0.0029 M

10-87. $Pt(OH)_6^{2-}$ *(aq)* + H_2O *(l)* $\rightleftarrows$ $Pt(OH)_5(OH_2)^-$ *(aq)* + OH^- *(aq)*

CHAPTER 11 - THERMOCHEMISTRY

11-1. The heat comes from the friction of the drill as it grinds against, and tears apart, the wood. The energy for the heat comes from the mechanical energy of the motor, which in turn comes from electrical energy.

11-3. The specific heat of water is over five times that of iron (Table 11-1). So the ranking is: 1 kg iron ball < 2 kg iron plate < 1 kg water < 2 kg water

11-5. The molar heat capacity is equal to the specific heat multiplied by the mass of one mole of the element.

Element	Specific heat ($J\ K^{-1}\ g^{-1}$)	Atomic mass	Molar heat capacity ($J\ K^{-1}\ mol^{-1}$)
Lithium	3.57	6.941	24.8
Sodium	1.23	22.990	28.3
Potassium	0.756	39.098	29.6
Rubidium	0.363	85.468	31.0
Cesium	0.242	132.905	32.2

The molar heat capacity of all of the elements is a gradually increasing -- about 1 $J\ K^{-1}\ mol^{-1}$ per row of the periodic table (the jump from Li to Na is slightly more). Thus, we expect the heat capacity for Fr to be around 33.5 $J\ K^{-1}\ mol^{-1}$.

11-7.

Element	Specific heat ($J\ K^{-1}\ g^{-1}$)	Atomic mass	Molar heat capacity ($J\ K^{-1}\ mol^{-1}$)
Nickel	0.444	58.6934	26.1
Zinc	0.388	65.39	25.4
Rhodium	0.243	102.906	25.0

11-7. (continued)

Element	Specific heat ($J\ K^{-1}\ g^{-1}$)	Atomic mass	Molar heat capacity ($J\ K^{-1}\ mol^{-1}$)
Tungsten	0.132	183.84	24.3
Gold	0.129	196.965	25.4
Uranium	0.116	238.029	27.6

11-9. The molar mass of P_4 is 4 × 30.974 = 123.896 g mol^{-1}, so the molar heat capacity of P_4 is: 0.757 J K^{-1} g^{-1} × 123.896 g mol^{-1} = **93.8 J K^{-1} mol^{-1}.**

11-11. The equation for equilibrating two masses at different temperatures is:

$$m_1\, c_{s1}\, \Delta t_1 = -\, m_2\, c_{s2}\, \Delta t_2$$

For this problem, substance 1 will be the water ("w") and substance 2 will be the zinc ("Zn"). The final temperature for each substance is the same. Then:

$$m_w\, c_{s,w}\, (t_f - t_{w,i}) = -\, m_{Zn}\, c_{s,Zn}\, (t_f - t_{Zn,i})$$

We have

m_w = 200.0 g $\qquad m_{Zn}$ = 60.0 g

$c_{s,w}$ = 4.22 J $(^oC)^{-1}$ g^{-1} $\qquad c_{s,Zn}$ = 0.389 J $(^oC)^{-1}$ g^{-1}

$t_{w,i}$ = 100.0 ^oC $\qquad t_{Zn,i}$ = 20^oC

This set-up uses temperature as small "*t*," and units of degrees Celsius. This is permissible because we are only concerned with *changes* or *differences* in temperature, and the kelvin and the degree Celsius are the same size. Then the equation becomes:

$$200.0\text{ g} \times 4.22\text{ J }(^oC)^{-1}\text{ g}^{-1}\ (t_f - 100.0^oC) = -\ 60.0\text{ g} \times 0.389\text{ J }(^oC)^{-1}\text{ g}^{-1}\ (t_f - 20.0^oC)$$

$$844\ t_f - 84{,}400 = -23.34\ t_f + 466.8$$

$$(844 + 23.34)\ t_f = 84{,}400 + 466.8$$

$$t_f = 84{,}867 / 867.3 = \mathbf{97.8^oC}$$

11-13. (a) For a heat transfer *q* and a temperature change Δt:

$$q = C\,\Delta t \qquad \Rightarrow \qquad C = q / \Delta t = 5682\text{ J} / 2.31^oC$$

$$= 2460\text{ J }^oC^{-1} = \mathbf{2460\ J\ K^{-1}}$$

11-13. (continued)

(b) $q = C\Delta t = 2460 \text{ J K}^{-1} \times 4.40 \text{ K} = 10820 \text{ K} = \mathbf{10.8 \text{ kJ}}$

This is the heat evolved by the reaction and absorbed by the calorimeter. Thus, q is positive for the calorimeter, and negative for this reaction.

11-15. The increase in temperature is an indication that the reacting chemical system is releasing energy as heat. The reaction is exothermic and **ΔH < 0 (is negative).**

11-17. (a) There are two moles of Na_2O and the evolution of 828 kJ of heat. Therefore:

$$\Delta H = \left(\frac{-828 \text{ kJ}}{2 \text{ mol Na}_2\text{O}}\right) \times \left(\frac{1 \text{ mol Na}_2\text{O}}{61.979 \text{ g Na}_2\text{O}}\right) = \mathbf{-6.68 \text{ kJ (g Na}_2\text{O)}^{-1}}.$$

(b) There is one mole of MgO indicated, and the uptake of 303 kJ of heat.

Therefore : $$\Delta H = \left(\frac{+302 \text{ kJ}}{1 \text{ mol MgO}}\right) \times \left(\frac{1 \text{ mol MgO}}{40.3044 \text{ g MgO}}\right) = \mathbf{+7.49 \text{ kJ (g MgO)}^{-1}}$$

(c) There are two moles of CO and the uptake of 33.3 kJ of heat.

Therefore: $$\Delta H = \left(\frac{+33.3 \text{ kJ}}{2 \text{ mol CO}}\right) \times \left(\frac{1 \text{ mol CO}}{28.010 \text{ g CO}}\right) = \mathbf{+ 0.594 \text{ kJ (g CO)}^{-1}}$$

11-19. The heat due to *just* the reaction of the bromine with the excess NaOH is the difference between the value for the bromine experiment and the "blank" without the bromine. Specifically: $\Delta H_{reac} = 121.3 \text{ J} - 2.34 \text{ J} = 118.9 \text{ J}$

This is the enthalpy change for 2.88×10^{-3} mol of Br_2 *(l)*. To convert this to the enthalpy change per mole of bromine:

$$\frac{118.9 \text{ J}}{2.88 \times 10^{-3} \text{mol Br}_2} = 41{,}300 \text{ J mol}^{-1} \text{ Br}_2 = \mathbf{41.3 \text{ kJ (mol Br}_2)^{-1}}$$

11-21. (a) This is a vaporization reaction : **ΔH > 0** (heat is needed to drive reaction)

(b) This is a condensation reaction to a solid: **ΔH < 0** (heat is given off)

(c) This is the freezing of a liquid: **ΔH < 0** (heat is given off)

11-23. The molar mass of CBr_4 is 331.63 g mol^{-1}, so 10.000 g of the compound is 0.030154 mol CBr_4. We then have: $\dfrac{1.359 \text{ kJ}}{0.030154 \text{ mol CBr}_4} = \mathbf{\dfrac{45.07 \text{ kJ}}{\text{mol CBr}_4}}$.

11-25. $$\left(\frac{6.04 \text{ kJ}}{1 \text{ mol CO}}\right) \times \left(\frac{1 \text{ mol CO}}{28.0104 \text{ g CO}}\right) \times 2.38 \text{ g CO} = \mathbf{+0.513 \text{ kJ} = 513 \text{ J}}$$

11-27. $Cs\ (l) + O_2\ (g) \rightarrow CsO_2\ (s)$ $\Delta H = -268.8\text{ kJ}$

$CsO_2\ (s) \rightarrow Cs\ (s) + O_2\ (g)$ $\Delta H = +266.1\text{ kJ}$

$Cs\ (l) \rightarrow Cs\ (s)$ $\Delta H = +266.1\text{ kJ} + (-268.8\text{ kJ}) = \mathbf{-\ 2.7\ kJ}$

11-29. $2\ CO_2\ (g) + H_2O\ (g) \rightarrow CH_2CO\ (g) + 2\ O_2\ (g)$ $-\Delta H_1 = +981.1$

$2\ CH_4\ (g) + 4\ O_2\ (g) \rightarrow 2\ CO_2\ (g) + 4\ H_2O\ (g)$ $2 \times \Delta H_2 = -1604.6$

$2\ CH_4\ (g) + 2\ O_2\ (g) \rightarrow CH_2CO\ (g) + 3\ H_2O\ (g)$ $\mathbf{\Delta H = -\ 623.5\ kJ}$

11-31. A pound of diamonds. They lie at higher enthalpy than graphite, so burning releases more enthalpy (heat in this case) on the path to the very low enthalpy product, carbon dioxide.

11-33. Tabulations of enthalpies of formation and similar thermodynamic quantities, such as those we will see in Chapter 12, are almost always done on a per mole basis. Enthalpy data and other thermodynamic data for reactions are given *for the reaction as written.* To determine the enthalpy change for a reaction we multiply molar enthalpies of formation by the number of moles of the substances *in the reaction as written.* So when we write "$2 \times \Delta H_f^o (NO_2)$" we are really saying "the heat of formation of two moles of NO_2."

$$\Delta H^o = 2 \times \Delta H_f^o (NO_2\ (g)) + 2 \times \Delta H_f^o (H_2O\ (l)) - 3 \times \Delta H_f^o (O_2\ (g)) - \Delta H_f^o (N_2H_4\ (l))$$

$$= 2\text{ mol} \times (+33.18\ \frac{\text{kJ}}{\text{mol}}) + 2\text{ mol} \times (-285.83\ \frac{\text{kJ}}{\text{mol}}) - 3\text{ mol} \times (0.0\frac{\text{kJ}}{\text{mol}}) - 1\text{ mol} \times (50.63\frac{\text{kJ}}{\text{mol}}) = \mathbf{-555.93\ kJ}$$

11-35. (a) $$\Delta H^o = 2 \times \Delta H_f^o (ZnO\ (s)) + 2 \times \Delta H_f^o (SO_2\ (g)) - 3 \times \Delta H_f^o (O_2\ (g)) - 2 \times \Delta H_f^o (ZnS\ (s))$$

$$= 2\text{ mol} \times (-348.28\frac{\text{kJ}}{\text{mol}}) + 2\text{ mol} \times (-296.83\frac{\text{kJ}}{\text{mol}}) - 3\text{ mol} \times (0.0\frac{\text{kJ}}{\text{mol}}) - 2\text{ mol} \times (-205.98\frac{\text{kJ}}{\text{mol}}) = \mathbf{-878.26\ kJ}$$

11-35. (continued)

(b) The molar mass of sphalerite is 97.46 g mol^{-1}, so 3.00 metric tons (= 3.00×10^6 g) will contain 3.078×10^4 mol. The value determined in (a) is for the reaction as written -- with *two* moles of ZnS. So the heat absorbed from the 3.00 metric ton sample is:

$$\Delta H = 3.078 \times 10^4 \text{ mol ZnS} \times \frac{-878.26 \text{ kJ}}{2 \text{ mol ZnS}} = \mathbf{-1.35 \times 10^7\ kJ}$$

11-37. (a) $\Delta H^o = \Delta H^o_f(Ca^{2+}\ (aq)) + 2 \times \Delta H^o_f(Cl^-\ (aq)) - \Delta H^o_f(CaCl_2\ (s))$

$$= 1 \text{ mol} \times (-542.83\frac{\text{kJ}}{\text{mol}}) + 2 \text{ mol} \times (-167.16\frac{\text{kJ}}{\text{mol}}) - 1 \text{ mol}\ (-795.8\frac{\text{kJ}}{\text{mol}})$$

$= \mathbf{-81.4\ kJ}$

(b) The value obtained is for the dissolution of one mole of $CaCl_2$. The molar mass of $CaCl_2$ is 110.96 g mol^{-1}, so 20.0 g $CaCl_2$ contains 0.1802 mol $CaCl_2$. The enthalpy change in this experiment is just:

$$q = \Delta H = 0.1802 \text{ mol CaCl}_2 \times \frac{-81.4 \text{ kJ}}{1 \text{ mol CaCl}_2} = -14.67 \text{ kJ} = -14{,}670 \text{ J}$$

This is the amount of heat given off to the surroundings by the reacting chemical system. In this case, the surroundings are the water.

$q_{water} = -q_{reaction} = C\,\Delta t,$ where $C = 418 \text{ J K}^{-1}$

$$\Delta t = \frac{-q_{reaction}}{C} = \frac{-(14{,}670)}{418 \text{ J K}^{-1}} = 35.1\ ^oC$$

The final temperature will be 20.0 ^{o}C + 35.1 ^{o}C = **55.1^{o}C**

11-39. For the combustion reaction ($\Delta H^o_f(O_2)$ = 0.0 and is omitted):

$$C_6H_{12}\ (l) + 9\ O_2\ (g) \rightarrow 6\ CO_2\ (g) + 6\ H_2O\ (l)$$

$$\Delta H^o_{comb.} = 6 \times \Delta H^o_f(CO_2\ (g)) + 6 \times \Delta H^o_f(H_2O\ (l)) - \Delta H^o_f(C_6H_{12}\ (l))$$

$$1 \text{ mol} \times \Delta H^o_f(C_6H_{12}\ (l)) = 6 \times \Delta H^o_f(CO_2\ (g)) + 6 \times \Delta H^o_f(H_2O\ (l)) - \Delta H^o_{comb.}$$

$$= 6 \text{ mol} \times (-393.51\frac{\text{kJ}}{\text{mol}}) + 6 \text{ mol} \times (-285.83\frac{\text{kJ}}{\text{mol}})$$

$$1 \text{ mol} \times - (-3923.7\frac{\text{kJ}}{\text{mol}}) \quad = -152.3 \text{ kJ}$$

$\Delta H^o_f(C_6H_{12}\ (l))$ = **152.5 kJ mol^{-1}**

11-41. The condensation reaction is:

$$CHCl_3\ (g) \rightarrow CHCl_3\ (l)$$

For this:

$$\Delta H^o = \Delta H^o_f(CHCl_3\ (l)) - \Delta H^o_f(CHCl_3\ (g))$$

$$= -134.5\frac{kJ}{mol} - (-103.1\frac{kJ}{mol}) = -31.4\ kJ\ mol^{-1}$$

For 2.5 mol: $2.5\ mol \times (-31.4\ \frac{kJ}{mol}) = \mathbf{-78.5\ kJ}$

11-43. The atomization reaction here is: $CCl_3F\ (g) \rightarrow C\ (g) + 3\ Cl\ (g) + F\ (g)$

The process involves, in list form:

Breaking three moles of C-Cl bonds:	+3 × 328	kJ
Breaking one mole of C-F bonds:	+441	kJ
TOTAL:	**+1425**	kJ

11-45. (a)

Breaking one mole of C-H bonds:	+413	kJ
Breaking one mole of C≡ N bonds:	+891	kJ
TOTAL:	**+1304**	kJ

(b)

Breaking one mole of C-H bonds:	+413	kJ
Breaking one mole of C≡ N bonds:	+891	kJ
Making $^1/_2$ mole of H-H bonds:	$-^1/_2$ × 436	kJ
Making $^1/_2$ mole of N≡ N bonds:	$-^1/_2$ × 945	kJ
TOTAL:	**+614**	kJ

(c)

Breaking one mole of C-H bonds:	+413	kJ
Breaking one mole of C≡ N bonds:	+891	kJ
Making mole of N-H bonds:	-391	kJ
Making one mole of C≡ N bonds:	-891	kJ
TOTAL:	**+22**	kJ

11-47. (a)

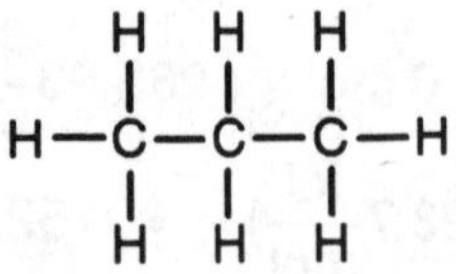

11-47. (continued)

(b) Note that CO_2 has two C=O double bonds and O_2 has one O=O double bond. Breaking eight moles of C-H bonds: +8(413) kJ

Breaking two moles of C-C bonds: +2(348) kJ

Breaking five moles of O=O bonds: +5(498) kJ

Making six moles of C=O bonds: -6(728) kJ

Making eight moles of O-H bonds: -8(463) kJ

TOTAL: **-1580** kJ.

11-49.

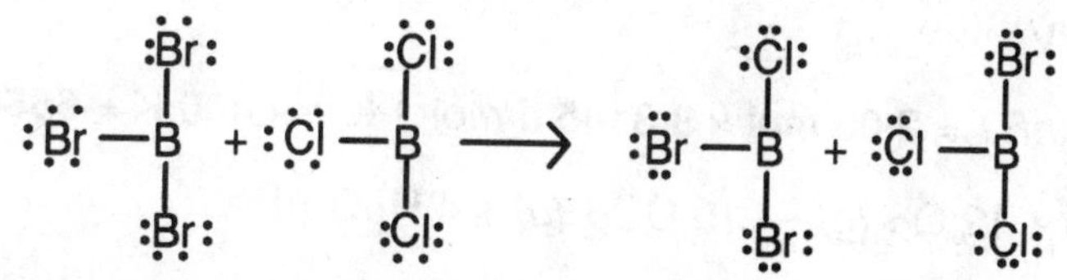

The reaction is completely neutral with respect to the type and number of the different bonds - three B-Br and three B-Cl bonds on the right and left. Thus, from the standpound of average bond enthalpies, $\Delta H = 0$.

11-51. The constant pressure input of heat into the nitrogen gas causes the gas to expand and perform pressure-volume work.

$$w = -P_{ext}\,\Delta V = -P_{ext}\,(V_{final} - V_{initial})$$

$$= -\ 50.0 \text{ atm} \times (974 \text{ L} - 542 \text{ L})$$

$$= \mathbf{-\ 21{,}600 \text{ L-atm}}$$

To convert this to the conventional energy unit the joule

$$-\ 21{,}600 \text{ L-atm} \times 101.325 \text{ J L}^{-1} \text{ atm}^{-1} = \mathbf{-\ 2.19 \times 10^{6} \text{ J}}$$

11-53.

$$w = -P_{ext}\,\Delta V = -\ 1.14 \text{ atm} \times (0.40 \text{ L} - 4.00 \text{ L}) = \mathbf{+\ 4.10 \text{ L-atm}}$$

$$= +\ 4.10 \text{ L-atm} \times 101.325 \text{ J L}^{-1} \text{ atm}^{-1} = \mathbf{+416 \text{ J}}$$

11-55. Because the gas is expanding against an external pressure of zero atmospheres, the work done is zero.

11-57. (a) The ΔE and q of the system are both positive as the thermal energy enters the system; w is zero because in the absence of a volume change work is not possible.

(b) The ΔE and q for the system are both negative as the thermal energy leaves the system. w is zero again.

(c) Because the system returns to its original temperature, the overall energy change is equal to the overal heat change, because we also know w is zero. Therefore: $q_1 + q_2 = \Delta E_1 + \Delta E_2$.

11-59.

$$H = E + PV$$

$$H - E = PV = nRT = 2.00 \text{ mol} \times 8.3145 \text{ J mol}^{-1} \text{ K}^{-1} \times 400 \text{ K} = \mathbf{6650 \text{ J}}$$

11-61. (a)

$$C_{10}H_8\ (s) + 12\ O_2\ (g) \rightarrow 10\ CO_2\ (g) + 4\ H_2O\ (l)$$

(b) The experiment used $^{0.6410 \text{ g}}/_{128.17 \text{ g mol}^{-1}}$ = 0.005001 mol and evolved 25.79 kJ. The heat absorbed at constant volume for the combustion of one mole of naphthalene is then $^{-25.79 \text{ kJ}}/_{0.005001 \text{ mol}} = -5157 \text{ kJ mol}^{-1}$.

Since the reaction is done at constant volume, this heat transfer is equal to the energy change for the reaction, and since the reaction is done at 25 °C, (=298.15 K), this is equal to the standard energy change: ΔE^o = **-5,157 kJ** ·

(c) For this reaction, there are 10 moles of product gases and 12 moles of reactant gases, so for the gas phase Δn = -2 mol.

$$\Delta H^o = \Delta E^o + RT\Delta n = -5{,}157{,}000 \text{ J} + (8.3145 \text{ J mol}^{-1} \text{ K}^{-1})(298.15 \text{ K})(2.00 \text{ mol})$$

$$= -5{,}162{,}000 \text{ J} = \mathbf{-5{,}162 \text{ kJ}}$$

(d)

$$\Delta H^o = 4 \times \Delta H_f^o (H_2O\ (l)) + 10 \times \Delta H_f^o (CO_2\ (g)) - 12 \times \Delta H_f^o (O_2\ (g)) - \Delta H_f^o (C_{10}H_8\ (s))$$

$$-5162 \text{ kJ} = 4 \text{ mol} \times (-285.83 \frac{\text{kJ}}{\text{mol}}) + 10 \times (-393.51 \frac{\text{kJ}}{\text{mol}}) - 12 \times (-0.00 \frac{\text{kJ}}{\text{mol}}) - 1 \text{ mol} \times \Delta H_f^o (C_{10}H_8)$$

$$1 \text{ mol} \times \Delta H_f^o (C_{10}H_8) = +84 \text{ kJ} \quad \Rightarrow \quad \mathbf{\Delta H_f^o (C_{10}H_8) = +84 \text{ kJ mol}^{-1}}$$

11-63. (a) molar heat capacity $= \left(0.215 \dfrac{\text{cal}}{\text{g K}}\right) \times \left(\dfrac{4.184\ \text{J}}{\text{cal}}\right) \times \left(\dfrac{26.9815\ \text{g Al}}{1\ \text{mol Al}}\right)$

$$= \mathbf{24.3}\ \frac{\mathbf{J}}{\mathbf{mol\ K^{-1}}}$$

(b) $$C_p = \left(0.215 \frac{\text{cal}}{\text{g K}}\right) \times \left(\frac{4.184\ \text{J}}{\text{cal}}\right) \times \left(\frac{1000\ \text{g}}{1\ \text{kg}}\right) \times \left(\frac{1000\ \text{kg}}{1\ \text{metric ton}}\right)$$

$$= \mathbf{9.0 \times 10^5\ J\ K^{-1}}$$

11-65. The equation for equilibrating two masses at different temperatures is:

$$m_1\ c_{s1}\ \Delta t_1 = -\ m_2\ c_{s2}\ \Delta t_2$$

For this problem, substance 1 will be the water ("w") and substance 2 will be the unknown ("u"). The final temperature for each substance is the same. Then:

$$m_w\ c_{s,w}\ (t_f - t_{w,i}) = -\ m_u\ c_{s,u}\ (t_f - t_{u,i})$$

We have $m_w = 100.0$ g $\qquad m_u = 61.0$ g

$c_{s,w} = 4.18\ \text{J}\ {}^{\circ}\text{C}^{-1}\ \text{g}^{-1} \qquad t_f = 26.39\ {}^{\circ}\text{C}$

$t_{w,i} = 20.00{}^{\circ}\text{C} \qquad t_{u,i} = 120.0{}^{\circ}\text{C}$

$$100.0\ \text{g} \times 4.18\ \text{J}\ ({}^{\circ}\text{C})^{-1}\ \text{g}^{-1}\ (26.39 - 20.00{}^{\circ}\text{C}) = c_{s,u}\ -61.0\ \text{g} \times\ (26.39 -\ 120.0{}^{\circ}\text{C})$$

$$2671\ \text{J} = c_{s,u} \times 5710\ \text{g}\ {}^{\circ}\text{C}$$

$$c_{s,u} = \left(\frac{2671\ \text{J}}{5710\ \text{g}\ {}^{\circ}\text{C}}\right) = \mathbf{0.468\ J\ g^{-1}\ ({}^{\circ}C)^{-1}}$$

11-67. The heat released in the combustion is:

$$q = 14.3\ \text{g glucose} \times \left(\frac{1\ \text{mol glucose}}{180.16\ \text{g glucose}}\right) \times \left(\frac{-2{,}820{,}000\ \text{J}}{1\ \text{mol glucose}}\right) = -2.24 \times 10^5\ \text{J}.$$

If this is absorbed by the water in the body, then $q_{water} = +2.24 \times 10^5$ J.

Then: $\quad m_w\ c_w\ \Delta t = 2.24 \times 10^5$ J; We have a mass of 50 kg = 50,000 g.

$$\Delta t = \frac{2.24 \times 10^5\ \text{J}}{(50{,}000\text{g}) \times \left(4.18\ \text{J}\ \text{K}^{-1}\ \text{g}^{-1}\right)} = 1.07\ \text{K} = \mathbf{1.07\ {}^{\circ}C}.$$

11-69. This problem is best done by a careful budget of the heat changes, knowing that the total heat change for all components of the system is zero:

0 = *q (ice melting)* + *q(water from ice warming)* + *q (water in glass cooling)*

The terms are listed separately for clarity.

11-69. (continued)

$$q \textit{ (ice melting)} = 36.0 \text{ g water} \times \left(\frac{+\ 333\text{J}}{1 \text{ g water}}\right) = 11{,}988 \text{ J}$$

$$q\textit{(water from ice warming)} = 36.0 \text{ g water} \times \left(\frac{4.18 \text{ J}}{1^{o}\text{ C g}^{-1}}\right) \times \left(t_{final} - 0.0\ ^{o}\text{C}\right)$$

$$= 150.48 \text{ J}\ ^{o}\text{C}^{-1}\ t_{final}$$

$$q \textit{ (water in glass cooling)} = 360 \text{ g water} \times \left(\frac{4.18 \text{ J}}{1^{o}\text{ C g}^{-1}}\right) \times \left(t_{final} - 20.0\ ^{o}\text{C}\right)$$

$$= 1504.8 \text{ J}\ ^{o}\text{C}^{-1}\ t_{final} - 30{,}096 \text{ J}$$

Then in our original heat budget equation:

$$0 = 11{,}988 \text{ J} + 150.48 \text{ J } (^{o}\text{C})^{-1}\ t_{final} + 1504.8 \text{ J } (^{o}\text{C})^{-1}\ t_{final} - 30{,}096 \text{ J}$$

$$1655 \text{ J } (^{o}\text{C})^{-1}\ t_{final} = 30{,}096 \text{ J} - 11{,}988 \text{ J} = 18{,}108 \text{ J}$$

$$t_{final} = \frac{18{,}108 \text{ J}}{1{,}655 \text{ J } (^{o}\text{C})^{-1}} = \mathbf{10.9\ ^{o}C.}$$

11-71. The cooling ability "*near its boiling point*" is connected to the specific heat. The cooling ability "at its boiling point" is connected to the enthalpy of vaporization. Helium can absorb more heat per gram near the boiling point, so helium is a better coolant **near** the boiling point. However, nitrogen requires more heat per gram for vaporization. It is a better coolant **at** its boiling point.

11-73. (a) $\Delta H^{o} = 2\ \Delta H_f^{o}(CO_2) + \Delta H_f^{o}(H_2O\ (g)) - \Delta H_f^{o}(C_2H_2) - 5/2\ \Delta H_f^{o}(O_2)$

$$= 2 \text{ mol} \times (-393.51 \text{ kJ mol}^{-1}) + 1 \text{ mol } (-241.82 \text{ kJ mol}^{-1})$$

$$- 1 \text{ mol } (+226.73 \text{ kJ mol}^{-1}) - 5/2 \text{ mol } (0 \text{ kJ mol}^{-1})$$

$$= - 1255.57 \text{ kJ} = \mathbf{1{,}255{,}570\ J}$$

(b) $C_p = C_{p,\text{carbon dioxide}} + C_{p,\text{water}}$

$$= 2.00 \text{ mol } CO_2 \times \left(\frac{37 \text{ J}}{\text{K-mol } CO_2}\right) + 1.00 \text{ mol } H_2O \times \left(\frac{36 \text{ J}}{\text{K-mol } H_2O}\right)$$

$$= \mathbf{110\ J\ K^{-1}}.$$

(c) The heat released in the combustion of one mol of acetylene (1,255,570 J) goes into warming the two mol of CO_2 and one mol of H_2O produced.

11-73 (continued)

The combined heat capacity of the gases is 110 J K^{-1}.

$$q_{gases} = -q_{reaction} = +1{,}255{,}570 \text{ J}$$

$$c_{p,gases}\,\Delta T = 1{,}255{,}570 \text{ J}$$

$$\Delta T = {}^{1{,}255{,}570 \text{ J}}/_{110 \text{ J K}^{-1}} = 11{,}400 \text{ K } (= 11{,}100^{o}\text{C})$$

Given an initial temperature of 20°C, the final temparature will be **~ 11,100^{o}C.**

11-75. We only need $\Delta H_f^o(CO_2)$ and $\Delta H_f^o(SiO_2)$, because we know $\Delta H_f^o(N_2) = \Delta H_f^o(C) = 0$ kJ mol^{-1}.

11-77. The hint reminds us to go entirely with one system of units - SI in this case. Then the heat capacity of the ball becomes 850 J K^{-1} kg^{-1}. We also know that the change in temperature must be 1.00^{o}C = 1.00 K

The heat transfers must equal zero in the end:

$$0 = q(\text{generated in falling ball}) + q\ (\text{absorbed in warming the ball})$$

where q(generated in falling ball) is the ball's decrease in potential energy.

$$0 = m_{ball}g\Delta h + m_{ball}\, c_{s,ball}\, \Delta t = m_{ball}\,(g\Delta h + c_{s,ball}\,\Delta t)$$

The common factor m_{ball} is cancels out, so:

$$0 = g\Delta h + c_{s,ball}\,\Delta t$$

Or: $$\Delta h = \frac{-c_{s,ball}\,\Delta t}{g} = \frac{\left(850 \text{ J K}^{-1}\text{ kg}^{-1}\right)\times(1.00 \text{ K})}{9.81 \text{ m s}^{-2}}$$

$$= 86.6 \text{ J}\left(\frac{\text{s}^2}{\text{kg-m}}\right) = 86.6\left(\frac{\text{kg-m}^2}{\text{s}^2}\right)\times\left(\frac{\text{s}^2}{\text{kg-m}}\right) = \mathbf{86.6\ m}$$

11-79. The work done by the expanding gas is equal to the work done by the paddle on the water. Hence:

$$w_{gas} = q_{water}$$

$$P_{ext}\,\Delta V = m\, c_s\,\Delta T$$

$$1.00 \text{ atm } (13.00 - 5.00 \text{ L}) = (1{,}000 \text{ g}) \times (4.18 \text{ J K}^{-1}\text{ g}^{-1}) \times \Delta T$$

$$(8.00 \text{ L-atm}) \times (101.325 \text{ J}/\text{L-atm}) = 4180 \text{ J K}^{-1} \times \Delta T$$

$$(810.5 \text{ J}/4180 \text{ J K}^{-1}) = \Delta T = 0.194 \text{ K} = \mathbf{0.194^{o}C}$$

CHAPTER 12 - SPONTANEOUS CHANGE AND EQUILIBRIUM

12-1. (a) $4\ Fe\ (s) + 3\ O_2\ (g) \rightarrow 2\ Fe_2O_3\ (s)$

This reaction is exothermic and spontaneous at room temperatures.

(b) $NH_4NO_3\ (s) \rightarrow NH_4^+\ (aq) + NO_3^-\ (aq)$

This reaction is endothermic and spontaneous at room temperatures.

12-3. Good examples are given by procedures used for cooling:

(i) vaporization of isopropyl alcohol ("rubbing alcohol") from skin.

(ii) melting ice in warm water.

(iii) use of a "cold pack," possibly based on dissolving NH_4NO_3 in water

12-5. (a) This is best done by enumeration. There are six states for die 1. Each can be paired with six states of die 2. Thus: No. microstates = 6 × 6 = **36**

(b) This combination represents one of thirty-six equally probable states, so the probability of two sixes is $^1/_{36}$ = **0.02778.**

12-7. (a) *Any* melting process of a pure substance has **$\Delta S > 0$.**

(b) Any reduction of structure (literally in this case) is a reduction in order and therefore has **$\Delta S > 0$.**

(c) Any separation of a mixture represents an increase in order: **$\Delta S < 0$.**

12-9. (a) This reaction has two moles of gas reacting to form one mole of gas so **$\Delta S < 0$.**

(b) This reaction two moles of gas condense to a solid and **$\Delta S < 0$.**

(c) Simple warming without any chemical change (including a phase change), as occurs here, always has **$\Delta S > 0$.**

(d) This involves vaporization of a pure substance so **$\Delta S < 0$.**

12-11. (a) $\Delta S^o = 2 \times S^o (H_2O\ (l)) + 2S^o (NO_2\ (g)) - S^o (N_2H_4\ (l)) - 3S^o (O_2\ (g))$

$= 2\ \text{mol}\ (69.91\ \text{J K}^{-1}\ \text{mol}^{-1}) + 2\ \text{mol}\ (239.95\ \text{J K}^{-1}\ \text{mol}^{-1})$

$- 1\ \text{mol}\ (121.21\ \text{J K}^{-1}\ \text{mol}^{-1}) - 3\ \text{mol}\ (205.03\ \text{J K}^{-1}\ \text{mol}^{-1})$

$= \mathbf{-116.58\ J\ K^{-1}}$

(b) The reaction that must be combined with the one given is:

$$N_2H_4\ (g) \rightarrow N_2H_4\ (l)$$

This reaction will have $\Delta S < 0$ because it is a condensation reaction. Therefore, the oxidation of gaseous hydrazine will have a **more negative** ΔS^o.

12-13. All reactions involve $Cl_2\ (g)$ as a reactant. $S^o (Cl_2\ (g)) = 222.96$. The other data and results may be presented in a table:

M	S^o(M) J K^{-1} mol^{-1}	S^o(MCl) J K^{-1} mol^{-1}	$\Delta S^o = 2S^o(MCl) - 2S^o(M) - S^o(Cl_2)$ J K^{-1}
Li	29.12	59.33	**-162.54**
Na	51.21	72.13	**-181.12**
K	64.18	82.59	**-186.14**
Rb	76.78	95.90	**-184.72**
Cs	85.23	101.17	**-191.08**

Except for Rb, ΔS^o becomes **increasingly negative** down the group.

12-15. $\Delta S = S^o(BaCl_2\ (s)) - S^o(Ba^{2+} (aq)) - 2S^o\ (Cl^- (aq))$

$= 1\ \text{mol}\ (123.68\ \text{J K}^{-1}\ \text{mol}^{-1}) - 1\ \text{mol}\ (9.6\ \text{J K}^{-1}\ \text{mol}^{-1})$

$- 2\ \text{mol}\ (56.5\ \text{J K}^{-1}\ \text{mol}^{-1})$

$= \mathbf{+1.1\ J\ K^{-1}}$

12-17. The reaction is largely driven by an increase in entropy, for there is now a new chemical species -- HOD -- in the mixture.

12-19. Spontaneity in a chemical change is determined by the sign of the change in the entropy of the system plus its surroundings. An increase of the entropy of the surroundings can offset decreases of entropy (= increases in order) within a system.

12-21. The entropy of the surroundings must increase by ***at least*** **44.7 J K^{-1}**.

12-23. $\Delta S_{fus} = \dfrac{\Delta H_{fus}}{T_{fus}} = \dfrac{35{,}400 \text{ J mol}^{-1}}{(3410 + 273) \text{ K}} = \mathbf{+9.61 \text{ J K}^{-1} \text{ mol}^{-1}}$

12-25. (a) $\Delta G = \Delta H - T\Delta S$

$= +5{,}650 \text{ J K}^{-1} - (170 \text{ K})(28.9 \text{ J K}^{-1} \text{ mol}^{-1})$

$= \mathbf{+740 \text{ J mol}^{-1}}$

(b) $(737 \text{ J mol}^{-1}) \times (3.60 \text{ mol}) = 2650 \text{ J} = \mathbf{2.65 \text{ kJ}}$

(c) The answer is **no**. The melting of ammonia is non-spontaneous at 170 K

(d) $\Delta G = 0 = \Delta H = T\Delta S$

$$T = \frac{\Delta H}{\Delta S} = \frac{5{,}650 \text{ J mol}^{-1}}{28.9 \text{ J mol K}^{-1}} = \mathbf{196 \text{ K}}$$

12-27. Trouton's rule: $\Delta S_{vap} \sim 88 \text{ J K}^{-1} \text{ mol}^{-1}$

$$\frac{\Delta H_{vap}}{T_{vap}} \sim 88 \text{ J K}^{-1} \text{ mol}^{-1}$$

$\Delta H_{vap} \sim (T_{vap})(88 \text{ J K mol}^{-1})$

$\sim (56.2 + 273.15 \text{ K})(88 \text{ J K}^{-1} \text{ mol}^{-1}) = 29{,}000 \text{ J K}^{-1} = \mathbf{29 \text{ kJ mol}^{-1}}$

12-29. (a) $\Delta G^o = \Delta G_f^o(\text{Sr } (s)) + \Delta G_f^o(\text{CaCl}_2 (s)) - \Delta G_f^o(\text{Ca } (s)) - \Delta G_f^o(\text{SrCl}_2 (s))$

$= 1 \text{ mol } (0 \text{ kJ mol}^{-1}) + 1 \text{ mol } (-748.1 \text{ kJ mol}^{-1})$

$- 1 \text{ mol } (0 \text{ kJ mol}^{-1}) - 1 \text{ mol } (-781.1 \text{ kJ mol}^{-1}) = \mathbf{+33.0 \text{ kJ}}$

(b) $\Delta G^o = \Delta G_f^o(\text{Al}_2\text{O}_3 (s)) + 2 \times \Delta G_f^o(\text{Fe } (s))$

$- 2 \times \Delta G_f^o(\text{Al } (s)) - \Delta G_f^o(\text{Fe}_2\text{O}_3 (s))$

$= 1 \text{ mol } (-1582.3 \text{ kJ mol}^{-1}) + 2 \text{ mol } (0 \text{ kJ mol}^{-1})$

$- 2 \text{ mol } (0 \text{ kJ mol}^{-1}) - 1 \text{ mol } (-742.2 \text{ kJ mol}^{-1}) = \mathbf{-840.1 \text{ kJ}}$

12-31. $\Delta H^o = \Delta H_f^o\ (CoCl_2 \bullet 6H_2O\ (s)) - \Delta H_f^o\ (CoCl_2\ (s)) - 6 \times \Delta H_f^o\ (H_2O\ (l))$

$= 1\text{ mol } (-2115.4\text{ kJ mol}^{-1}) - 1\text{ mol } (-312.5\text{ kJ mol}^{-1})$

$- 6\text{ mol } (-285.83\text{ kJ mol}^{-1}) = \mathbf{-87.92\ kJ}$

$\Delta S^o = S^o\ (CoCl_2 \bullet 6\ H_2O\ (s)) - S^o\ (CoCl_2\ (s)) - 6 \times S^o\ (H_2O\ (l))$

$= 1\text{ mol } (343\text{ J K}^{-1}\text{ mol}^{-1}) - 1\text{ mol } (109.16\text{ J K}^{-1}\text{ mol}^{-1})$

$- 6\text{ mol } (69.99\text{ J K}^{-1}\text{ mol}^{-1}) = \mathbf{-186\ J\ K^{-1}}$

$\Delta G^o = \Delta G_f^o\ (CoCl_2 \bullet 6\ H_2O\ (s)) - \Delta G_f^o\ (CoCl_2\ (s)) - 6 \times \Delta G_f^o\ (H_2O\ (l))$

$= 1\text{ mol } (-1725.2\text{ kJ mol}^{-1}) - 1\text{ mol } (-269.8\text{ kJ mol}^{-1})$

$- 6\text{ mol } (0 - 237.18\text{ kJ mol}^{-1}) = \mathbf{-32.3\ kJ}$

12-33. At *low* temperature, $T\Delta S$ becomes small, so the enthalpy change is most important in determining ΔG.

(a) $\Delta G < 0$ (b) $\Delta G < 0$ (c) $\Delta G > 0$ (d) $\Delta G > 0$

12-35. (a) $\Delta H^o = 2 \times \Delta H_f^o\ (Fe_2O_3\ (s)) - 4 \times \Delta H_f^o\ (Fe\ (s)) - 3 \times \Delta H_f^o\ (O_2\ (g))$

$= 2\text{ mol } (-824.2\text{ kJ mol}^{-1}) - 4\text{ mol } (0\text{ kJ mol}^{-1}) - 3\text{ mol } (0\text{ kJ mol}^{-1})$

$= -1648.4\text{ kJ}$

$\Delta S^o = 2 \times S^o\ (Fe_2O_3\ (s)) - 4 \times S^o\ (Fe\ (s)) - 3\ S^o\ (O_2\ (g))$

$= 2\text{ mol } (87.40\text{ J K}^{-1}\text{ mol}^{-1}) - 4\text{ mol } (27.28\text{ J K}^{-1}\text{ mol}^{-1})$

$- 3\text{ mol } (205.03\text{ J K}^{-1}\text{ mol}^{-1}) = \mathbf{-549\ J\ K^{-1}}$

$\Delta H^o - T\Delta S^o = \Delta G^o$

$\Delta H^o - T\Delta S^o = 0$ at equilibrium

$$T = \frac{\Delta H}{\Delta S} = \frac{-1648.400\text{ J}}{-549\text{ J K}^{-1}} = 3000\text{ K}$$

Since both ΔH^o and ΔS^o are positive, the reaction will be spontaneous at temperatures *higher* than 3000 K: ***T* > 3000 K.**

12-35.(continued)

(b) $\Delta H^o = \Delta H_f^o\ (SO_3\ (g)) - \Delta H_f^o\ (SO_2\ (g)) - \frac{1}{2}\ \Delta H_f^o\ (O_2\ (g))$

$= 1\ \text{mol}\ (-395.72\ \text{kJ mol}^{-1}) - 1\ \text{mol}\ (-296.83\ \text{kJ mol}^{-1})$

$- \frac{1}{2}\ \text{mol}\ (0\ \text{kJ mol}^{-1}) = -98.89\ \text{kJ} = -98{,}890\ \text{J}$

$\Delta S^o = S^o\ (SO_3) - S^o\ (SO_2) - \frac{1}{2}\ S^o\ (O_2)$

$= 1\ \text{mol}\ (256.65\ \text{J K}^{-1}\ \text{mol}^{-1}) - 1\ \text{mol}\ (248.11\ \text{J K}^{-1}\ \text{mol}^{-1})$

$- \frac{1}{2}\ \text{mol}(205.03\ \text{J K}^{-1}\ \text{mol}^{-1}) = -93.97\ \text{J K}^{-1}$

$\Delta H - T\Delta S = 0$ at equilibrium

$$\frac{\Delta H}{\Delta S} = T = \frac{-98{,}890\ \text{J}}{-93.97\ \text{J K}^{-1}} = 1052\text{K}$$

Since both ΔH^o and ΔS^o are negative, the reaction will be spontaneous at temperatures *lower* than 1050 K: $0 < T < 1050$ K.

(c) $\Delta H^o = \Delta H_f^o\ (N_2O\ (g)) + 2 \times \Delta H_f^o\ (H_2O\ (g)) - \Delta H_f^o\ (NH_4NO_3\ (s))$

$= 1\ \text{mol}\ (82.05\ \text{kJ mol}^{-1}) + 2\ \text{mol}\ (-241.82\ \text{kJ mol}^{-1})$

$- 1\ \text{mol}\ (-365.56\ \text{kJ mol}^{-1}) = -36.03\ \text{kJ} = -36{,}030\ \text{J}$

$\Delta S^o = S^o\ (N_2O\ (g)) + 2 \times S^o\ (H_2O\ (g)) - S^o\ (NH_4NO_3\ (s))$

$= 1\ \text{mol}\ (219.74\ \text{J K}^{-1}\ \text{mol}^{-1}) + 2\ \text{mol}\ (118.72\ \text{J K}^{-1}\ \text{mol}^{-1})$

$- 1\ \text{mol}\ (151.08\ \text{J K}^{-1}\ \text{mol}^{-1}) = +306.1\ \text{J K}^{-1}$

With $\Delta H^o < 0$ and $\Delta S^o > 0$, the reaction will be **spontaneous at all T.**

12-37. The reaction is: $WO_3\ (s) + 3\ H_2\ (g) \rightarrow W\ (s) + 3\ H_2O\ (g)$

$\Delta H^o = \Delta H_f^o(W\ (s)) + 3\ \Delta H_f^o(H_2O\ (g)) - \Delta H_f^o(WO_3\ (s)) - 3\ \Delta H_f^o(H_2\ (g))$

$= 1\ \text{mol}\ (0.0\ \text{kJ mol}^{-1}) + 3\ \text{mol}\ (-241.82\ \text{kJ mol}^{-1})$

$- 1\ \text{mol}\ (-842.87\ \text{kJ mol}^{-1}) - 3\ \text{mol}\ (-0.0\ \text{kJ mol}^{-1}) = \mathbf{+\ 117.41\ kJ}$

$\Delta S^o = S^o(W\ (s)) + 3\ S^o(H_2O\ (g)) - S^o(WO_3\ (s)) - 3\ S^o(H_2\ (g))$

$= 1\ \text{mol}\ (32.64\ \text{J K}^{-1}\ \text{mol}^{-1}) + 3\ \text{mol}\ (\ 188.72\ \text{J K}^{-1}\ \text{mol}^{-1})$

$- 1\ \text{mol}\ (75.90\ \text{J mol}^{-1}\ \text{K}^{-1}) - 3\ \text{K}\ (130.57\ \text{J mol}^{-1}\ \text{mol}^{-1}) = \mathbf{+\ 131.19\ J\ K^{-1}}$

12-37. (continued)

The significant positive standard entropy change indicates that, at high enough temperatures, the $-T\Delta S^o$ term in the expression for the free energy will become large and negative -- large enough to overcome the positive ΔH^o.

$$\Delta G < 0 \text{ for } T > \frac{\Delta H^o}{\Delta S^o} = \frac{117{,}410 \text{ J}}{131.19 \text{ J K}^{-1}} = \mathbf{895\ K}$$

12-39.

$$\Delta G^o = 3 \times \Delta G_f^o(\text{H}_2\text{O}(g)) + 2 \times \Delta G_f^o(\text{NO}_2(g)) - \frac{7}{2}\Delta G_f^o(\text{O}_2(g)) - 2 \times \Delta G_f^o(\text{NH}_3(g))$$

$$= 3 \text{ mol}(-228.59 \text{ kJ mol}^{-1}) + 2 \text{ mol}(51.29 \text{ kJ mol}^{-1}) - \frac{7}{2} \text{ mol}(0 \text{ kJ mol}^{-1}) - 2 \text{ mol}(-16.48 \text{ kJ mol}^{-1})$$

$$= -550.23 \text{ kJ} = \mathbf{-550{,}230\ J} = -550{,}230 \text{ J per mol of reaction}$$

$$K = e^{-(\Delta G^o/RT)} = e^{-(-550{,}230 \text{ J mol}^{-1}/(8.3145 \text{J mol}^{-1} \text{K}^{-1} \times 298.15 \text{ K}))} = \mathbf{2.5 \times 10^{+96}}$$

12-41. (a)

$$\Delta G^o = \Delta G_f^o(\text{SO}_3(g)) - \Delta G_f^o(\text{SO}_2(g)) - \frac{1}{2}\Delta G_f^o(\text{O}_2(g))$$

$$= 1\text{mol}(-371.08 \text{ kJ mol}^{-1}) - 1\text{mol}(-300.19 \text{ kJ mol}^{-1}) - \frac{1}{2}\text{mol}(0 \text{ kJ mol}^{-1})$$

$$= -70.89 \text{ kJ} = -70{,}890 \text{ J} = -70.890 \text{ J per mol of reaction}$$

$$K = e^{-(-70{,}890 \text{ Jmol}^{-1}/(8.3145 \text{J mol}^{-1} \text{K}^{-1})(298.15 \text{ K}))} = e^{+28.60} = \mathbf{2.6 \times 10^{12}}$$

$$K = \frac{P_{SO_3}}{(P_{SO_2})(P_{O_2})^{1/2}}$$

(b)

$$\Delta G^o = 2 \times \Delta G_f^o(\text{Fe}_3\text{O}_4(s)) + \frac{1}{2}\Delta G_f^o(\text{O}_2(g)) - 3 \times \Delta G_f^o(\text{Fe}_2\text{O}_3(s))$$

$$= 2 \text{ mol}(-1015.5 \text{ kJ mol}^{-1}) + \frac{1}{2} \text{ mol}(0 \text{ kJ mol}^{-1}) - 3 \text{ mol}(-742.2 \text{ kJ mol}^{-1})$$

$$= +195.6 \text{ kJ} = +195{,}600 \text{ J} = +195{,}600 \text{ J per mol of reaction}$$

$$K = e^{-(+195{,}600 \text{ J mol}^{-1}/(8.3145 \text{J mol}^{-1} \text{K}^{-1})(298.15 \text{ K}))} = e^{-78.90} = \mathbf{5.4 \times 10^{-35}}$$

$$K = (P_{O_2})^{1/2}$$

12-41. (continued)

(c) $\Delta G^o = \Delta G^o_f\,(Cu^{2+}\,(aq)) + 2 \times \Delta G^o_f\,(Cl^-\,(aq)) - \Delta G^o_f\,(CuCl_2\,(s))$

$= 1\text{ mol }(+65.49\text{ kJ mol}^{-1}) + 2\text{ mol }(-131.23\text{ kJ mol}^{-1})$

$-1\text{ mol }(-175.7\text{ kJ mol}^{-1})$

$= -21.27\text{ kJ} = \mathbf{-21{,}270\ J} = -21{,}270\text{ J per mol of reaction}$

$$K = e^{-\left(-21{,}270\text{ J mol}^{-1} / \left(8.3145\text{J mol}^{-1}\text{ K}^{-1}\right)(298.15\text{ K})\right)} = e^{+8.58} = \mathbf{5300}$$

$K = \mathbf{[Cu^{2+}]\,[Cl^-]^2}$

12-43. $\Delta G^o = \Delta G^o_f\,(HPO_4^{2-}\,(aq)) + \Delta G^o_f\,(H_3O^+\,(aq))$

$- \Delta G^o_f\,(H_2PO_4^-\,(aq)) - \Delta G^o_f\,(H_2O\,(l))$

$= 1\text{ mol }(-1089.15\text{ kJ mol}^{-1}) + 1\text{ mol }(-237.18\text{ kJ mol}^{-1})$

$- 1\text{ mol }(-1130.28\text{ kJ mol}^{-1}) - 1\text{ mol }(-237.18\text{ kJ mol}^{-1})$

$= +41.13\text{ kJ} = +41{,}130\text{ J} = 41{,}130\text{ J per mol of reaction}$

$$K = e^{-\left(+41{,}130\text{ J mol}^{-1}/\left(8.3145\text{J mol}^{-1}\text{ K}^{-1}\right)(298.15\text{ K})\right)} = e^{-16.59} = \mathbf{6.2 \times 10^{-8}}$$

12-45. All that is required is that ΔS be sufficiently negative to "overwhelm" ΔH. It makes sense that ΔS is very negative, because the reaction involves trapping (condensing) a gas in a liquid.

12-47. $\Delta G^o_{590} = 29{,}400\text{ J} = 29{,}400\text{ per mol of reaction}$

$$K = e^{-\left(+29{,}400\text{ J mol}^{-1}/\left(8.3145\text{J mol}^{-1}\text{ K}^{-1}\right)(590\text{ K})\right)} = e^{-5.99} = \mathbf{0.0025}$$

12-49. The information in the problem indicates that heat drives O_2 out of water, so that process must be endothermic. The reaction written in the problem is for dissolving O_2 *into* water. This must be exothermic, or $\Delta H < 0$.

12-51. Since the reaction gives fewer moles of gaseous products than gaseous reactants, increasing pressure will . The reaction is exothermic and decreasing temperatures will likewise drive the reaction to the right.

12-53. $\Delta H^o = 2\Delta H_f^o\,(NH_3\,(g)) - 3\Delta H_f^o\,(H_2\,(g)) - \Delta H_f^o\,(N_2\,(g))$

$= 2\text{ mol }(-46.11\text{ kJ mol}^{-1}) - 3\text{ mol }(0\text{ kJ mol}^{-1}) - 1\text{ mol }(0\text{ kJ mol}^{-1})$

$= -92.22\text{ kJ} = -92{,}220\text{ J}$

$\Delta S^o = 2\,S^o\,(NH_3\,(g)) - 3\,S^o\,(H_2\,(g)) - S^o\,(N_2\,(g))$

$= 2\text{ mol }(+192.34\text{ J mol}^{-1}\text{ K}^{-1}) - 3\text{ mol }(+130.57\text{ J mol}^{-1}\text{ K}^{-1})$

$- 1\text{ mol }(191.50\text{ J mol}^{-1}\text{ K}^{-1})$

$= -198.53\text{ J K}^{-1}$

$\Delta G\,(600\text{ K}) = \Delta H^o - 600\,\Delta S^o$

$= -92{,}220\text{ J} - (600\text{ K})(-198.53\text{ J K}^{-1}) = 26{,}898\text{ J}$

$= 26{,}898$ J per mol of the reaction

$$K = e^{-\left(26{,}898\text{ J mol}^{-1}/\left(8.3145\text{J mol}^{-1}\text{ K}^{-1}\right)(600\text{ K})\right)} = e^{-5.39} = \mathbf{0.0046}$$

12-55. The assumption that ΔH and ΔS are independent of temperature permits the use of the van't Hoff equation.

$$\ln\left(\frac{K_2}{K_1}\right) = \frac{\Delta H^o}{R}\left(\frac{1}{T_1} - \frac{1}{T_2}\right)$$

$K_2 = 1.21 \times 10^{-3};\ T_2 = 200^oC = 473.15\text{ K}$

$K_1 = 6.8;\ T_1 = 25^oC = 298.15\text{ K}$

$$\ln\left(\frac{1.21 \times 10^{-3}}{6.8}\right) = \frac{\Delta H^o}{8.3145\text{ J K}^{-1}\text{ mol}^{-1}}\left(1.2405 \times 10^{-3}\text{ K}^{-1}\right)$$

$$\frac{8.3145\text{ J mol}^{-1}\text{ K}^{-1}}{1.2405 \times 10^{-3}\text{ K}^{-1}}(-8.634) = \Delta H^o = -58{,}000\text{ J mol}^{-1} = -58\text{ kJ mol}^{-1}$$

This answer gives the enthalpy change for "one mole of the reaction" For the reaction as written, we will have $\boldsymbol{\Delta H^o = -58}$ **kJ.**

12-57. $K_2 = 2900;\quad T_2 = 28\ ^oC = 301.15\text{ K}$

$K_1 = 40\quad\quad T_1 = 48\ ^oC = 321.15\text{ K}$

$$\ln\left(\frac{2900}{40}\right) = \frac{\Delta H^o}{8.3145\text{ J K}^{-1}\text{ mol}^{-1}}\left(\frac{1}{321.15\text{ K}} - \frac{1}{301.15\text{ K}}\right)$$

This yields $\quad\quad \Delta H^o = -172{,}000\text{ J mol}^{-1}$

12-57. (continued) ΔH for the reaction as written is **-172,000 J = -172 kJ.**

At 28 °C:

$$\Delta G^o = -RT\ln K = -(8.3145\ \frac{\text{J}}{\text{K mol}^{-1}})\ (301.15\ \text{K})\ (\ln 2900) = -19{,}960\ \text{J mol}^{-1}$$

For the reaction as written, ΔG^o = -19,960 J.

$$\Delta S^o = -\frac{\Delta G^o - \Delta H^o}{T} = -\frac{(-19{,}960\ \text{J})-(-172{,}200\ \text{J})}{301.15\ \text{K}} = \mathbf{-506\ J\ K^{-1}}$$

12-59. (a) $\Delta G^o = -RT\ln K = -(8.3145\ \frac{\text{J}}{\text{K mol}^{-1}})\ (298\ \text{K})\ \ln(9.3 \times 10^9) = -56{,}872\ \text{J mol-1}$

For the reaction as written, ΔG^o = -56,900 J = **-56.9 kJ**

(b) For ΔH^o, we employ the van't Hoff equation:

$$\ln\left(\frac{K_2}{K_1}\right) = \frac{\Delta H^o}{R}\left(\frac{1}{T_1} - \frac{1}{T_2}\right)$$

$$\ln\left(\frac{3.3 \times 10^7}{9.3 \times 10^9}\right) = \frac{\Delta H^o}{8.3145\ \text{J K}^{-1}\ \text{mol}^{-1}}\left(\frac{1}{298\ \text{K}} - \frac{1}{398\ \text{K}}\right)$$

$$-5.64 = \Delta H^o\ \frac{\left(8.43 \times 10^{-4}\ \text{K}^{-1}\right)}{8.3145\ \text{J K}^{-1}\ \text{mol}^{-1}}$$

$$\Delta H^o = -5.64 \times \left(\frac{8.3145\ \text{J mol}^{-1}}{8.43 \times 10^{-4}}\right) = -\ 55{,}630\ \text{J mol}^{-1}$$

For the reaction as written, ΔH^o = -55,630 J = **-55.6 kJ**

$$\Delta S^o = -\frac{\Delta G^o - \Delta H^o}{T} = -\frac{(-56{,}872\ \text{J})-(-55{,}630\ \text{J})}{298.15\ \text{K}} = \mathbf{+4.2\ J\ K^{-1}}$$

12-61. The Clausius-Clapeyron equation is used here:

P_1 = 0.4034 atm $\quad T_1$ = -50 °C = 223.15 K

P_2 = 4.2380 atm $\quad T_2$ = 0 °C = 273.15 K

$$\ln\left(\frac{P_2}{P_1}\right) = \frac{\Delta H_{vap}}{R}\left(\frac{1}{T_1} - \frac{1}{T_2}\right)$$

$$\ln\left(\frac{4.2380}{0.4034}\right) = \frac{\Delta H_{vap}}{8.3145\ \text{J K}^{-1}\ \text{mol}^{-1}}\left(\frac{1}{223.15\ \text{K}} - \frac{1}{273.15\ \text{K}}\right)$$

$$2.3915 = \frac{\Delta H_{vap}}{8.3145\ \text{J K}^{-1}\ \text{mol}^{-1}}\left(-8.203 \times 10^{-4}\ \text{K}^{-1}\right)$$

$$\frac{\left(8.3145\ \text{J mol}^{-1}\right)(2.3519)}{\left(8.203 \times 10^{-4}\right)} = \Delta H_{vap} = +23{,}800\ \text{J mol}^{-1} = \mathbf{+23.8\ kJ\ mol^{-1}}$$

12-61. (continued)

(b) The normal boiling point is when P_{vap} = 1 atm. If we set this equal to P_1 and $T_1 = T_b$, then:

$$\ln(P_2) = \frac{\Delta H_{vap}}{R}\left(\frac{1}{T_b} - \frac{1}{T_2}\right)$$

$$\frac{R\ln(P_2)}{\Delta H_{vap}} = \left(\frac{1}{T_b} - \frac{1}{T_2}\right)$$

$$\frac{1}{T_b} = \frac{R\ln(P_2)}{\Delta H_{vap}} + \frac{1}{T_2}$$

$$= \frac{8.3145 \text{ J mol}^{-1}\text{ K}^{-1} \ln(0.4034)}{23{,}800 \text{ J mol}^{-1}} + \frac{1}{223.15 \text{ K}}$$

$$= 0.004164 \text{ K}^{-1}$$

$$\mathbf{T_b = 240 \text{ K}}$$

12-63. These data imply: P_2 = 1.00 atm T_2 = 124°C = 397.15 K

P_1 = 0.63 atm T_1 = 107°C = 380.15 K

$$\ln\left(\frac{1.00}{0.63}\right) = \frac{\Delta H_{vap}}{8.3145 \text{ J K}^{-1}\text{ mol}^{-1}}\left(\frac{1}{380.15 \text{ K}} - \frac{1}{397.15 \text{ K}}\right)$$

$$\frac{\left(8.3145 \text{ J mol}^{-1}\right)(0.462)}{\left(1.126 \times 10^{-4}\right)} = \Delta H_{vap} = +34{,}000 \text{ J mol}^{-1} = \mathbf{+34 \text{ kJ mol}^{-1}}$$

12-65. The data in section 12-8 are, for $6\ CO_2\ (g) + 12\ H_2O\ (l) \rightarrow C_6H_{12}O_6 + 6\ O_2\ (g)$:

ΔG^o = +2872 kJ ΔS^o = -207 J K^{-1}

$$\Delta H^o - T\Delta S^o = \Delta G^o$$

$$\Delta H^o = \Delta G^o + T\Delta S^o$$

$$= (2{,}872{,}000 \text{ J}) + (298.15 \text{ K})(-207 \text{ J K}^{-1})$$

$$= 2{,}810{,}000 \text{ J} = \mathbf{2{,}810 \text{ kJ}}$$

12-67. (a) Each individual keystroke has a $\frac{1}{2}$ chance of producing the value specified, since there are 50 even and 50 odd numbers in the range between 1 and 100. The question gives 10 results in *specific* order, so the probability is:

$$\frac{1}{2}\times\frac{1}{2}\times\frac{1}{2}\times\frac{1}{2}\times\frac{1}{2}\times\frac{1}{2}\times\frac{1}{2}\times\frac{1}{2}\times\frac{1}{2}\times\frac{1}{2} = \left(\frac{1}{2}\right)^{10} = \mathbf{9.77 \times 10^{-4}}$$

12-67. (continued)

(b) Here the pattern involves 9 even results and 1 odd result in *random* order. Picture the case where all ten numbers are even. This has a probability of 9.76 × 10^{-4}, just as in part **(a)**. If we allow *any* individual keystroke to yield an odd number, then this can happen ten different ways--the first keystroke, the second, etc. Thus the probability is 10 × 9.77 × 10^{-4} = **9.77 × 10^{-3}**

12-69. (a) The **random**, less ordered structure will have **higher** entropy.

(b) With each site having 2 possible orientations, "up" or "down," the number of possible states is $(2)^{6.022 \times 10^{23}}$.

12-71. The area under the curve from 0 to 200 K is larger for gold. **Gold** has higher absolute entropy.

12-73. (a) This is **false**. Energy is *transformed* in power plants.

(b) This is **false**. Scientists have found *no* exceptions to the second law of thermodynamics.

(c) This is **true**.

(d) This is **false**. The second law of thermodynamics allows scientists to predict the *tendancy*, in terms of spontaneity vs. non-spontaneity, of reactions.

(e) This is **false**. Classical thermodynamics is derived from the *observed laws of thermodynamics. These laws are independent of any theory of matter.*

12-75. (a)

$$\Delta H^o = 3\Delta H_f^o\ (S_8\ (g)) - 4\Delta H_f^o\ (S_6\ (g))$$
$$= 3\text{ mol } (101.55\text{ kJ mol}^{-1}) - 4\text{ mol } (103.72\text{ kJ mol}^{-1})$$
$$= \mathbf{-110.23\ kJ}$$

The energetics favor S_8 *(g)*.

(b) The reaction has fewer gaseous molecules in the products, so $\Delta S^o < 0$. Thus the entropy change favors the reactant S_6 *(g)*

12-77. $\Delta S^o = \dfrac{\Delta H_{vap}}{T_{vap}} = \dfrac{38{,}740 \text{ J mol}^{-1}}{(273.15 \text{ K} + 78.4 \text{ K})} = \mathbf{+110 \text{ J K}^{-1} \text{ mol}^{-1}}$

Trouton's rule predicts $\Delta S_{vap} = 88 \pm 5$ kJ mol^{-1}

The vaporization of ethanol has a larger entropy change than expected. This suggests ethanol is more ordered in the liquid phase than most compounds. One reason may be extensive hydrogen bonding networks.

12-79.
$$\Delta G^o = 3\Delta G_f^o (SiO_2, \text{quartz}) + 2\Delta G_f^o (N_2 (g)) + 3\Delta G_f^o (\text{C, gr}) - 3\Delta G_f^o (CO_2 (g)) - \Delta G_f^o (Si_3N_4 (s))$$

$$= 3 \text{ mol } (-856.67 \frac{\text{kJ}}{\text{mol}}) + 2 \text{ mol } (0 \frac{\text{kJ}}{\text{mol}}) + 3 \text{ mol } (0 \frac{\text{kJ}}{\text{mol}}) - 3 \text{ mol } (-394.36 \frac{\text{kJ}}{\text{mol}}) - 1 \text{ mol } (-642.6 \frac{\text{kJ}}{\text{mol}})$$

$$= \mathbf{-744.3 \text{ kJ}}$$

12-81. (a)
$$\Delta H^o = 2\Delta H_f^o (\text{CuCl}) + \Delta H_f^o (Cl_2) - 2\Delta H_f^o (CuCl_2)$$

$$= 2 \text{ mol } (-137.2 \text{ kJ/mol}) + 1 \text{ mol } (0 \text{ kJ/mol}) - 2 \text{ mol } (-220.1 \text{ kJ/mol})$$

$$= \mathbf{+165.8 \text{ kJ}}$$

$$\Delta S^o = 2S^o (\text{CuCl}) + S^o (Cl_2) - 2S^o (CuCl_2)$$

$$= 2 \text{ mol } (86.2 \text{ J K}^{-1} \text{ mol}^{-1}) + 1 \text{ mol } (222.96 \text{ J K}^{-1} \text{ mol}^{-1}) - 2 \text{ mol } (108.07 \text{ J K}^{-1} \text{ mol}^{-1})$$

$$= \mathbf{+179.2 \text{ J K}^{-1}}$$

(b) $\Delta G^o_{590} \approx \Delta H^o - T\Delta S^o$

$$\approx 165{,}800 \text{ J} - (590 \text{ K})(179.2 \text{ J K}^{-1}) = 60{,}072 \text{ J} = \mathbf{60.07 \text{ kJ}}$$

(c) $\Delta G^o_{590} = \Delta H^o_{590} - T\Delta S^o_{590}$

$$= 158{,}360 \text{ J} - (590 \text{ K})(177.74 \text{ J K}^{-1}) = 53{,}493 \text{ J} = \mathbf{53.49 \text{ kJ}}$$

$$\% \text{ error} = \frac{\Delta G^o_{incorrect} - \Delta G^o_{correct}}{\Delta G^o_{correct}} \times 100\%$$

$$= \frac{60.07 \text{ kJ} - 53.49 \text{ kJ}}{53.49 \text{ kJ}} \times 100\% = \mathbf{12.3\%}$$

12-83. (a)

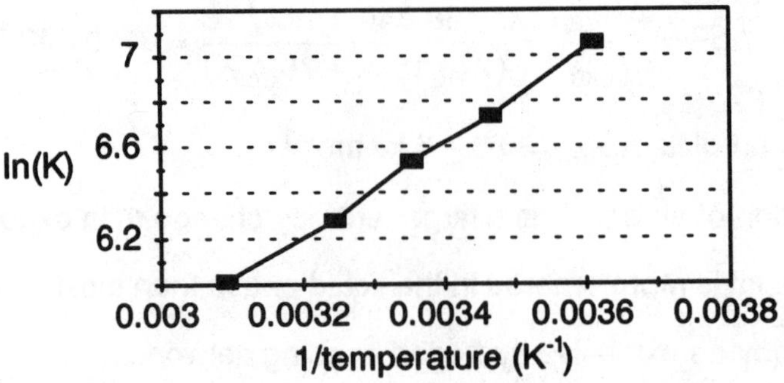

(b) The slope of the graph is equal to $-\dfrac{\Delta H^o}{R}$, and here the slope has a value, determined by linear regression (it can also be done by hand) of +2020 K, so:

$$-\frac{\Delta H^o}{R} = \text{slope}$$

$$\Delta H^o = -\text{slope} \times R = -2020\ \text{K} \times 8.3145\ \text{J mol}^{-1}\ \text{K}^{-1}$$

$$= -16{,}800\ \text{J mol}^{-1}$$

For the reaction as written, ΔH^o = **- 16.8 kJ**

The reaction is exothermic. Higher temperatures reduce K, shifting the reaction to the **right.**

12-85. The table of changes must be arranged to include the variable x, which indicates the fraction of N_2 that undergoes dissociation, and the variable y, which indicates the initial pressure of N_2:

ALL P IN ATM	N_2	N
INITIAL PRESSURE	y	0
CHANGE IN PRESSURE	$-yx$	$+2yx$
FINAL PRESSURE	$y(1-x)$	$2yx$

We know: $P_{TOTAL} = P_{N_2} + P_N$

$$1.00\ \text{atm} = y(1-x) + (2yx) = y(1+x)$$

Therefore: $y = 1.00 / (1 + x)$

12-85. (continued)

$P_N = {}^{1-x}/_{1+x}$ $\quad\quad$ $P_{N_2} = {}^{2x}/_{1+x}$

Therefore:
$$K = \frac{\dfrac{(2x)^2}{(1.00+x)^2}}{\dfrac{(1.00-x)}{(1.00+x)}} = \frac{4x^2}{1-x^2}$$

At 5000 K, $x = 0.65\% = 0.0065$ $\quad K_1 = \dfrac{4(0.0065)^2}{1-(0.0065)^2} = 1.690 \times 10^{-4}$

At 6000 K, $x = 11.6\% = 0.116$ $\quad K_2 = \dfrac{4(0.116)^2}{1-(0.116)^2} = 5.456 \times 10^{-2}$

From van't Hoff:
$$\ln\left(\frac{K_2}{K_1}\right) = \frac{\Delta H^o}{R}\left(\frac{1}{T_1} - \frac{1}{T_2}\right)$$

$$\ln\left(\frac{5.456 \times 10^{-2}}{1.690 \times 10^{-4}}\right) = \frac{\Delta H^o}{(8.3145 \text{ J mol}^{-1}\text{ K}^{-1})}\left(\frac{1}{5000 \text{ K}} - \frac{1}{6000 \text{ K}}\right)$$

$$\frac{(8.3145)(5.777)}{3.33 \times 10^{-5}} = \Delta H^o = \mathbf{1442\ kJ}$$

12-87. To an outside observer, a system at equilibrium never changes -- like a dead object. But the fact that equilibria are dynamic on a microscopic level -- constantly going backwards and forwards--means the system is in fact very active.

12-89. (a) $\quad \Delta H^o - T\Delta S^o = \Delta G^o$

$$\Delta S^o = -\frac{\Delta G^o - \Delta H^o}{T} = -\frac{(-34{,}500 \text{ J}) - (-19{,}700 \text{ J})}{298.15 \text{ K}}$$

$= \mathbf{+49.7\ J\ K^{-1}}$

(b) Formation of 38 mol of ATP from ADP requires 38 × (34.5 kJ) = 1311 kJ. Conversion of glucose and O_2 to carbon dioxide and water yields 2872 kJ. The efficiency is then 0.456 = **45.6%**

CHAPTER 13 - REDOX REACTIONS AND ELECTROCHEMISTRY

13-1. $MnO_2\ (s) + {}^4/_3\ Al\ (s) \rightarrow Mn\ (s) + {}^2/_3\ Al_2O_3\ (s)$

$$\Delta H^o = \Delta H_f^o(Mn\ (s)) + {}^2/_3\ \Delta H_f^o(Al_2O_3\ (s)) - \Delta H_f^o(MnO_2\ (s)) - {}^4/_3\ \Delta H_f^o(Al\ (s))$$

$$= 1\ mol\ (0.0\ \frac{kJ}{mol}) + {}^2/_3\ mol\ (-1675.7\ \frac{kJ}{mol}) - mol\ (-520.03\ \frac{kJ}{mol}) - {}^4/_3\ mol\ (0.0\ \frac{kJ}{mol}) .. = \mathbf{-5971\ kJ}$$

$$\Delta G^o = \Delta G_f^o(Mn\ (s)) + {}^2/_3\ \Delta G_f^o(Al_2O_3\ (s)) - \Delta G_f^o(MnO_2\ (s)) - {}^4/_3\ \Delta G_f^o(Al\ (s))$$

$$= 1\ mol\ (0.0\ \frac{kJ}{mol}) + {}^2/_3\ mol\ (-1582.3\ \frac{kJ}{mol}) - 1\ mol\ (-465.17\ \frac{kJ}{mol}) - {}^4/_3\ mol\ (0.0\ \frac{kJ}{mol}) = \mathbf{-589.7\ kJ}$$

13-3. The reaction is: $2\ HgO\ (s) \rightarrow 2\ Hg\ (l) + O_2\ (g)$

$$\Delta H^o = 2\ \Delta H_f^o(Hg\ (l)) + \Delta H_f^o(O_2\ (g)) - 2\ \Delta H_f^o(HgO\ (s))$$

$$= 2\ mol(0.0\ \frac{kJ}{mol}) + 1\ mol\ (0.0\ \frac{kJ}{mol}) - 2\ mol\ (-90.83\ \frac{kJ}{mol})$$

$$= \mathbf{181.66\ kJ}$$

$$\Delta S^o = 2\ S^o(Hg\ (l)) + S^o(O_2\ (g)) - 2\ S^o(HgO\ (s))$$

$$= 2\ mol\ (76.02\ JK^{-1}\ mol^{-1}) + 1\ mol\ (205.03\ JK^{-1}\ mol^{-1}) - 2\ mol\ (70.29\ JK^{-1}\ mol^{-1})$$

$$= \mathbf{+\ 216.49\ J\ K^{-1}}$$

As we saw repeatedly in Chapter 12, when ΔG^o equals zero:

$$T = \Delta H^o / \Delta S^o = {}^{181{,}660\ J}/_{216.49\ J\ K^{-1}} = 839\ K = 566^oC$$

Because ΔH and ΔS are both greater than zero, the reaction will be spontaneous at higher temperatures: **T > 566°C**

13-5. The calculation of the mass of contained copper must take into account the number of grams of the copper compound in 1 metric ton of ore and the fraction of copper in a mass of the compound. There are 1,000,000 grams in one metric ton, so 1% of this amount is 10,000 grams. For neatness' sake, a table is best for keeping track of the contributions of the different compounds to the mass of copper in the ore.

ORE	grams in 1 metric ton	molar mass (g mol^{-1})	mass fraction Cu	mass of Cu (g)
$CuFeS_2$	11,000 g	183.525	0.346	3,809
CuS	4200 g	95.612	0.665	2,791
Cu_5FeS_4	5100 g	501.84	0.633	3,229
			TOTAL:	9,829 g =9.8 kg

13-7. (a) #1: $Fe_2O_3\ (s) + 3\ CO\ (g) \rightarrow 2\ Fe\ (s) + 3\ CO_2\ (g)$

#2: $Fe_3O_4\ (s) + 4\ CO\ (g) \rightarrow 3\ Fe\ (s) + 4\ CO_2\ (g)$

#3: $FeCO_3\ (s) + CO\ (g) \rightarrow Fe\ (s) + 2\ CO_2\ (g)$

(b) For all three reactions, the term for ΔG_f^o(Fe) is omitted, because it is zero.

#1: $\Delta G^o = 3\ \Delta G_f^o(CO_2) - \Delta G_f^o(Fe_2O_3) - 3\ \Delta G_f^o(CO)$

$= 3\text{ mol }(-394.36\frac{kJ}{mol}) - 1\text{ mol }(-742.2\frac{kJ}{mol}) - 3\text{ mol }(-137.15\frac{kJ}{mol})$

$= -29.43$ kJ for the reaction, $\Delta G^o =$ **-14.7 kJ (mol Fe)$^{-1}$**

#2: $\Delta G^o = 4\ \Delta G_f^o(CO_2) - \Delta G_f^o(Fe_3O_4) - 4\ \Delta G_f^o(CO)$

$= 4\text{ mol }(-394.36\ \frac{kJ}{mol}) - 1\text{ mol }(-1015.5\ \frac{kJ}{mol}) - 4\text{ mol }(-137.15\ \frac{kJ}{mol})$

$= -13.34$ kJ for the reaction, $\Delta G^o =$ **-4.4 kJ (mol Fe)$^{-1}$**

#3: $\Delta G^o = 2\ \Delta G_f^o(CO_2) - \Delta G_f^o(FeCO_3) - \Delta G_f^o(CO)$

$= 2\text{ mol }(-394.36\ \frac{kJ}{mol}) - 1\text{ mol }(-666.72\frac{kJ}{mol}) - 1\text{ mol }(-137.15\ \frac{kJ}{mol})$

$= +15.1$ kJ for the reaction, $\Delta G^o =$ **+15.1 kJ (mol Fe)$^{-1}$**

Per mole of iron produced, **Fe_2O_3** is thermodynamically easiest to reduce with CO as reductant.

13-9. (a) Reduction: $2\ H^+\ (aq) + H_2O_2\ (aq) + 2\ e^- \rightarrow 2\ H_2O\ (l)$

Oxidation: $Fe^{2+} (aq) \rightarrow Fe^{3+}\ (aq) + e^-$

(b) In this problem H^+ and H_2O appear in *both* the reduction and the oxidation reaction. The half-equations must be reconstructed by considering the reduced and oxidized species:

Reduction: $MnO_4^- \rightarrow Mn^{2+}$

Add H_2O to balance O: $MnO_4^- \rightarrow Mn^{2+} + 4\ H_2O$

Add H^+ to balance H: $8\ H^+ + MnO_4^- \rightarrow Mn^{2+} + 4\ H_2O$

Add e^- to balance charge: $5\ e^- + 8\ H^+ + MnO_4^- \rightarrow Mn^{2+} + 4\ H_2O$

Add appropriate phase descriptions:

$$5\ e^- + 8\ H^+\ (aq) + MnO_4^-\ (aq) \rightarrow Mn^{2+}\ (aq) + 4\ H_2O\ (l)$$

Oxidation: $SO_2 \rightarrow HSO_4^-$

Add H_2O to balance O: $2\ H_2O + SO_2 \rightarrow HSO_4^-$

Add H^+ to balance H: $2\ H_2O + SO_2 \rightarrow HSO_4^- + 3\ H^+$

Add e^- to balance charge: $2\ H_2O + SO_2 \rightarrow HSO_4^- + 3\ H^+ + 2\ e^-$

Add appropriate phase descriptions:

$$2\ H_2O\ (l) + SO_2\ (aq) \rightarrow HSO_4^-\ (aq) + 3\ H^+\ (aq) + 2\ e^-$$

(c) This is a disproportionation reaction, where a single substance (here ClO_2^-) is both reduced (to Cl^-) *and* oxidized (to ClO_2).

Reduction: $ClO_2^- \rightarrow Cl^-$

Add H_2O to balance O: $ClO_2^- \rightarrow Cl^- + 2\ H_2O$

Add H^+ to balance H: $4\ H^+ + ClO_2^- \rightarrow Cl^- + 2\ H_2O$

Add e^- to balance charge: $4\ e^- + 4\ H^+ + ClO_2^- \rightarrow Cl^- + 2\ H_2O$

Add appropriate phase descriptions:

$$4\ e^- + 4\ H^+\ (aq) + ClO_2^-\ (aq) \rightarrow Cl^-\ (aq) + 2\ H_2O\ (l)$$

13-9 (c) (continued)

Oxidation: $ClO_2^- \rightarrow ClO_2$

Add H_2O to balance O (not needed):

Add H^+ to balance H (not needed):

Add e^- to balance charge: $ClO_2^- \rightarrow ClO_2 + e^-$

Add appropriate phase descriptions:

$$ClO_2^- \,(aq) \rightarrow ClO_2 \,(g) + e^-$$

13-11. Alternate reactions will be balanced in full detail. For the others the balanced half-reactions and the final equation are presented.

(a) Reduction: $VO_2^+ \rightarrow VO^{2+}$

Add H_2O to balance O: $VO_2^+ \rightarrow VO^{2+} + H_2O$

Add H^+ to balance H: $2\,H^+ + VO_2^+ \rightarrow VO^{2+} + H_2O$

Add e^- to balance charge: $e^- + 2\,H^+ + VO_2^+ \rightarrow VO^{2+} + H_2O$

Add appropriate phase descriptions:

$$e^- + 2\,H^+ \,(aq) + VO_2^+ \,(aq) \rightarrow VO^{2+} \,(aq) + H_2O \,(l)$$

Oxidation: $SO_2 \rightarrow SO_4^{2-}$

Add H_2O to balance O: $2\,H_2O + SO_2 \rightarrow SO_4^{2-}$

Add H^+ to balance H : $2\,H_2O + SO_2 \rightarrow SO_4^{2-} + 4\,H^+$

Add e^- to balance charge: $2\,H_2O + SO_2 \rightarrow SO_4^{2-} + 4\,H^+ + 2\,e^-$

Add appropriate phase descriptions:

$$2\,H_2O \,(l) + SO_2 \,(g) \rightarrow SO_4^{2-} \,(aq) + 4\,H^+ \,(aq) + 2\,e^-$$

Combine: The reduction reaction has 1 e^- transferred; the oxidation reaction has 2 e^-. So the reduction reaction must be multiplied by 2 and the reduction reaction must be multiplied by 1 to cancel electrons. The final balanced equation is:

$$SO_2 \,(g) + 2\,VO_2^+ \,(aq) \rightarrow 2\,VO^{2+} \,(aq) + SO_4^{2-} \,(aq)$$

13-11. (continued)

(b) Oxidation: $2\ H_2O\ (l) + SO_2\ (g) \rightarrow SO_4^{2-}\ (aq) + 4\ H^+\ (aq) + 2\ e^-$

Reduction: $Br_2\ (l) + 2\ e^- \rightarrow 2\ Br^-\ (aq)$

Combine: $Br_2\ (l) + 2\ H_2O\ (l) + SO_2\ (g) \rightarrow SO_4^{2-}\ (aq) + 4\ H^+\ (aq) + 2\ Br^-\ (aq)$

(c) Reduction: $Cr_2O_7^{2-} \rightarrow Cr^{3+}$

Balance all but H and O: $Cr_2O_7^{2-} \rightarrow 2\ Cr^{3+}$

Add H_2O to balance O: $Cr_2O_7^{2-} \rightarrow 2\ Cr^{3+} + 7\ H_2O$

Add H^+ to balance H: $14\ H^+ + Cr_2O_7^{2-} \rightarrow 2\ Cr^{3+} + 7\ H_2O$

Add e^- to balance charge: $6e^- + 14\ H^+ + Cr_2O_7^{2-} \rightarrow 2\ Cr^{3+} + 7\ H_2O$

Add appropriate phase descriptions:

$$6\ e^- + 14\ H^+\ (aq) + Cr_2O_7^{2-}\ (aq) \rightarrow 2\ Cr^{3+}\ (aq) + 7\ H_2O\ (l)$$

Oxidation: $Np^{4+} \rightarrow NpO_2^{2+}$

Add H_2O to balance O: $2\ H_2O + Np^{4+} \rightarrow NpO_2^{2+}$

Add H^+ to balance H : $2\ H_2O + Np^{4+} \rightarrow NpO_2^{2+} + 4\ H^+$

Add e^- to balance charge: $2\ H_2O + Np^{4+} \rightarrow NpO_2^{2+} + 4\ H^+ + 2\ e^-$

Add appropriate phase descriptions:

$$2\ H_2O\ (l) + Np^{4+}\ (aq) \rightarrow NpO_2^{2+}\ (aq) + 4\ H^+\ (aq) + 2\ e^-$$

Combine: The oxidation reaction involves two electrons, the reduction six. We must multiply the oxidation reaction by three before adding it to the oxidation reaction. The final balanced equation is:

$$2\ H^+ (aq) + 3\ Np^{4+} (aq) + Cr_2O_7^{2-} (aq) \rightarrow 2\ Cr^{3+} (aq) + 3\ NpO_2^{2+} (aq) + H_2O (l)$$

(d) Oxidation: $HCOOH\ (aq) \rightarrow CO_2 + 2\ H^+\ (aq) + 2\ e^-$

Reduction: $5\ e^- + 8\ H^+\ (aq) + MnO_4^-\ (aq) \rightarrow Mn^{2+}\ (aq) + 4\ H_2O\ (l)$

Combine: $5\ HCOOH\ (aq) + 2\ MnO_4^-\ (aq) + 6\ H^+\ (aq)$

$$\rightarrow 5\ CO_2\ (g) + 2\ Mn^{2+}\ (aq) + 8\ H_2O\ (l)$$

13-11. (continued)

(e) In this disproportionation Pb_3O_4 is reduced to Pb^{2+} and oxidized to PbO_2

Reduction: $Pb_3O_4 \rightarrow Pb^{2+}$

Balance all but H and O: $Pb_3O_4 \rightarrow 3\ Pb^{2+}$

Add H_2O to balance O: $Pb_3O_4 \rightarrow 3\ Pb^{2+} + 4\ H_2O$

Add H^+ to balance H: $8\ H^+ + Pb_3O_4 \rightarrow 3\ Pb^{2+} + 4\ H_2O$

Add e^- to balance charge: $2e^- + 8\ H^+ + Pb_3O_4 \rightarrow 3\ Pb^{2+} + 4\ H_2O$

Add appropriate phase descriptions:

$$2e^- + 8\ H^+\ (aq) + Pb_3O_4\ (s) \rightarrow 3\ Pb^{2+} + 4\ H_2O\ (l)$$

Oxidation: $Pb_3O_4 \rightarrow PbO_2$

Balance all but H and O: $Pb_3O_4 \rightarrow 3\ PbO_2$

Add H_2O to balance O: $2\ H_2O + Pb_3O_4 \rightarrow 3\ PbO_2$

Add H^+ to balance H : $2\ H_2O + Pb_3O_4 \rightarrow 3\ PbO_2 + 4\ H^+$

Add e^- to balance charge: $2\ H_2O + Pb_3O_4 \rightarrow 3\ PbO_2 + 4\ H^+ + 4\ e^-$

Add appropriate phase descriptions:

$$2\ H_2O\ (l) + Pb_3O_4\ (s) \rightarrow 3\ PbO_2\ (s) + 4\ H^+\ (aq) + 4\ e^-$$

Combine: The oxidation reaction involves four electrons, the reduction two. We must multiply the reduction reaction by two before adding it to the oxidation reaction.

$$12\ H^+\ (aq) + 3\ Pb_3O_4\ (s) \rightarrow 6\ Pb^{2+} + 3\ PbO_2\ (s) + 6\ H_2O\ (l)$$

This can be simplified by dividing through by 3:

$$4\ H^+\ (aq) + Pb_3O_4\ (s) \rightarrow 2\ Pb^{2+} + PbO_2\ (s) + 2\ H_2O\ (l)$$

13-11. (continued)

(f) There are two points to make about this problem. First, *three* elements might change oxidation numbers -- Hg, P, and Au. But P appears on both sides in some form of phosphate, so a change oxidation numbers occurs only with Hg and P. Secondly, in combining the oxidation reaction (three electrons transferred) and the reduction reaction (two electrons transferred), we must multiply *both* by an integer to make the electrons equal.

<u>Oxidation:</u> $Au\ (s) + 4\ Cl^-\ (aq) \rightarrow AuCl_4^-\ (aq) + 3\ e^-$

<u>Reduction:</u> $2\ e^- + Hg_2HPO_4\ (s) + H^+\ (aq) \rightarrow 2\ Hg\ (l) + H_2PO_4^-\ (aq)$

<u>Combine:</u> $3\ Hg_2HPO_4\ (s) + 3\ H^+\ (aq) + 2\ Au\ (s) + 8\ Cl^-\ (aq)$

$\rightarrow 6\ Hg\ (l) + 3\ H_2PO_4^-\ (aq) + 2\ AuCl_4^-\ (aq)$

13-13. As with No. 11 above, only some parts (here, a and d) are worked in detail.

(a) <u>Reduction:</u> $Br_2 \rightarrow Br^-$

Balance all but H and O: $Br_2 \rightarrow 2\ Br^-$

Add H_2O to balance O, Add H^+ to balance H: *neither* needed here.

Add e^- to balance charge: $2\ e^- + Br_2 \rightarrow 2\ Br^-$

Add appropriate phase descriptions: $2\ e^- + Br_2\ (aq) \rightarrow 2\ Br^-\ (aq)$

<u>Oxidation:</u> $Cr(OH)_3 \rightarrow CrO_4^{2-}$

Add H_2O to balance O: $H_2O + Cr(OH)_3 \rightarrow CrO_4^{2-}$

Add H^+ to balance H : $H_2O + Cr(OH)_3 \rightarrow CrO_4^{2-} + 5\ H^+$

"Neutralize" H^+ with OH^- added to both sides; make $H^+ + OH^-$ into H_2O:

$H_2O + 5\ OH^- + Cr(OH)_3 \rightarrow CrO_4^{2-} + 5\ H_2O$

Simplify: $5\ OH^- + Cr(OH)_3 \rightarrow CrO_4^{2-} + 4\ H_2O$

Add e^- to balance charge: $5\ OH^- + Cr(OH)_3 \rightarrow CrO_4^{2-} + 4\ H_2O + 3\ e^-$

Add appropriate phase descriptions:

$5\ OH^-\ (aq) + Cr(OH)_3\ (s) \rightarrow CrO_4^{2-}\ (aq) + 4\ H_2O\ (l) + 3\ e^-$

13-13. (continued)

Combine: The reduction reaction has two e^- transferred; the oxidation reaction has 3 e^-. So the reduction reaction must be multiplied by **3** and the reduction reaction must be multiplied by **2** to cancel electrons. The final equation is:

$10\ OH^-(aq) + 2\ Cr(OH)_3(s) + 3\ Br_2(aq) \rightarrow 6\ Br^-(aq) + 2\ CrO_4^{2-}(aq) + 8H_2O(l)$

(b) Briefly:

Reduction: $4\ e^- + H_2O\ (l) + ZrO(OH)_2\ (s) \rightarrow Zr\ (aq) + 4\ OH^-\ (aq)$

Oxidation: $2\ OH^-\ (aq) + SO_3^{2-}\ (aq) \rightarrow SO_4^{2-}\ (aq) + H_2O\ (l) + 2\ e^-$

Combined: $ZrO(OH)_2\ (s) + 2\ SO_3^{2-}\ (aq) \rightarrow 2\ SO_4^{2-}\ (aq) + Zr\ (aq) + H_2O\ (l)$

(c) Briefly:

Reduction: $2\ e^- + H_2O\ (l) + HPbO_2^-\ (aq) \rightarrow Pb\ (s) + 3\ OH^-\ (aq)$

Oxidation: $8\ OH^-\ (aq) + Re\ (s) \rightarrow ReO_4^-\ (aq) + 4\ H_2O\ (l) + 7\ e^-$

Combined: $7\ HPbO_2^-\ (aq) + 2\ Re\ (s) \rightarrow$

$2\ ReO_4^-\ (aq) + 7\ Pb\ (s) + 5\ OH^-\ (aq) + H_2O\ (l)$

(d) Reduction: $HXeO_4^- \rightarrow Xe$

Add H_2O to balance O: $HXeO_4^- \rightarrow Xe + 4\ H_2O$

Add H^+ to balance H: $7\ H^+ + HXeO_4^- \rightarrow Xe + 4\ H_2O$

"Neutralize" H^+ with OH^- added to both sides; make $H^+ + OH^-$ into H_2O:

$7\ H_2O + HXeO_4^- \rightarrow Xe + 4\ H_2O + 7\ OH^-$

Simplify: $3\ H_2O + HXeO_4^- \rightarrow Xe + 7\ OH^-$

Add e^- to balance charge: $6\ e^- + 3\ H_2O + HXeO_4^- \rightarrow Xe + 7\ OH^-$

Add appropriate phase descriptions:

$6\ e^- + 3\ H_2O\ (l) + HXeO_4^-\ (aq) \rightarrow Xe\ (g) + 7\ OH^-\ (aq)$

13-13. (continued)

<u>Oxidation:</u> $HXeO_4^- \rightarrow XeO_6^{4-}$

Add H_2O to balance O: $2\ H_2O + HXeO_4^- \rightarrow XeO_6^{4-}$

Add H^+ to balance H : $2\ H_2O + HXeO_4^- \rightarrow XeO_6^{4-} + 5\ H^+$

"Neutralize" H^+ with OH^- added to both sides; make $H^+ + OH^-$ into H_2O:

$$2\ H_2O + 5\ OH^- + HXeO_4^- \rightarrow XeO_6^{4-} + 5\ H_2O$$

Simplify: $5\ OH^- + HXeO_4^- \rightarrow XeO_6^{4-} + 3\ H_2O$

Insert e^- to balance charge: $5\ OH^- + HXeO_4^- \rightarrow XeO_6^{4-} + 3\ H_2O + 2\ e^-$

Add appropriate phase descriptions:

$$5\ OH^-\ (aq) + HXeO_4^-\ (aq) \rightarrow XeO_6^{4-}\ (aq) + 3\ H_2O\ (l) + 2\ e^-$$

<u>Combine:</u> The reduction reaction has six e^- transferred; the oxidation reaction has 2 e^-. So the oxidation reaction must be multiplied by **3** to cancel electrons.

The final equation is:

$$8\ OH^-\ (aq) + 4\ HXeO_4^-\ (aq) \rightarrow Xe\ (g) + 3\ XeO_6^{4-}\ (aq) + 6\ H_2O\ (l)$$

(e) Briefly:

<u>Reduction:</u> $2\ e^- + H_2O\ (l) + Ag_2S\ (s) \rightarrow 2\ Ag\ (s) + HS^-\ (aq) + OH^-\ (aq)$

<u>Oxidation:</u> $5\ OH^-(aq) + Cr(OH)_3(s) \rightarrow CrO_4^{2-}\ (aq) + 4\ H_2O\ (l) + 3\ e^-$

<u>Combined:</u> $7\ OH^-\ (aq) + 2\ Cr(OH)_3\ (s) + 3\ Ag_2S\ (s)$

$$\rightarrow 6\ Ag\ (s) + 3\ HS^-\ (aq) + 2\ CrO_4^{2-}\ (aq) + 5\ H_2O\ (l)$$

(f) Briefly:

<u>Reduction:</u> $2\ e^- + 2\ H_2O\ (l) + CO_3^{2-}\ (aq) \rightarrow CO\ (g) + 4\ OH^-\ (aq)$

<u>Oxidation:</u> $4\ OH^-\ (aq) + N_2H_4\ (aq) \rightarrow N_2\ (g) + 4\ H_2O\ (l) + 4\ e^-$

<u>Combined:</u> $N_2H_4\ (aq) + 2\ CO_3^{2-}\ (aq) \rightarrow 2\ CO\ (g) + 4\ OH^-\ (aq) + N_2\ (g)$

13-15. This problem may seem unusual because the one element -- oxygen with a 2- oxidation number -- is present in *four* different substances: PbO_2^{2-}, SO_4^{2-}, H_2O, and OH^-. But systematic use of the half-reaction method described in the text will lead to the correct answer without a problem. We develop a half-reaction for oxygen involving the only species containing oxygen and hydrogen -- water, hydroxide and oxygen gas. Generally, w*henever oxygen changes its oxidation number to or from 2-, its half reaction should be balanced against* ***water.***

Reduction: $O_2 \rightarrow H_2O$

Add H_2O to balance O: $O_2 \rightarrow 2\ H_2O$

Add H^+ to balance H: $4\ H^+ + O_2 \rightarrow 2\ H_2O$

Add e^- to balance charge: $4\ e^- + 4\ H^+ + O_2 \rightarrow 2\ H_2O$

"Neutralize" H^+ with OH^- added to both sides; make $H^+ + OH^-$ into H_2O:

$$4\ e^- + 4\ H_2O + O_2 \rightarrow 2\ H_2O + 4\ OH^-$$

Simplify: $4\ e^- + 2\ H_2O + O_2 \rightarrow 4\ OH^-$

Add appropriate phase descriptions: $4\ e^- + 2\ H_2O\ (l) + O_2\ (g) \rightarrow 4\ OH^-\ (aq)$

Oxidation: $PbS \rightarrow PbO_2^{2-} + SO_4^{2-}$

(note: both the Pb and the S are balanced already)

Add H_2O to balance O: $6\ H_2O + PbS \rightarrow PbO_2^{2-} + SO_4^{2-}$

Add H^+ to balance H : $6\ H_2O + PbS \rightarrow PbO_2^{2-} + SO_4^{2-} + 12\ H^+$

"Neutralize H^+ with OH^- added to both sides; make $H^+ + OH^-$ into H_2O:

$$12\ OH^- + 6\ H_2O + PbS \rightarrow PbO_2^{2-} + SO_4^{2-} + 12\ H_2O$$

Simplify: $12\ OH^- + PbS \rightarrow PbO_2^{2-} + SO_4^{2-} + 6\ H_2O$

Add e^- to balance charge: $12\ OH^- + PbS \rightarrow PbO_2^{2-} + SO_4^{2-} + 6\ H_2O + 8\ e^-$

Add appropriate phase descriptions:

$$12\ OH^-\ (aq) + PbS\ (s) \rightarrow PbO_2^{2-}\ (aq) + SO_4^{2-}\ (aq) + 6\ H_2O\ (l) + 8\ e^-$$

13-15. (continued)

Combine: The reduction reaction has four e^- transferred; the oxidation reaction has eight e^- transferred. So the reduction reaction must be multiplied by **2** to cancel electrons. The final equation is:

$$4\ OH^-\ (aq) + PbS\ (s) + 2\ O_2\ (g) \rightarrow PbO_2^{2-}\ (aq) + SO_4^{2-}\ (aq) + 2\ H_2O\ (l)$$

13-17. (a) $Ca\ (s) + Cl_2\ (g) \rightarrow CaCl_2\ (s)$

(b) $2\ Fe^{3+}\ (aq) + Sn^{2+}\ (aq) \rightarrow 2\ Fe^{2+}\ (aq) + Sn^{4+}\ (aq)$

(c) $Fe_2O_3\ (s) + 3\ H_2\ (g) \rightarrow 2\ Fe\ (s) + 3\ H_2O\ (g)$

(d) $2\ K\ (s) + H_2O_2\ (aq) \rightarrow 2\ KOH\ (aq)$

13-19. Half reactions aren't required here, but they make the solution much clearer.

Reduction: $e^- + H^+\ (aq) + HNO_2\ (aq) \rightarrow NO\ (g) + H_2O\ (l)$

Oxidation: $H_2O\ (l) + HNO_2\ (aq) \rightarrow NO_3^-\ (aq) + 3\ H^+ + 2\ e^-$

Combined: $3\ HNO_2\ (aq) \rightarrow 2\ NO\ (g) + NO_3^-\ (aq) + H^+ + H_2O\ (l)$

13-21. 1 amp = 1 C sec^{-1}, so 45 A = 45 C sec^{-1}, and the charge is:

$$Q = (45\ C\ s^{-1}) \times 1.2\ s = \mathbf{54\ C}$$

13-23. $\left(\dfrac{6.5\times10^3\ C}{18\ min}\right)\times\left(\dfrac{1\ min}{60\ s}\right) = 6.0\ C\ s^{-1} = \mathbf{6.0\ A}$

13-25. Cathode: $2e^- + 2\ H^+\ (aq) \rightarrow H_2\ (g)$

Anode: $2\ H_2O\ (l) \rightarrow 4\ H^+\ (aq) + O_2\ (g) + 4\ e^-$

Total: $2\ H_2O\ (l) \rightarrow 2\ H_2\ (g) + O_2\ (g)$

$H_2O \rightarrow H_2 + O_2$ $\quad H_2O \rightarrow O_2$

$H_2O \rightarrow H_2$

13-27.

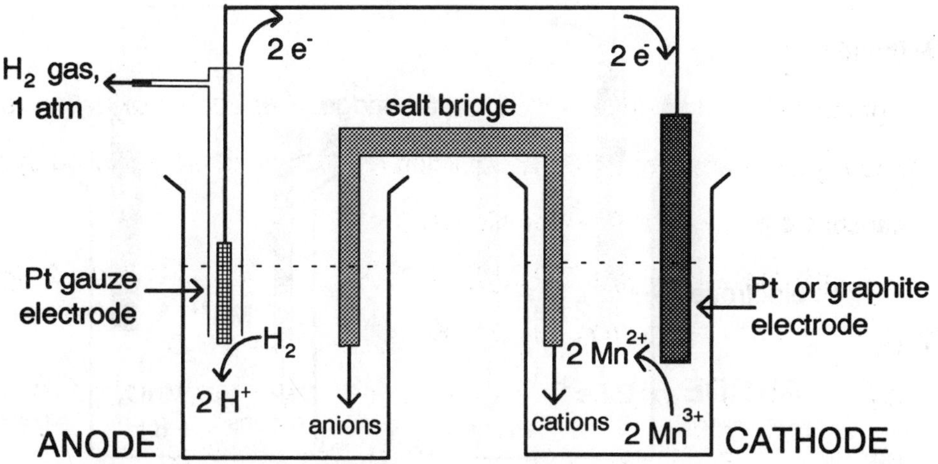

During the reaction electrons are released at the anode, where hydrogen gas becomes hydrogen ion. The electrons flow through an external circuit to the cathode, where manganese (III) ions are reduced to manganese (II) ions.

13-29.

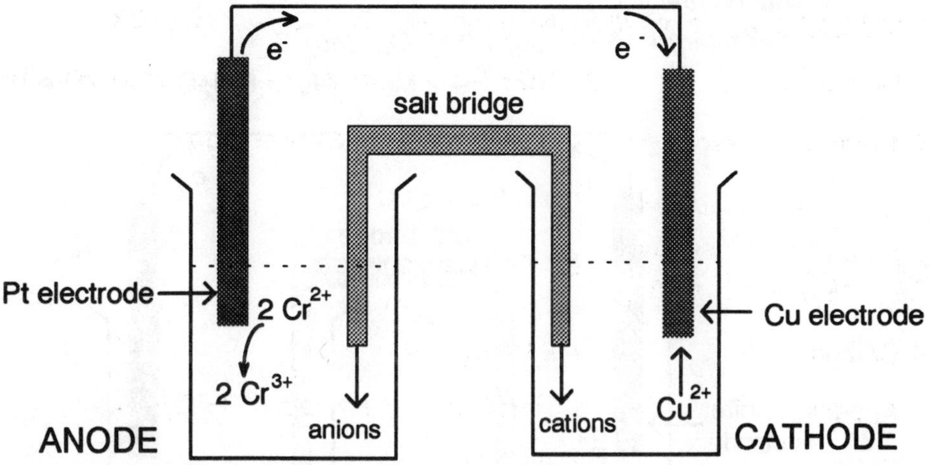

During the reaction electrons are released at the anode, where chromium (II) ion becomes chromium (III) ions. The electrons flow through an external circuit to the cathode, where copper (II) ions are reduced to copper metal, which deposits on the copper electrode. The overall reaction is:

$$2\ Cr^{2+}\ (aq) + Cu^{2+}\ (aq) \rightarrow Cu\ (s) + 2\ Cr^{3+}\ (aq)$$

13-31. (a)

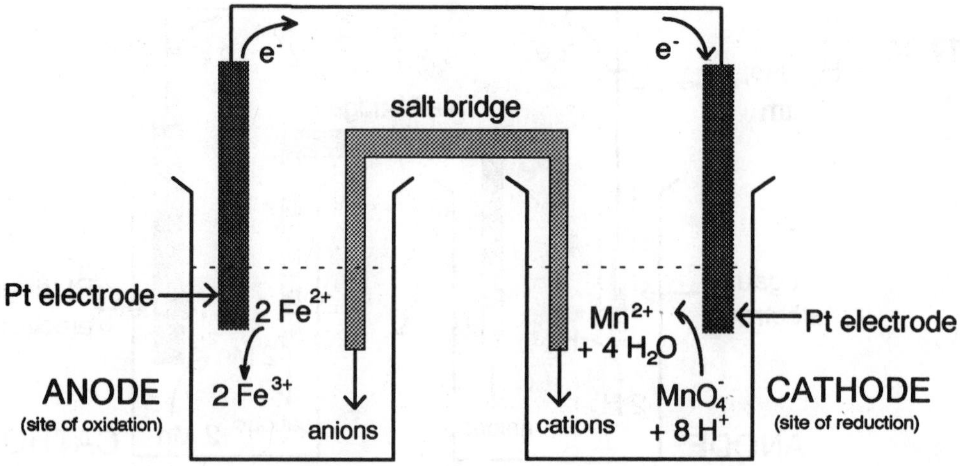

Anode (oxidation) reaction:

$$2\ Fe^{2+}\ (aq) \rightarrow 2\ Fe^{3+}\ (aq) + 2\ e^-$$

Cathode (reduction) reaction:

$$5\ e^- + 8\ H^+\ (aq) + MnO_4^-\ (aq) \rightarrow Mn^{2+}\ (aq) + 4\ H_2O\ (l)$$

Balanced reaction:

$$10\ Fe^{2+}\ (aq) + 16\ H^+\ (aq) + 2\ MnO_4^-\ (aq) \rightarrow 2\ Mn^{2+}\ (aq) + 8\ H_2O\ (l) + 10\ Fe^{3+}\ (aq)$$

(b)

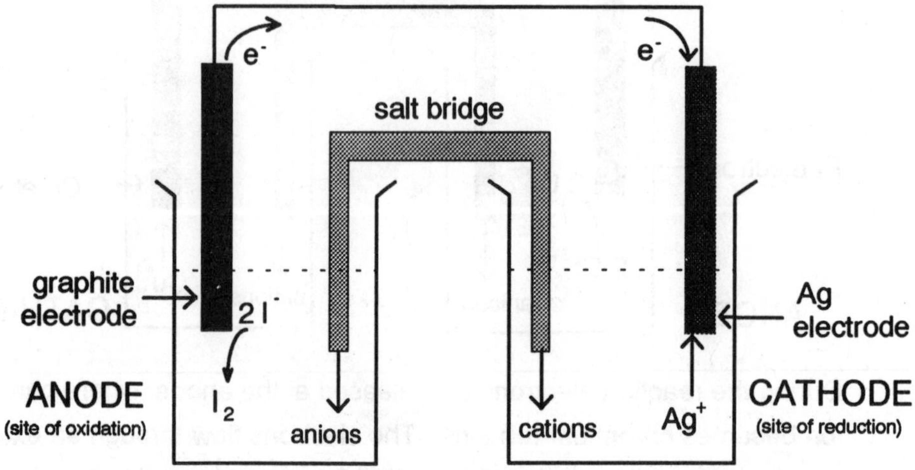

Anode (oxidation) reaction:

$$2\ I^-\ (aq) \rightarrow I_2\ (aq) + 2\ e^-$$

Cathode (reduction) reaction:

$$e^- + Ag^+\ (aq) \rightarrow Ag\ (s)$$

Balanced reaction:

$$2\ Ag^+\ (aq) + 2\ I^-\ (aq) \rightarrow I_2\ (aq) + 2\ Ag\ (s)$$

13-33. $2.5\ \text{A} \times \left(\frac{60\ \text{s}}{\text{min}}\right) \times \left(\frac{1\ \text{C s}^{-1}}{1\ \text{A}}\right) \times \left(\frac{6.0221 \times 10^{23}\ \text{e}^-\ \text{mol}^{-1}}{96,485\ \text{C mol}^{-1}}\right) = \mathbf{9.36 \times 10^{20}\ e^-\ min^{-1}}$

13-35. (a) $\left(1.00\ \text{mol Ag}^+\right) \times \left(\frac{1\ \text{mol e}^-}{1\ \text{mol Ag}^+}\right) \times \left(\frac{96,485\ \text{C}}{1\ \text{mol e}^-}\right) = \mathbf{96{,}500\ C}$

(b) $(2.00\ \text{mol H}_2\text{O}) \times \left(\frac{2\ \text{mol e}^-}{1\ \text{mol H}_2\text{O}}\right) \times \left(\frac{96,485\ \text{C}}{1\ \text{mol e}^-}\right) = \mathbf{386{,}000\ C}$

(c) $\left(1.50\ \text{mol Mn}^{3+}\right) \times \left(\frac{1\ \text{mol e}^-}{1\ \text{mol Mn}^{3+}}\right) \times \left(\frac{96,485\ \text{C}}{1\ \text{mol e}^-}\right) = \mathbf{145{,}000\ C}$

(d) $\left(3.00\ \text{mol ClO}_4{}^-\right) \times \left(\frac{8\ \text{mol e}^-}{1\ \text{mol ClO}_4{}^-}\right) \times \left(\frac{96,485\ \text{C}}{1\ \text{mol e}^-}\right) = \mathbf{2.32 \times 10^6\ C}$

13-37. The reduction of Sn^{4+} requires four moles of electrons per mol of Sn. Therefore:

$$\text{mol Sn} = \left(\frac{69,500\ \text{C}}{96,485\ \text{C}\ \left(\text{mol e}^-\right)^{-1}}\right) \times \left(\frac{1\ \text{mol Sn}}{4\ \text{mol e}^-}\right) = \mathbf{0.180\ mol\ Sn}$$

This corresponds to $0.180\ \text{mol} \times 118.71\ \text{g mol}^{-1}$ = **21.4 g Sn.**

13-39. (a) $\text{Zn}\ (s) + \text{Cl}_2\ (g) \rightarrow \text{Zn}^{2+}\ (aq) + 2\ \text{Cl}^-\ (aq)$

(b) $Q = 0.800\ \text{C s}^{-1} \times 25\ \text{min} \times 60\ \text{s min}^{-1} = \mathbf{1200\ C}$

$\text{mol e}^- = 1200\ \text{C} / 96,485\ \text{C}\ (\text{mol e}^-)^{-1} = 0.01244 = \mathbf{0.0124\ mol\ e^-}$

(c) Two electrons must pass through the circuit for each zinc atom oxidized. So the number of moles of zinc deposited is one-half the number of mole of e^-:

$\text{mol Zn} = 0.01244 / 2 = 0.00622\ \text{mol Zn}$

$\text{g Zn} = 0.00622\ \text{mol} \times 65.39\ \text{g mol}^{-1} = \mathbf{0.407\ g\ Zn}$

(d) The number of mol of Cl_2 consumed is equal the number of mol of Zn, or 0.00622 mol Cl_2. This corresponds to a volume of:

$$V = \frac{nRT}{P} = \frac{(0.00622\ \text{mol})\left(0.08206\frac{\text{L-atm}}{\text{mol-K}}\right)(298.15\ \text{K})}{1\ \text{atm}} = \mathbf{0.152\ L\ Cl_2}$$

13-41. The experimental setup requires the electrons that cause the reduction of Ag^+ also to cause the reduction of Cd^{2+}. The production of Ag requires one mole of electrons per mole of Ag and the production of Cd requires two moles of electrons per mole of Cd. The mole ratio of Cd to Ag is:

$$\left(\frac{1\text{ mol e}^-}{1\text{ mol Ag}}\right)\times\left(\frac{1\text{ mol Cd}}{2\text{ mol e}^-}\right)=\frac{1\text{ mol Cd}}{2\text{ mol Ag}}$$

And we then have:

$$0.475\text{ g Ag}\times\left(\frac{1\text{ mol Ag}}{107.87\text{ g Ag}}\right)\times\left(\frac{1\text{ mol Cd}}{2\text{ mol Ag}}\right)\times\left(\frac{112.41\text{ g Cd}}{1\text{ mol Cd}}\right)=\mathbf{0.248\text{ g Cd}}$$

13-43. The number of electrons used in oxidation of O in H_2O to O_2 (4 mol e^- per mol O_2) equals the number of electrons used in the reduction of dissolved copper. The number of moles of O_2 is $16.0\text{ g} / 31.9988\text{ g mol}^{-1} = 0.500\text{ mol } O_2$.

Therefore, the number of moles of electrons passed is 2.00 mol e^-.

The mass of Cu produced is $63.5\text{ g} / 63.546\text{ g mol}^{-1} = 1.00$ mol.

Therefore, each Cu gains 2 electrons, so the initial oxidation state must be +2.

13-45. Anode: $2\,Cl^- \rightarrow Cl_2\,(g) + 2\,e^-$

Cathode: $Na^+ + e^- \rightarrow Na\,(l)$

13-47. In the Hall-Heroult process 3 mol e^- is required per mole of Al, or mol Al = $^1/_3$ mol e^-. But in this case the charge flows through a *series* of cells, so each Coulomb of charge is "used" 100 times. The total number of electrons moved through *each* cell is

$$Q = 55{,}000\text{ C s}^{-1}\times 86{,}400\text{ s} = 4.75\times10^9\text{ C}$$

$$\text{mol e}^- = (4.75\times10^9\text{ C}) \div (96{,}485\text{ C mol}^{-1}) = 49{,}250\text{ mol e}^-$$

$$\text{mol Al} = 0.3333\times 49{,}250\text{ mol e}^- = 1.64\times10^4\text{ mol Al}$$

In 100 cells, the mol of Al produced will be: $100\times1.64\times10^4 = 1.64\times10^4$ mol Al

$$\text{g Al} = (1.64\times10^6\text{ mol Al})\times(26.982\text{ g mol}^{-1}\text{ Al})$$

$$= \mathbf{4.42\times10^7\text{ g Al}}$$

13-49. $2\ Mg\ (s) + TiCl_4\ (l) \rightarrow Ti\ (s) + 2\ MgCl_2\ (s)$

The mol of Ti in 100 kg (=100,000 g) is

$$\text{mol Ti} = {}^{100{,}000\ g}/_{47.88\ g\ mol^{-1}} = 2{,}088\ \text{mol Ti}$$

Two moles of Mg are required for every mole of Ti produced, so we need 4,176 mol Mg. This weighs 4,176 mol × 24.305 g mol^{-1} = 101,000 g = **101 kg.**

13-51. The cathode reaction is $Zn^{2+}\ (aq) + 2\ e^- \rightarrow Zn\ (s)$.

$$\text{mol Zn} = {}^{7.32\ g}/_{65.39\ g\ mol^{-1}} = 0.112\ \text{mol Zn}$$

$$\text{mol } e^- = 2 \times \text{mol Zn} = 0.224\ \text{mol } e^-$$

$$Q = 0.224\ \text{mol } e^- \times 96{,}485\ C\ mol^{-1} = 21{,}600\ C$$

$$\text{current} = {}^{Q}/_{\text{time}}$$

$$\text{time} = {}^{Q}/_{\text{current}} = {}^{21{,}600\ C}/_{8.50\ C\ s^{-1}}$$

$$= 2540\ s = \mathbf{42.4\ min}$$

13-53. The answers are found in the text's section on "Iron and Steel."

Si: Production: $Si\ (s) + O_2\ (g) \rightarrow SiO_2\ (s)$

Trapping: $CaO\ (s) + Al_2O_3\ (s) + SiO_2\ (s) \rightarrow CaO{\bullet}Al_2O_3{\bullet}(SiO_2)_2\ (l)$

P: Production: $P_4\ (s) + 5\ O_2\ (g) \rightarrow 2\ P_2O_5\ (s)$

Trapping: $3\ CaO\ (s) + P_2O_5\ (s) \rightarrow$ "$(CaO)_3{\bullet}P_2O_5\ (s)$

Both trapping reactions consist in part of a Lewis acid-base reaction between a basic oxide (CaO) and an acidic oxide (SiO_2 and P_2O_5). The actual species present are complex derivatives of silicate, SiO_4^{4-} and phosphate, PO_4^{3-} (see Chapter 22, in particular Table 22-1, for more details).

13-55. The only important substances for calculating the free energy change in this reaction are $FeCr_2O_4$ and CO (ΔG_f^o = -137.15 kJ mol^{-1}).

$$\Delta G^o = 4\Delta G_f^o(CO) - \Delta G_f^o(FeCr_2O_4)$$

$$= 4\ \text{mol} \times (-137.15\ kJ\ mol^{-1}) - 1\ \text{mol} \times (-1344\ kJ\ mol^{-1})$$

$$= \mathbf{+\ 795\ kJ.}$$

13-57. The presence of a large amount of hydroxide means this redox reaction is occurring in *basic, aqueous* solution:

$$2\ Al\ (s) + 2\ OH^-\ (aq) + 6\ H_2O\ (l) \rightarrow 2\ Al(OH)_4^-\ (aq) + 3\ H_2\ (g)$$

13-59. The reaction to yield hydrogen and chlorate from aqueous sodium chloride is not favored thermodynamically. We can infer that the reverse reaction (of chlorate and hydrogen gas to give chloride ion and water) is spontaneous:

$$ClO_3^-\ (aq) + 3\ H_2\ (g) \rightarrow Cl^-\ (aq) + 3\ H_2O\ (l)$$

13-61. All of these reactions are balanced in the absence of water.

(a) $Cl_2O\ (g) + N_2O_5\ (g) \rightarrow 2\ NO_2Cl\ (g) + O_2\ (g)$

(b) $Cl_2O\ (g) + N_2O_5\ (g) \rightarrow 2\ NO_3Cl\ (g)$

(c) $4\ N_2O_5\ (l) + Au\ (s) \rightarrow (NO_2)Au(NO_3)_4\ (s) + 3\ NO_2\ (g)$

(d) $3\ TiCl_4\ (l) + 2\ NO_2Cl\ (g) \rightarrow 2\ Cl_2\ (g) + 2\ TiOCl_2\ (s) + (NO)_2TiCl_6\ (s)$

(e) $8\ NHBr_2\ (s) \rightarrow 2\ NH_4Br\ (s) + 3\ N_2\ (g) + 7\ Br_2\ (g)$

(f) $3\ NaN_3\ (s) + 8\ NO_2Cl\ (g) \rightarrow 7\ N_2O\ (g) + 3\ NaNO_3\ (s) + 4\ Cl_2\ (g)$

(g) $2\ KSCN\ (s) + 2\ NOCl\ (g) \rightarrow (SCN)_2\ (g) + 2\ NO\ (g) + 2\ KCl\ (s)$

(h) $2\ K_2MnF_6\ (s) + 4\ SbF_5\ (s) \rightarrow 4\ KSbF_6\ (s) + 2\ MnF_3\ (s) + F_2\ (g)$

(i) $2\ NF_4SbF_6\ (s) + 14\ H_2O(l)$

$\rightarrow 2\ NF_3\ (g) + 2\ HSb(OH)_6\ (s) + O_2\ (g) + 14\ HF\ (g)$

13-63. $$\frac{96{,}485.31\ C\ mol^{-1}}{6.022137 \times 10^{23}\ electrons\ mol^{-1}} = \mathbf{1.602177 \times 10^{-19}\ C\ electron^{-1}}$$

13-65. 1.83 g of Zn corresponds to $^{1.83}/_{65.39}$ = 0.0280 mol of Zn, and given 2 e^- passed for every Zn atom, the number of moles of electrons that passed through the cathode is 0.0560 mol e^-. This equals 5400 C of charge. But the cathode only sampled 0.25% of the electricity used. The total charge was $^{5400\ C}/_{0.025}$ = **2.16×10^6 C.**

13-67. The reaction in the cell is:

$$Zn\ (s) + Ni^{2+}\ (aq) \rightarrow Ni\ (s) + Zn^{2+}\ (aq)$$

(a) mol Zn = $^{32.68\text{ g}}/_{65.39\text{ g mol}^{-1}}$ = 0.500 mol

mol Ni^{2+} = 0.575 L × 1.00 mol L^{-1} = 0.575 mol

The **Zn** is the limiting reactant.

(b) Oxidation of 0.500 mol of Zn will require 1.00 mol of electrons, or 96,485 C.

The time for this amount of charge to flow, given a current of 0.0715 C s^{-1}, is

$^{96,485\text{ C}}/_{0.0715\text{ C s}^{-1}}$ = 1.35 × 10^6 s = 375 hr = **15.6 days.**

(c) The nickel electrode will gain 0.500 mol of Ni, with a mass of **29.3 g.**

(d) The Ni^{2+} solution will lose 0.500 mol of Ni^{2+}, leaving 0.075 mol of Ni^{2+} in 0.575 L of solution, for a final $[Ni^{2+}]$ = $^{0.075\text{ mol}}/_{0.575\text{ L}}$ = **0.13 M.**

13-69. There are three stages in the production process to compare and contrast: extraction / initial separation, preparation of electrolysis materials, and the final electrolysis process.

The extraction of magnesium involves a solid base, for example the ore, dolomite (itself a source of Mg), and seawater, which contains free Mg^{2+} *(aq)*. The initial separation is in the form of *solid* magnesium hydroxide. Base is also important in the extraction and separation of aluminum, but the aluminum source is exclusively an ore, bauxite, and base is used to *dissolve* the aluminum as $Al(OH)_4^-$.

Further processing is needed to prepare both elements for electrolysis. For magnesium, this involves conversion to anhydrous $MgCl_2$ *(s)* by treatment with HCl and evaporation. For aluminum, the oxide is required for hydrolysis, and it is directly formed from the intermediate $Al(OH)_4^-$ by crystallization followed by drying.

13-69. (continued)

The final electrolysis to make Mg can be done on a $MgCl_2$ melt; a by-product is Cl_2, which is recycled. Al, in contrast, requires molten cryolite as a medium for the electrolysis. The other product of aluminum reduction is CO_2 from graphite.

13-71. (a) The reaction is balanced most easily by inspection:

Balancing Fe: $2\ FeCr_2O_4 \rightarrow Fe_2O_3$

Balancing Cr : $2\ FeCr_2O_4 \rightarrow Fe_2O_3 + 4\ Na_2CrO_4$

" Na : $4\ Na_2CO_3 + 2\ FeCrO_4 \rightarrow Fe_2O_3 + 4\ Na_2CrO_4$

" C: $4\ Na_2CO_3 + 2\ FeCrO_4 \rightarrow Fe_2O_3 + 4\ Na_2CrO_4 + 4\ CO_2$

" O: $^7/_2\ O_2 + 4\ Na_2CO_3 + 2\ FeCrO_4 \rightarrow Fe_2O_3 + 4\ Na_2CrO_4 + 4\ CO_2$

Converting to integers and inserting the apppropiriate phase descriptions yields:

$$7\ O_2\ (g) + 8\ Na_2CO_3\ (l) + 4\ FeCrO_4 \rightarrow 2\ Fe_2O_3\ (s) + 8\ Na_2CrO_4\ (l) + 8\ CO_2$$

(b)

Data required*	Value			
$+ 8 \times \Delta H_f^o(Na_2CrO_4\ (l))$	$8\ mol \times (-1342\ kJ\ mol^{-1})$	=	- 10,736	kJ
$+ 8 \times \Delta H_f^o(CO_2\ (g))$	$8\ mol \times (-393.51\ kJ\ mol^{-1})$	=	- 3148.08	kJ
$+ 2\ \Delta H_f^o(Fe_2O_3\ (s))$	$4\ mol \times (-824.2\ kJ\ mol^{-1})$	=	- 1648.6	kJ
$- 8\ \Delta H_f^o(Na_2CO_3\ (l))$	$-8\ mol \times (-1130.68\ kJ\ mol^{-1})$	=	+ 9045.44	kJ
$- 4\ \Delta H_f^o(FeCr_2O_4\ (s))$	$-4\ mol \times (-1445\ kJ\ mol^{-1})$	=	+ 5780	kJ
	ΔH^o	=	**-707**	kJ

* We cannot get data easily for the enthalpy change associated with melting Na_2CO_3 or Na_2CrO_4. However, both of these substances are present in equal chemical amounts, one is a reactant and the other is a product and, finally, both are 2:1 sodium salts of an oxyanion. They should have similar molar enthalpies of fusion, and neglecting that number should have an equal and opposite affect: on the reaction.

(c) The sodium chromate should be leached from the mixture by water. Then it should be isolated by evaporation of the water, and perhaps used directly in some kind of electrolysis cell or reduced by an appropriate element - for example, C, Si, or Mg.

CHAPTER 14 - ELECTROCHEMISTRY AND CELL VOLTAGE

14-1. $150 \text{ watts} \times \frac{1 \text{ kilowatt}}{1000 \text{ watts}} \times \frac{\$0.10}{1 \text{ kilowatt-hour}} \times 10 \text{ hours} = \mathbf{\$0.15}$

14-3. One volt is one J C^{-1}. One amp is one C sec^{-1}. The rate of energy production $(1.34 \text{ J C}^{-1}) \times (0.800 \text{ C s}^{-1}) = 1.072 \text{ J s}^{-1}$. The time to produce 1 J of energy is: $\frac{1.00 \text{ J}}{1.072 \text{ J s}^{-1}} = \mathbf{0.933 \text{ s}}$.

14-5. (a) $Pb\ (s) + Cu^{2+}\ (aq) \rightarrow Pb^{2+}\ (aq) + Cu\ (s)$

$\Delta\mathcal{E}^o = \mathcal{E}^o(Cu^{2+} \mid Cu) - \mathcal{E}^o(Pb^{2+} \mid Pb)$

$= (0.3402 \text{ V}) - (-0.1263 \text{ V}) = \mathbf{0.4665 \text{ V}} = 0.4665 \text{ J C}^{-1}$

$\Delta G^o = -n\mathcal{F}\Delta\mathcal{E}^o$ (Note: $n = 2$ mol e^- transferred)

$= -(2 \text{ mol e}^-)(96{,}485 \text{ C (mol e}^-)^{-1})(0.4665 \text{ J C}^{-1})$

$= -90{,}020 \text{ J} = \mathbf{-90.02 \text{ kJ}}$

(b) $MnO_4^-\ (aq) + 8\ H^+\ (aq) + 5\ Fe^{2+}\ (aq)$

$\rightarrow 4\ H_2O\ (l) + Mn^{2+}\ (aq) + 5\ Fe^{3+}\ (aq)$

$\Delta\mathcal{E}^o = \mathcal{E}^o(MnO_4^- \mid Mn^{2+}) - \mathcal{E}^o(Fe^{3+} \mid Fe^{2+})$

$= +(1.471 \text{ V}) - (0.770 \text{ V}) = \mathbf{+0.721} \text{ V}$

$\Delta G^o = -n\mathcal{F}\Delta\mathcal{E}^o$ (Note: $n = 5$ mol e^- transferred)

$= -(5 \text{ mol e}^-)(96{,}485 \text{ C (mol e}^-)^{-1})(0.721 \text{ J C}^{-1})$

$= -348{,}000 \text{ J} = \mathbf{-348 \text{ kJ}}$

(c) $2\ Ag^+\ (aq) + 2\ I^-\ (aq) \rightarrow I_2\ (s) + 2\ Ag\ (s)$

$\Delta\mathcal{E}^o = \mathcal{E}^o(Ag^+ \mid Ag) - \mathcal{E}^o(I_2, I^-)$ $n = 2$ mol e^- per I_2

$= (+0.7996) - (+0.535 \text{ V}) = \mathbf{+0.265 \text{ V}}$

$\Delta G^o = -n\mathcal{F}\Delta\mathcal{E}^o$ (Note: $n = 2$ mol e^- transferred)

$\Delta G^o = -(2 \text{ mol e}^-)(96{,}485 \text{ C (mol e}^-)^{-1})(+0.265 \text{ J C}^{-1})$

$= -51{,}140 \text{ J} = \mathbf{-51.1 \text{ kJ}}$

14-7. The reaction is: Ni *(s)* + 2 Ag^+ *(aq)* → Ni^{2+} *(aq)* + 2 Ag *(s)*

$$\Delta\mathcal{E}^o = \mathcal{E}^o\,(\,Ag \mid Ag^+\,) - \mathcal{E}^o\,(\,Ni^{2+} \mid Ni\,)$$
$$= (0.7996) - (-0.23) = +1.03 \text{ V}$$

Note: n = 2 mol e^- in the reaction as written.

$$\Delta G^o = -(2 \text{ mol } e^-)\,(96{,}485 \text{ C (mol } e^-)^{-1})\,(+1.03 \text{ J C}^{-1})$$
$$= -198.8 \text{ kJ}$$

$w_{elec,max}$ = ΔG (= ΔG^o in this case with all substances in standard states)

$$w_{elec,max} = -\frac{198{,}800 \text{ J}}{2 \text{ mol Ag}} \times \frac{1 \text{ mol Ag}}{107.87 \text{ g Ag}} \times 1.00 \text{ g Ag} = \mathbf{-921\ J}$$

This is the work absorbed by the system. The maxiumum work *done by the system* is -921 J.

14-9. (a)

Cathode: Br_2 *(l)* + $2e^-$ → 2 Br^- *(aq)*

Anode: Co *(s)* → Co^{2+} *(aq)* + $2e^-$

Overall: Br_2 *(l)* + Co *(s)* → 2 Br^- *(aq)* + Co^{2+} *(aq)*

(b) $\Delta\mathcal{E}^o = \mathcal{E}^o\,(\,Br_2 \mid Br^-\,) - \mathcal{E}^o\,(\,Co^{2+} \mid Co\,)$ = 1.065 V - (-0.28 V) = **+1.34 V**

14-11. (a) Indium plating out implies indium is the cathode and zinc is anode.

Cathode: In^{3+} *(aq)* + $3e^-$ → In *(s)*

Anode: Zn *(s)* → Zn^{2+} *(aq)* + $2e^-$

(b) $\Delta\mathcal{E}^o = \mathcal{E}^o\,(\,In^{3+} \mid In\,) - \mathcal{E}^o\,(\,Zn^{2+} \mid Zn\,)$

$\mathcal{E}^o\,(\,In^{3+} \mid In\,) = \Delta\mathcal{E}^o + \mathcal{E}^o\,(\,Zn^{2+} \mid Zn\,)$ = (+0.425 V) + (-0.7628 V) = **-0.338 V**

14-13. The possible reduction half-reaction reaction is: Mn^{2+} *(aq)* + $2e^-$→ Mn *(s)*

The possible oxidation half-reaction is: Mn^{2+} *(aq)* → Mn^{3+} *(aq)* + e^-

The cell potential would be: $\Delta\mathcal{E}^o = \mathcal{E}^o\,(\,Mn^{2+} \mid Mn\,) - \mathcal{E}^o\,(\,Mn^{3+} \mid Mn^{2+}\,)$

= (-1.029 V) - (+1.51 V) = **-2.54 V**

The reaction is **non-spontaneous**, because $\Delta\mathcal{E}^o$ is negative.

14-15. $2\ Fe^{3+}\ (aq) + Fe\ (s) \rightarrow 3\ Fe^{2+}\ (aq)$

Reduction: $Fe^{3+}\ (aq) + e^- \rightarrow Fe^{2+}\ (aq)$

Oxidation: $Fe\ (s) \rightarrow Fe^{2+}\ (aq) + 2\ e^-$

$$\Delta\mathcal{E}^o = \mathcal{E}^o\ (\ Fe^{3+}\ |\ Fe^{2+}\ ) - \mathcal{E}^o\ (\ Fe^{2+}\ |\ Fe\ )$$

$$= (+0.770) - (-0.409) = \mathbf{1.179\ V}$$

14-17. **Solid aluminum will readily lose electrons. It will be a good reducing agent.**

14-19. Compare $\mathcal{E}^o\ (\ Br_2\ |\ Br^-\ ) = +1.065$ V and $\mathcal{E}^o\ (\ Cl_2\ |\ Cl^-\ ) = +1.3583$ V. **Chlorine is a stronger oxidant, and should be a better disinfectant.**

14-21. The reduction half-reaction is:

$MnO_4^-\ (aq) + 8H^+\ (aq) + 5e^- \rightarrow 4H_2O\ (l) + Mn^{2+}\ (aq)$ $\qquad \mathcal{E}^o = +1.491$ V

If a reductant appears in a reduction half reaction with $\mathcal{E}^o > +1.491$ V, then MnO_4^- *(aq)* will *not* oxidize it. Here:

	reductant	$\mathcal{E}^o$ (ox | red)	MnO_4^- capable of oxidizing it?
(a)	F^- *(aq)*	+2.87 V	**No**
(b)	Cl^- *(aq)*	+1.3583 V	**Yes**
(c)	Cr^{3+} *(aq)*	+1.33 V	**Yes**
(d)	ClO_4^- *(aq)*	*	**No**

* ClO_4^- is not listed in appendix E anywhere as a reductant. It is "impossible" to oxidize.

14-23. (a) The whole cell reaction that is important here has a $P_4\ |\ PH_3$ cathode and a $H_2PO_2^-\ |\ P_4$ anode. In that case:

$$\Delta\mathcal{E}^o = \mathcal{E}^o\ (\ P_4\ |\ PH_3\ ) - \mathcal{E}^o\ (\ H_2PO_2\ |\ P_4\ )$$

$$= -0.89 - (-2.05) = +1.16\ V$$

Yes, **P_4 will disproportionate.**

(b) **P_4 is the stronger reducing agent,** because -(-2.05 V) > -(-0.89 V).

14-25. For this reaction: $\Delta\mathcal{E}^o = \mathcal{E}^o\,(Pb^{2+} \mid Pb) - \mathcal{E}^o\,(Cr^{3+} \mid Cr^{2+})$

$$= (-0.1263) - (-0.424) = +0.2977\text{ V}$$

$$Q = \frac{[Cr^{3+}]^2}{[Cr^{2+}]^2\,[Pb^{2+}]} = \frac{(0.0030)^2}{(0.20)^2\ (0.15)} = 0.00150$$

$n = 2$ for this reaction, so: $\Delta\mathcal{E} = \Delta\mathcal{E}^o - \frac{0.0592\text{ V}}{2}\log_{10}Q$

$$= 0.2977 - \frac{0.0592\text{ V}}{2}\log_{10}(0.00150) = \mathbf{+0.381\ V}$$

14-27. (a) $Cu\,(s) + Pb^{2+}\,(aq) \rightarrow Pb\,(s) + Cu^{2+}\,(aq)$

$$\Delta\mathcal{E}^o = \mathcal{E}^o\,(Cu^{2+} \mid Cu) - \mathcal{E}^o\,(Pb^{2+} \mid Pb)$$

$$= 0.3402\text{ V} - (-0.1263\text{ V}) = +0.4665\text{ V}$$

$$Q = \frac{[Pb^{2+}]}{[Cu^{2+}]} = \frac{.0020}{.075} = 0.02667$$

$$\Delta\mathcal{E} = +0.4665\text{ V} - \frac{0.0592\text{ V}}{2}\log 0.02667 = \mathbf{+0.513\ V}$$

(b) $MnO_4^-\,(aq) + 8\,H^+\,(aq) + 5\,Fe^{2+}\,(aq)$

$$\rightarrow 5\,Fe^{3+}\,(aq) + 4\,H_2O\,(l) + Mn^{2+}\,(aq)$$

$$\Delta\mathcal{E}^o = \mathcal{E}^o\,(MnO_4^- \mid Mn^{2+}) - \mathcal{E}^o\,(Fe^{3+} \mid Fe^{2+})$$

$$= 1.491\text{ V} - (0.770\text{ V}) = 0.721\text{ V}$$

$$Q = \frac{[Mn^{2+}][Fe^{3+}]^5}{[MnO_4^-][Fe^{2+}]^5\,[H^+]^8} = \frac{(0.95)\,(0.010)^5}{(0.050)(0.020)^5\,(0.10)^8} = 5.94 \times 10^7$$

Note: $n = 5$

$$\Delta\mathcal{E} = +0.721\text{ V} - \frac{0.0592\text{ V}}{5}\log\left(5.94\ \times 10^7\right) = \mathbf{+0.629\ V}$$

(c) $2\,I^-\,(aq) + 2\,Ag^+\,(aq) \rightarrow 2\,Ag\,(s) + I_2\,(s)$

$$\Delta\mathcal{E}^o = \mathcal{E}^o\,(Ag^+ \mid Ag) - \mathcal{E}^o\,(I_2 \mid I^-)$$

$$= 0.7996\text{ V} - (+0.535) = +0.2646\text{ V}$$

$$Q = [I^-]^{-2}\,[Ag^+]^{-2} = (0.10)^{-2}\,(0.10)^{-2} = 1.0 \times 10^{+4};\ \ (n = 2)$$

$$\Delta\mathcal{E} = +0.2646\text{ V} - \frac{0.0592\text{ V}}{2}\log_{10}\left(1.0 \times 10^4\right) = +0.2646 - 0.1184 = \mathbf{+0.146\ V}$$

14-29. The standard reduction potential for this half-reaction is -0.41 V. This will be modified by non-standard-state conditions. We use the Nernst equation for half-reactions the same way we use it for whole reactions.

$$\mathcal{E} = \mathcal{E}^{o} - \frac{0.0592\text{ V}}{n_{hc}} \log Q_{hc} \quad \text{and:} \quad Q_{hc} = \frac{[Cr^{2+}]}{[Cr^{3+}]} = \frac{0.0019}{0.15} = 0.0127$$

$$\mathcal{E} = -0.41 - \frac{0.0592\text{ V}}{1} \log(0.0127) = \mathbf{-0.30\text{ V}}$$

14-31. The standard reduction potential for a Cd^{2+} | Cd half-reaction is -0.4026 V. The half cell with the *more negative* reduction potential will be the anode in a Galvanic cell. This is the **Cd^{2+} | Cd** standard half cell.

14-33. $H_2\,(g) + I_2\,(s) \rightarrow 2I^-\,(aq) + 2H^+\,(aq) \qquad n = 2$

$$\Delta\mathcal{E}^{o} = \mathcal{E}^{o}(I_2 \mid I^-) - \mathcal{E}^{o}(H^+ \mid H_2) = +0.535 - 0 = +0.535\text{ V}$$

$$\Delta\mathcal{E} = \Delta\mathcal{E}^{o} - \frac{0.0592}{2} \log_{10} Q$$

$$\log_{10} Q = -\frac{2(\Delta\mathcal{E} - \Delta\mathcal{E}^{o})}{0.0592} = -\frac{2(0.841 - 0.535)}{0.0592} = -10.33$$

$$Q = 10^{-10.33} = 4.59 \times 10^{-11} = \frac{[H^+]^2[I^-]^2}{P_{H_2}}$$

$$[H^+] = \sqrt{\frac{Q \times P_{H_2}}{[I^-]^2}} = \sqrt{\frac{4.59 \times 10^{-11} \times 1.00}{(1.00)^2}} = 6.77 \times 10^{-6}\text{ M}; \quad \mathbf{pH = 5.17}$$

14-35. (a) $\Delta\mathcal{E}^{o} = \mathcal{E}^{o}(HClO_2 \mid HClO) - \mathcal{E}^{o}(Cr_2O_7^{2-} \mid Cr^{3+})$

$$= (+1.64) - (1.33) = \mathbf{+0.31} \qquad (n = 6)$$

(b) $$\Delta\mathcal{E} = \Delta\mathcal{E}^{o} - \frac{0.0592\text{ V}}{6} \log_{10} Q$$

$$\log_{10} Q = -\frac{(\Delta\mathcal{E} - \Delta\mathcal{E}^{o})6}{0.0592} = -\frac{(0.15 - 0.31)6}{.0592} = +16.21$$

$$Q = 10^{+16.21} = 1.6 \times 10^{16} = \frac{[H^+]^8[Cr_2O_7^{2-}][HClO]^3}{[Cr^{3+}]^2[HClO_2]^3}$$

$$[Cr^{3+}] = \sqrt{\frac{[H^+]^8[Cr_2O_7^{2-}][HClO]^3}{Q[HClO_2]^3}} = \sqrt{\frac{(1)^8(0.80)(0.20)^3}{(1.645 \times 10^{16})(0.15)^3}} = \mathbf{1 \times 10^{-8}\text{ M}}$$

14-37. (a) Anode: $Ni\ (s) \rightarrow Ni^{2+}\ (aq) + 2e^-$

Cathode: $Ag^+\ (aq) + e^- \rightarrow Ag\ (s)$

Overall: $2Ag^+\ (aq) + Ni\ (s) \rightarrow Ni^{2+}\ (aq) + 2Ag\ (s)$

(b) $\Delta\mathcal{E}^o = \mathcal{E}^o\,(Ag^+ \mid Ag) - \mathcal{E}^o\,(Ni^{2+} \mid Ni)\ \ +0.7996 - (-0.23) = +1.03\ V$

$$\Delta\mathcal{E} = 1.03 - \frac{0.0592}{2}\log\frac{(0.10)}{(0.10)^2} = 1.03 - 0.030\ V = \mathbf{1.00\ V}$$

(c) $$\Delta\mathcal{E}^o = \frac{0.0592\ V}{n}\log_{10} K$$

$$\log_{10} K = \frac{n\Delta E^o}{0.0592} = \frac{(2)(1.03)}{0.0592} = 34.8 \Rightarrow K = 10^{34.8} = \mathbf{6 \times 10^{34}}$$

14-39. In problem 35, we had $\Delta\mathcal{E}^o = +0.31$ V and $n = 6$. Therefore:

$$\log_{10} K = \frac{(6)(0.31)}{0.0592} = 31.42$$

$$K = 10^{+31.42} = \mathbf{3 \times 10^{31}}$$

This large equilibrium constant indicates the reaction will go essentially all the way to the right. The Cr^{3+} : $HClO_2$ molar ratio is 1 : 2, compared to a ratio in the reaction of 2 : 3. Hence, there is *excess $HClO_2$*. The Cr^{3+} will all be consumed and the solution after the reaction will be **orange**.

14-41. $\Delta\mathcal{E}^o = \mathcal{E}^o\,(In^+ \mid In) - \mathcal{E}^o\,(In^{3+} \mid In) = (-0.21\ V) - (-0.40\ V) = +0.19\ V$

$$\log_{10} K = \frac{n\Delta E^o}{0.0592} = \frac{(2)(0.19)}{0.0592} = 6.419 \Rightarrow K = 10^{+6.419} = \mathbf{3 \times 10^6}$$

14-43. The whole cell reaction is:

$$2\,H^+\ (1\ M) + H_2\ (1\ atm) \rightarrow 2\,H^+\ (unknown) + H_2\ (1\ atm)$$

Note that the standard cell potential for this reaction is 0.00 V.

$$\Delta\mathcal{E} = 0.00 - \frac{0.0592}{2}\log\frac{\left[H^+(unknown)\right]^2(1.00)}{(1.00)^2(1.00)}$$

$$= -\,0.0296\log\left[H^+\ (unknown)\right]^2$$

$$= -(2)(0.0296)\log\left[H^+\ (unknown)\right] = 0.0592\ pH\ (unknown)$$

$$pH\ (unknown) = \frac{\Delta\mathcal{E}}{0.0592} = \frac{0.150}{0.0592} = \mathbf{2.53}$$

14-43. (continued)

A buffer made with equal concentrations of a weak acid and its conjugate base has the characteristic that $pK_a \approx pH$. Here, $pK_a = 2.53$, so

$K_a = 10^{-2.53} = \mathbf{0.0029}$.

14-45. (a)

$$\Delta\mathcal{E}^\circ = \mathcal{E}^\circ(Br_2 \mid Br^-) - \mathcal{E}^\circ(H^+ \mid H_2)$$

$$= 1.065 - 0 = \mathbf{+1.065\ V}$$

(b)

$$\Delta\mathcal{E} = \Delta\mathcal{E}^\circ - \frac{.0592\ V}{2}\log_{10}\left(\frac{[Br^-]^2[H^+]^2}{P_{H_2}}\right)$$

$$1.710\ V = 1.065\ V - \frac{.0592\ V}{2}\log_{10}\left(\frac{[Br^-]^2(1)^2}{(1)}\right)$$

$$0.645\ V = -\frac{.0592\ V}{2}\log_{10}[Br^-]^2$$

$$0.645\ V = -.0592\ V\log_{10}[Br^-]$$

$$\log_{10}[Br^-] = \frac{0.645\ V}{-0.0592\ V} = -10.90$$

$$[Br^-] = 10^{-10.90} = \mathbf{1.3 \times 10^{-11}\ M}.$$

(c) We know $[Ag^+] = 0.060$ M, so:

$$K_{sp} = [Ag^+][Br^-] = (0.060)(1.27 \times 10^{-11}) = \mathbf{7.6 \times 10^{-13}}$$

14-47.

$$\Delta\mathcal{E}^\circ = \mathcal{E}^\circ(PbO_2 \mid PbSO_4) - \mathcal{E}^\circ(PbSO_4 \mid Pb)$$

$$= 1.685\ V - (-0.356\ V) = \mathbf{+2.041\ V}$$

Six such cells in series would generate an electrical potential of

6(2.041 V) = **12.25 V.**

14-49. The reaction yields $2e^-$ per Pb reacted.

$$10\text{ kg of Pb} = 10{,}000\text{ g}/207.2\text{ g mol}^{-1} = 48.26\text{ mol Pb}$$

$$\text{mol of }e^- = 48.26\text{ mol} \times 2 = 96.5\text{ mol }e^-$$

$$\text{C of }e^- = 96.5\text{ mol} \times 96{,}485\text{ C mol}^{-1} = \mathbf{9.3 \times 10^6\ C}.$$

14-51. In problem No. 49 we discovered that the voltage for the six cells in series was six times that for one cell. But in evaluating the maximum work we can obtain it is much clearer treat the system as 10,000 g of Pb all reacting to give a single cell potential of +2.041 V. Then, for the charge (determined in No. 51) passed in this system:

$$w_{max} = \Delta G = \text{charge} \times \text{potential}$$
$$= 9.3 \times 10^6 \text{ C} \times 2.041 \text{ V J C}^{-1}$$
$$= 1.9 \times 10^7 \text{ J} = \mathbf{19{,}000 \text{ kJ}}$$

14-53. Not entirely, because the cell reaction also consumes Pb and PbO_2. If these are not replenished, the battery will remain rundown. On the other hand, if excess Pb and PbO_2 are present, replenishment with more H_2SO_4 will (temporarily) restore the battery's action.

14-55.
$$\Delta\mathcal{E}^o = \mathcal{E}^o(O_2 \mid H_2O) - \mathcal{E}^o(H_2 \mid H^+) = 1.229 \text{ V}$$
$$w_{max} = \left(1.229 \frac{\text{J}}{\text{C}}\right)\left(\frac{96485 \text{ C}}{\text{mol e}^-}\right)\left(\frac{2 \text{ mol e}^-}{1 \text{ mol } H_2O}\right)\left(\frac{1 \text{ mol } H_2O}{18.015 \text{ g } H_2O}\right)$$
$$= 13{,}200 \text{ J g}^{-1} \qquad \text{60\% of this is } \mathbf{7{,}900 \text{ J g}^{-1}}$$

14-57. Since the reaction is done in basic aqueous conditions, we must use the water / hydrogen half cell for those conditions.

$$\Delta\mathcal{E}^o = \mathcal{E}^o(H_2O \mid H_2) - \mathcal{E}^o(Fe^{2+} \mid Fe) = (-0.8277) - (-0.409) = \mathbf{-0.42 \text{ V}}$$

This reaction is **non-spontaneous**. Because hydroxide is a product, the reaction will become more favorable as $[OH^-]$ decreases--as one moves to pH's lower than 14.

14-59. Sodium would make an excellent sacrificial anode, except for the fact that it is far too reactive *with water* to be stable when exposed to a marine environment.

14-61. $$Q = \left(\frac{1.5 \times 10^{13}\text{ g Al}}{26.98\text{ g mol}^{-1}}\right)\left(\frac{3\text{ mol e}^-}{1\text{ mol Al}}\right)\left(\frac{96{,}485\text{ C}}{1\text{ mol e}^-}\right) = 1.61 \times 10^{17}\text{ C.}$$

$$\text{Energy} = 1.61 \times 10^{17}\text{ C} \times 5\frac{\text{J}}{\text{C}} \times \frac{1\text{ kW-hr}}{3.6 \times 10^{6}\text{ J}} = 2.24 \times 10^{11}\text{ kW-hr}$$

Cost = 2.24×10^{11} kW-hr $\times$($0.10 (kW-hr) $^{-1}$) = $2.24 $\times 10^{10}$ = **$22.4 billion.**

14-63. (a) Appendix E gives these two reduction half-reactions:

$MnO_2\ (s) + 4H^+\ (aq) + 2e^- \rightarrow Mn^{2+}\ (aq) + 2H_2O\ (l)$ $\quad \mathcal{E}^o = +1.208$ V

$2H^+\ (aq) + O_2\ (g) + 2e^- \rightarrow H_2O_2\ (aq)$ $\quad \mathcal{E}^o = +0.682$ V

Since the reaction is carried out under standard state conditions, the cathode is the reaction at more positive $\mathcal{E}^o$--the $MnO_2\ |\ Mn^{2+}$ reaction.

Cathode: $MnO_2\ (s) + 4H^+\ (aq) + 2e^- \rightarrow Mn^{2+}\ (aq) + 2H_2O\ (l)$

Anode: $H_2O_2\ (aq) \rightarrow 2H^+\ (aq) + O_2 + (g) + 2e^-$

Whole cell: $MnO_2(s) + 2H^+(aq) + H_2O_2(aq) \rightarrow Mn^{2+}(aq) + 2H_2O(l) + O_2(g)$

(b) $\Delta\mathcal{E}^o$ = (+1.208 V) - (0.682 V) = **+0.526 V**

14-65. We need to drive the non-spontaneous reaction:

$Ni^{2+}\ (aq) + 2I^-\ (aq) \rightarrow Ni\ (s) + I_2\ (s)$

For which: $\Delta\mathcal{E}^o = \mathcal{E}^o\ (Ni^{2+}\ |\ Ni) - \mathcal{E}^o\ (I_2\ |\ I^-)$

= (-0.23 V) - (0.535 V) = **-0.76 V**

A potential of +0.765 V must be applied to drive this reaction.

Anode: $2I^-\ (aq) \rightarrow I_2\ (s) + 2e^-$

Cathode: $Ni^{2+}\ (aq) + 2e^- \rightarrow Ni\ (s)$

14-67. The standard reduction potential for reduction to $PH_3\ (g)$ is more negative than the standard reduction potential for reduction to $HS^-\ (g)$. Therefore, it is harder to form PH_3--so PH_3 must be a stronger reducing agent.

14-69. Cathode: $Ag^+\ (aq) + e^- \rightarrow Ag\ (s)$

Anode: $Zn\ (s) \rightarrow Zn^{2+}\ (aq) + 2e^-$

$\Delta\mathcal{E}^o = \mathcal{E}^o\ (Ag^+\ |\ Ag) - \mathcal{E}^o\ (Zn^{2+}\ |\ Zn)$

= (+0.7996 V) - (-0.7628 V) = +1.5624 V

14-69. (continued)

If she makes a cell that uses the solutions that she has without altering them, then the voltage would be:

$$\Delta\mathcal{E} = \Delta\mathcal{E}^{o} - \frac{0.0592\text{ V}}{2}\log_{10}\frac{[Zn^{2+}]}{[Ag^{+}]^{2}}$$

$$= 1.5624\text{ V} - (0.0296\text{V})\log\left(\frac{.10}{(.01)^{2}}\right)$$

$$= 1.5624\text{ V} - (0.0296\text{ V} \times 3) = 1.47\text{ V}.$$

This is *not* the voltage she needs, so one of the solutions must be diluted to give the correct voltage. Being a careful student of the Nernst equation, she knows the logarithmic term is the source of possible variations. So she writes:

$$1.50\text{ V} = 1.5624\text{ V} - \frac{0.0592\text{ V}}{2}\log_{10} Q$$

Rearranging: $+\dfrac{0.0624\text{ V}}{0.0296\text{ V}} = \log_{10} Q$

$10^{+2.108}$ = $\boldsymbol{Q = 128}$ This is the reaction quotient she needs.

The Q for the solutions available is: $Q = \dfrac{[Zn^{2+}]}{[Ag^{+}]^{2}} = 1000$

So Q must be decreased. She decides to lower the concentration of $[Zn^{2+}]$ so $Q = 123$. In this case, keeping $[Ag^{+}] = 0.0100$ M:

$$[Zn^{2+}] = 123\,[Ag^{+}]^{2} = 123\,(0.010)^{2} = 0.0123\text{ M}$$

So she prepares a solution with $[Zn^{2+}] = 0.0123$ M from her stock solution and places it in the apparatus sketched on the next page.

14-69. (continued)

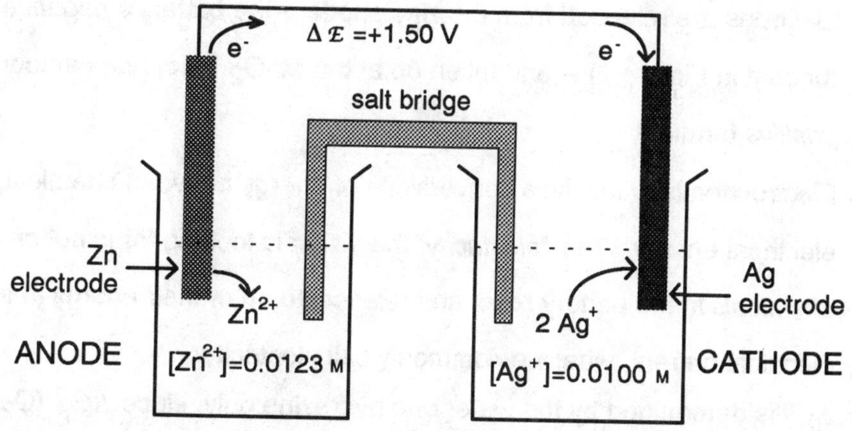

14-71. (a) The spontaneous reaction will tend to *decrease* the concentration in the cell with higher [Pb^{2+}] (0.10 M) and *increase* the concentration in the cell with lewer [Pb^{2+}] (0.010 M). So the whole cell reaction will be:

$$Pb^{2+}\ (0.10\ M) + Pb\ (s) \rightarrow Pb\ (s) + Pb^{2+}\ (0.010\ M)$$

The product Pb^{2+} is in the cell with the lower [Pb^{2+}]. Thus, for a spontaneous reaction, we want to write $Q = \dfrac{[Pb^{2+}]_{lower}}{[Pb^{2+}]_{higher}} = \dfrac{(0.010)}{(0.100)} = 0.10$

$$\Delta\mathcal{E} = 0.0 - (0.0512\ V/2)\log 10^{-1} = \mathbf{+0.030\ V}$$

(b) After the addition of the sulfate, a significant amount of the Pb^{2+} in the solution will precipitate as lead sulfate. There will be a small concentration of Pb^{2+}, controlled by the common ion effect. The spontaneous reaction will now produce Pb^{2+} in the cell sulfate, in the reverse direction from that in part (a).

$$[Pb^{2+}]_{lower} = \frac{K_{sp}\,(PbSO_4)}{[SO_4{}^{2-}]} = \frac{1.1 \times 10^{-8}}{0.10\ M} = 1.1 \times 10^{-7}\ M$$

Then: $\Delta\mathcal{E} = 0.0\ -0.0296\ V \log \dfrac{(1.1 \times 10^{-7})}{(0.010)} = \mathbf{+\ 0.146\ V}$

14-73. The spontaneous reaction in the Leclanché cell is:

$$Zn\ (s) + 2\ MnO_2\ (s) + 2\ NH_4{}^+(aq) \rightarrow Zn^{2+}(aq) + Mn_2O_3\ (s) + 2\ NH_3\ (aq) + H_2O\ (l)$$

14-73. (continued)

Electrons are released from the zinc anode -- the battery's *negative* terminal (bottom in Fig. 14-2) -- and taken up at the MnO_2 | graphite cathode -- the *positive* terminal.

14-75. Electrochemistry involves conversions of energy between chemical energy and electrical energy. The *"electricity"* the visitor is looking for is not present until the *chemicals* in the battery react and release some of their energy in the form of an electrical current, what we commonly call electricity.

14-77. ΔG^o is determined by the water and hydrazine only, since ΔG_f^o (O_2 *(g)*) = ΔG_f^o (N_2 *(g)*) = 0.

Thus: $\Delta G^o = 2\,\Delta G_f^o(H_2O\ (l)) - \Delta G_f^o(N_2H_4\ (aq))$

$$= 2\text{ mol }(-237.18\text{ kJ mol}^{-1}) - 1\text{ mol}(+128.1\text{ kJ mol}^{-1}) = -346.36\text{ kJ}$$

The cell is thermodynamically feasible. And what the seller claims about the products is correct. N_2 is part of air and liquid water is, well, water.

The cell potential in this case, since four electrons are transferred, is:

$$\Delta\mathcal{E}^o = -\frac{\Delta G^o}{n\mathcal{F}} = -\frac{-346{,}360\text{ J}}{\left(4\text{ mol e}^-\right)\left(96{,}485\text{ C (mol e}^-)^{-1}\right)} = +0.897\,\frac{\text{J}}{\text{C}} = \mathbf{+0.897\ V}$$

14-79. The potentials are:

$Sn^{2+} + 2e^- \rightarrow Sn$ $\quad \mathcal{E}^o = -0.1364$ V $\qquad Fe^{2+} + 2e^- \rightarrow Fe$ $\quad \mathcal{E}^o = -0.409$ V

$Zn^{2+} + 2e^- \rightarrow Zn$ $\quad \mathcal{E}^o = -0.7628$ V

Sn is harder to oxidize than Fe. Thus, given access to Fe *(s)*, oxidants will more readily attack Fe. Of course, in an intact tin can the oxidant can only attack the less reactive tin because the tin covers all of the iron. With a galvanized object, in contrast, the zinc acts as a sacrificial anode as well as a coating. A section of iron, under assault by an oxidant, will be protected by the oxidation of Zn, even if the Zn is some distance away, provided a continuous electrical pathway between the Zn and Fe is available.

CHAPTER 15 - CHEMICAL KINETICS

15-1. The first mile marker was passed at 13 minutes and 16 seconds before noon; the second marker was passed at 2 minutes and 24 seconds *after* noon. So the time elapsed was 15 minutes and 40 seconds, or 15.667 minutes.

The distance traveled was 30.0 - 11.5 = 18.5 miles.

The rate of travel in miles per minute was: $\frac{18.5 \text{ miles}}{15.667 \text{ minutes}} = \mathbf{1.18 \text{ mile min}^{-1}}$.

This is equal to $(1.181 \text{ mile min}^{-1}) \times (60 \text{ min hr}^{-1}) = \mathbf{70.9 \text{ mile hr}^{-1}}$.

15-3.

TIME ELAPSED	MILES TRAVELED	RATE OF TRAVEL
11 hours	550 miles	**50 miles per hour**
12 hours	550 miles	**46 miles per hour**
13 hours	550 miles	**42 miles per hour**
18.5 hours	550 + 300= 850 miles	**46 miles per hour**

15-5. A line drawn as a tangent to the curve at t = 200 seconds has the following parameters: concentration change = 0.0320 - 0.0215 = 0.0105 M

time change = 200 seconds

$$\text{rate} = \frac{\text{concentration change}}{\text{time change}} = \frac{0.0105 \text{ M}}{200 \text{ s}} = \mathbf{5.25 \times 10^{-5} \text{ mol L}^{-1} \text{ s}^{-1}}$$

15-7. The related expressions for the rate reflect the stoichiometry of the reaction.

$$\text{rate} = -\frac{\Delta[N_2]}{\Delta t} = -\frac{1}{3}\frac{\Delta[H_2]}{\Delta t} = +\frac{1}{2}\frac{\Delta[NH_3]}{\Delta t}$$

15-9. (a) As determined in the last problem, the relationship between the expressions of the rate are:

$$-\frac{1}{3}\frac{\Delta[H_2]}{\Delta t} = +\frac{1}{2}\frac{\Delta[NH_3]}{\Delta t}$$

$$\frac{\Delta[H_2]}{\Delta t} = -\frac{3}{2}\left(-0.150\frac{\text{mol}}{\text{L-s}}\right) = \mathbf{0.225 \text{ mol L}^{-1} \text{ s}^{-1}}$$

(b) $$-\frac{\Delta[N_2]}{\Delta t} = +\frac{1}{2}\frac{\Delta[NH_3]}{\Delta t} \Rightarrow \frac{\Delta[N_2]}{\Delta t} = -\frac{1}{3}\left(0.150\frac{\text{mol}}{\text{L-s}}\right) = \mathbf{0.075 \text{ mol L}^{-1} \text{ s}^{-1}}$$

15-11. (a) **Second** order -- indicated by the lone exponent "2" on $[NO_2]$

(b) **First** order -- indicated by the implied exponent "1" on $[I_2]$

15-13. The overall rate expression will have: Rate = k [species A, B, C, ...]^3

The units of rate are mol L^{-1} sec^{-1}. The units of concentration are mol L^{-1}.

Therefore, we can rearrange for

$$k = \frac{\text{rate}}{[\text{species A, B, C..}]^3} = \frac{\text{mol L}^{-1}\text{s}^{-1}}{\left(\text{mol L}^{-1}\right)^3} = \frac{\text{L}^2}{\text{mol}^2\ \text{s}} = \mathbf{L^2\ mol^{-2}\ s^{-1}}$$

15-15. (a) As in Example 15-2, we can determine the order of a reaction with respect to a reactant by examining the dependence of the ratio of the rate on the ratio of the concentrations of that reactant. Using the first two data points:

$$\frac{\text{rate}_2}{\text{rate}_1} = \left(\frac{[\text{NOBr}]_2}{[\text{NOBr}]_1}\right)^n$$

$$\frac{6.2\times10^{-5}}{1.35\times10^{-4}} = \left(\frac{0.0088}{0.0130}\right)^n$$

$$0.4593 = (0.6769)^n$$

Clearly, n is not 1, and we must try out different values for n. If $n = 2$, then $(0.6769)^n = (0.6769)^2 = 0.4582$. This equals the experimental rate ratio, so we conclude the reaction is second order in NOBr.

We can verify this by checking the rate ratios vs. concentration ratios for the second and third data points:

$$\frac{\text{rate}_3}{\text{rate}_2} = \left(\frac{[\text{NOBr}]_3}{[\text{NOBr}]_2}\right)^2$$

$$\frac{1.92\times10^{-5}}{6.2\times10^{-5}} = \left(\frac{0.0049}{0.0088}\right)^2$$

$0.3097 = 0.3100$ This verifies our conclusion that $n = 2$.

The rate expression is then: **rate = k [NOBr]^2**

15-15. (continued)

(b) The rate constant can be determined from the experimental rate and the concentration of NOBr: $k = \dfrac{\text{rate}}{[\text{NOBr}]^2}$

For the first datum: $k = \dfrac{1.35 \times 10^{-4}\ \text{mol L}^{-1}\ \text{s}^{-1}}{(0.0130\ \text{mol L}^{-1})^2} = 0.799\ \text{L mol}^{-1}\ \text{s}^{-1}$

For the second: $k = 0.801\ \text{L mol}^{-1}\ \text{s}^{-1}$;

For the third: $k = 0.801\ \text{L mol}^{-1}\ \text{s}^{-1}$

The average of these three is **0.800 L mol^{-1} s^{-1}**.

15-17. (a) Increasing [I^-] by a factor of ten will increase the rate of the reaction by a factor of ten, since the reaction is first order in [I^-].

(b) Decreasing [H_2O_2] by a factor of four will decrease the rate by a factor of four, since the reaction is first order in [H_2O_2].

15-19. (a) The experimental data imply the following about the rate expression:

Cutting [H_2] in half cuts rate in half	⇒	The reaction is first order in [H_2]
Raising [NO] by 10 raises rate by 100	⇒	The reaction is second order in [NO]

$$\text{Rate} = k\,[H_2]\,[\text{NO}]^2$$

The units of k for this third-order reaction are $\text{L}^2\ \text{mol}^{-2}\ \text{s}^{-1}$

(b) Raising [H_2] by factor of 2 ⇒ Raise rate by factor of 2

Raising [NO] by 3 ⇒ Raise rate by factor of $3^2 = 9$

TOGETHER: Raise rate by factor of $\times$ 9 = 18

15-21. (a) The first two data differ in the concentration of *both* reactants, so we can't use them (yet). The second and third data differ in the concentration of CH_3I only, so they can be used to determine the order of the reaction in CH_3I:

$$\frac{\text{rate}_3}{\text{rate}_2} = \left(\frac{[CH_3I]_3}{[CH_3I]_2}\right)^n$$

$$\frac{6.0\times10^{-6}}{3.0\times10^{-6}} = \left(\frac{4.00\times10^{-4}}{2.00\times10^{-4}}\right)^n$$

$$2.0 = (2.00)^n, \text{ so } n = 1$$

We must now compare the first two data to obtain the order of the reaction order with respect to C_5H_5N. To do this analytically, we must include the both reactants in the ratio, but of course we now know the reaction order in CH_3I:

$$\frac{\text{rate}_2}{\text{rate}_1} = \left(\frac{[CH_3I]_2}{[CH_3I]_1}\right)^1 \times \left(\frac{[C_5H_5N]_2}{[C_5H_5N]_1}\right)^n$$

$$\frac{3.0\times10^{-6}}{7.5\times10^{-7}} = \left(\frac{2.00\times10^{-4}}{1.00\times10^{-4}}\right)^1 \times \left(\frac{2.00\times10^{-4}}{1.00\times10^{-4}}\right)^n$$

$$4.0 = (2.00) \times (2.00)^n$$

$$2.0 = (2.00)^n, \text{ so } n = 1$$

The overall rate expression is: rate = $\boldsymbol{k}$ **$[C_5H_5N]$ $[CH_3I]$**.

(b) We can solve for k by putting he rate and concentration of any data point in the equation: $k = \dfrac{rate}{[C_5H_5N][CH_3I]}$

For the first data point: $k = \dfrac{7.5\times10^{-7}\text{ mol L}^{-1}\text{ s}^{-1}}{(1.00\times10^{-4}\text{ mol L}^{-1})(1.00\times10^{-4}\text{ mol L}^{-1})}$

= 75 L mol^{-1} s^{-1}

(c) rate = $(75\text{ L mol}^{-1}\text{ s}^{-1})(5.0\times10^{-5}\text{ mol L}^{-1})(2.0\times10^{-5}\text{ mol L}^{-1})$

= 7.5 × 10^{-8} mol L^{-1} s^{-1}

15-23. (a) Comparing data in the first two lines, we get the order of the reaction in SCN^-:

$$\frac{\text{rate}_2}{\text{rate}_1} = \left(\frac{[SCN^-]_2}{[SCN^-]_1}\right)^n$$

$$\frac{3.5\times10^{-9}}{1.9\times10^{-9}} = \left(\frac{0.084}{0.045}\right)^n$$

$$1.84 = (1.87)^n \quad \text{so } n = 1 \text{ for } [SCN^-]$$

Comparing the data in the 2nd and 3rd lines we get the order of the reaction in

$Cr(H_2O)_6{}^{3+}$:
$$\frac{\text{rate}_3}{\text{rate}_2} = \left(\frac{\left[Cr(H_2O)_6^{3+}\right]_3}{\left[Cr(H_2O)_6^{3+}\right]_2}\right)^n$$

$$\frac{8.9\times10^{-9}}{3.5\times10^{-9}} = \left(\frac{0.053}{0.021}\right)^n$$

$$2.54 = (2.53)^n \quad \text{so } n = 1 \text{ for } \left[Cr(H_2O)_6^{3+}\right]$$

Together:
$$\text{rate} = \boldsymbol{k\left[Cr(H_2O)_6^{3+}\right][SCN^-]}$$

(b) For the first data point:
$$k = \frac{rate}{\left[Cr(H_2O)_6^{3+}\right][SCN^-]}$$

$$= \frac{1.9\times10^{-9}\ \text{mol L}^{-1}\ \text{s}^{-1}}{(0.021\ \text{mol L}^{-1})(0.045\ \text{mol L}^{-1})}$$

$$= \mathbf{2.0\times10^{-6}\ L\ mol^{-1}\ s^{-1}}.$$

15-25. (a) There is a general relationship between the rate constant *k* and the half-life $t_{1/2}$ for a first order reaction:

$$k = \frac{\ln 2}{t_{1/2}} = \frac{0.6931}{t_{1/2}} = \frac{0.6931}{4.5\times10^4\ \text{s}} = 1.54\times10^{-5}\ \text{s}^{-1} = \mathbf{1.5\times10^{-5}\ s^{-1}}$$

(b) Note that 16.2 hours = 58320 seconds. We seek the fraction *x* of an original amount that remains. This means:

$$x\,[SO_2Cl_2]_o = [SO_2Cl_2]_o\, e^{-kt}$$ Note the common $[SO_2Cl_2]_o$

Then:
$$x = e^{-(1.54\times10^{-5}\ \text{s}^{-1})(58320\ \text{s})} = e^{-0.8983} = \mathbf{0.41}$$

15-27. We can rearrange the basic equation for the time dependence of concentration to solve for k. Starting at $t = 0$, we have:

$$[C_2H_5Cl] = [C_2H_5Cl]_o\, e^{-kt}$$

$$\frac{[C_2H_5Cl]}{[C_2H_5Cl]_o} = e^{-kt}$$

$$\ln\left(\frac{[C_2H_5Cl]}{[C_2H_5Cl]_o}\right) = -kt$$

$$-\frac{1}{340\text{ s}}\ln\left(\frac{0.0016\text{ mol L}^{-1}}{0.0098\text{ mol L}^{-1}}\right) = k = \mathbf{0.0053\ s^{-1}}$$

15-29. (a) This is **true**, because rate is proportional to the concentration of A, which is decreasing with time.

(b) This is **false**. The rate constant merely indicates the "velocity" of the reaction, not the time it takes to complete the reaction.

(c) This is **true**, because the reaction is first order in A.

(d) This is **false**. The half life of a first-order reaction is $t_{1/2} = {}^{0.6931}/_{k}$.

(e) This is **false**. See the answer to (d) for the reason.

15-31. (a) For a second order reaction:

$$\frac{1}{[I]} = \frac{1}{[I]_o} + 2kt = \frac{1}{1.00 \times 10^{-4}\text{ mol L}^{-1}} + 2(8.2 \times 10^{9}\text{ L mol}^{-1}\text{ s}^{-1})(2.0 \times 10^{-6}\text{ s})$$

$$= (1.00 \times 10^{4}\text{ L mol}^{-1}) + (3.28 \times 10^{4}\text{ L mol}^{-1}) = 42{,}800\text{ L mol}^{-1}$$

$$[I] = \frac{1}{42{,}800\text{ L mol}^{-1}} = \mathbf{2.34 \times 10^{-5}\ mol\ L^{-1}}$$

15-33. The units of the rate constant -- s^{-1} -- indicate that this is a first-order reaction.

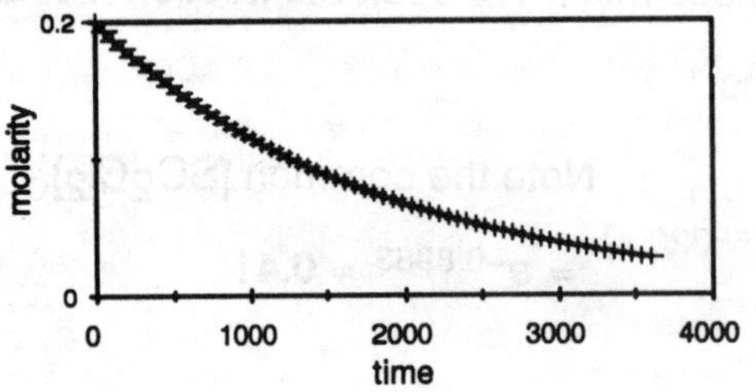

Note that the concentration decays exponentially, and reaches half its original value after 1300 seconds, the half-life for this reaction.

15-35. (a) bimolecular rate = $k\,[HCO][O_2]$

(b) termolecular rate = $k\,[CH_3][O_2][N_2]$

(c) unimolecular rate = $k\,[HO_2NO_2]$

15-37. (a) The first step is unimolecular, the others are all bimolecular.

(b) If we simply add all four reactions, we get:

$$H_2O_2 + \mathbf{O} + \mathbf{CF_2Cl_2} + \mathbf{ClO} + O_3 + \mathbf{Cl} + \mathbf{ClF_2Cl}$$
$$\rightarrow H_2O + \mathbf{O} + \mathbf{ClO} + \mathbf{CF_2Cl} + \mathbf{Cl} + 2\,O_2 + \mathbf{CF_2Cl_2}$$

Compounds in bold are common to both sides and can be eliminated in getting the overall equation: $H_2O_2 + O_3 \rightarrow H_2O + 2\,O_2$

(c) An intermediate species is one that is *formed and then destroyed* during a reaction. In this reaction O, ClO, CF_2Cl, and Cl are intermediates. Note that CF_2Cl_2 is *destroyed and then re-formed* in the reaction. It is **not** an intermediate (but see problem No. 55).

15-39. For a pair of elementary steps such as this, we have

$$K = \frac{\textit{rate constant forward}}{\textit{rate constant backward}}$$

$$\textit{rate constant backward} = \frac{\textit{rate constant forward}}{K} = \frac{1.3 \times 10^{10}\ \mathrm{L\ mol^{-1}\ s^{-1}}}{5.0 \times 10^{10}}$$

$$= 0.26\ \mathrm{L\ mol^{-1}\ s^{-1}}$$

15-41. (a) Overall: A + B + E → D + F

From the rate determining step: rate = $k_2[C][E]$

From the equilibrium: $K = \dfrac{k_1}{k_{-1}} = \dfrac{[C][D]}{[A][B]}$

Rearranging: $[C] = \dfrac{k_1}{k_{-1}}\dfrac{[A][B]}{[D]}$

Combining: rate = $\left(\dfrac{k_1 k_2}{k_{-1}}\right)\dfrac{[A][B][E]}{[D]}$

15-41. (continued)

(b) Overall: A + D → B + F

From the rate determining step: $\text{rate} = k_3[\text{E}]$

From the second equilibrium: $K_2 = \dfrac{k_2}{k_{-2}} = \dfrac{[\text{E}]}{[\text{C}][\text{D}]}$

Rearranging: $[\text{E}] = \dfrac{k_2}{k_{-2}}[\text{C}][\text{D}]$

From the first equilibrium: $K_1 = \dfrac{k_1}{k_{-1}} = \dfrac{[\text{B}][\text{C}]}{[\text{A}]}$

Rearranging: $[\text{C}] = \dfrac{k_1}{k_{-1}}\dfrac{[\text{A}]}{[\text{B}]}$

Therefore: $[\text{E}] = \dfrac{k_2}{k_{-2}}\dfrac{k_1}{k_{-1}}\dfrac{[\text{A}][\text{D}]}{[\text{B}]}$

And: $\text{rate} = \dfrac{k_1 k_2 k_3}{k_{-1}k_{-2}}\dfrac{[\text{A}][\text{D}]}{[\text{B}]}$

15-43. Only mechanism **(b)** is consistent with the rate expression. In it, the intermediates H_2Cl_2 and $CH_3CHClCH_2$, which both participate in the elementary rate-determining step, are generated in fast equilibria dependent on $[HCl]^2$ and $[HCl][CH_3CHCH_2]$. When these expressions are combined the dependence will be $[HCl]^3[CH_3CHCH_2]$.

Mechanism (a) is not consistent with the rate expression, because the last step is fast and is after the slow step, so it makes no difference to the reaction rate. Mechanism (c) also has two pre-equilibria, but only two molecules of HCl are involved.

15-45. Only mechanism **(a)** is consistent with the rate expression. Only the first step in it will matter to the rate expression, and this step is a unimolecular reaction involving just NO_2Cl. Both mechanisms (b) and (c) predict a second-order dependence on NO_2Cl.

15-47. Determining the activation energy and A can be done by choosing any two experimental points to get E_a and A.

$$k_1 = 5.49 \times 10^6 \qquad T_1 = 5000\text{ K} \qquad \frac{1}{T_1} = 2.0 \times 10^{-4}\text{ K}^{-1}$$

$$k_3 = 5.09 \times 10^9 \qquad T_2 = 15{,}000\text{ K} \qquad \frac{1}{T_2} = 6.67 \times 10^{-5}\text{ K}^{-1}$$

These are then used in the Arrhenius equation, cast as in Example 15-9 to make the determination of E_a and A convenient:

$$\ln\left(\frac{k_1}{k_3}\right) = -\frac{E_a}{R}\left(\frac{1}{T_1} - \frac{1}{T_3}\right)$$

$$\ln\left(\frac{5.49\times10^6}{5.09\times10^9}\right) = -\frac{E_a}{8.3145\text{ J mol}^{-1}\text{ K}^{-1}}\left(2.0\times10^{-4}\text{K}^{-1} - 6.67\times10^{-5}\text{K}^{-1}\right)$$

$$-6.832 = -E_a \times (1.6032 \times 10^{-5}\text{ mol J}^{-1})$$

$$E_a = \frac{6.832}{1.6032\times10^{-5}\text{ mol J}^{-1}} = \mathbf{4.25 \times 10^5\ J\ mol^{-1}}$$

(b) Using point 3 only:

$$\ln A = \ln k_3 + \frac{E_a}{RT_3} = \ln(5.09 \times 10^9) + \frac{4.25\times10^5\text{ J mol}^{-1}}{(8.3145\text{ J mol}^{-1}\text{ K}^{-1})(15000\text{ K})}$$

$$\ln A = +22.35 + 3.416 = 25.766$$

$$A = e^{25.766} = \mathbf{1.54 \times 10^{11}\ L\ mol^{-1}\ s^{-1}}$$

One may also get both $\ln A$ and E_a from a graph of $\ln k$ vs. $+^1/_T$:

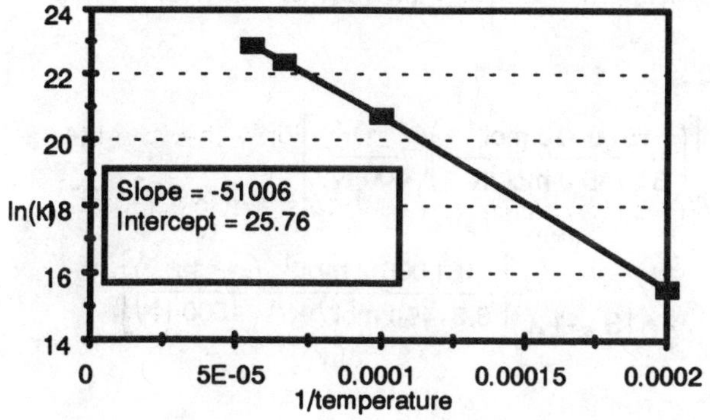

The slope of the graph equals $-\frac{E_a}{R}$, and has units of Kelvins and then:

$E_a = -\text{slope} \times R = 4.24 \times 10^5\text{ J mol}^{-1}$

We also have intercept = $\ln A$,

so $A = e^{\text{intercept}} = e^{25.76}$

$= 1.54 \times 10^{11}\text{ L mol}^{-1}\text{ s}^{-1}$

15-49. We have two expressions at the two temperatures:

$$k_1 = A\,e^{-E_a/RT_1}$$

$$k_2 = A\,e^{-E_a/RT_2}$$

If we divide the second by the second, we obtain:

$$\frac{k_2}{k_1} = \frac{Ae^{-E_a/RT_2}}{Ae^{-E_a/RT_1}} = e^{-E_a/RT_2}e^{+E_a/RT_1} = e^{-\left[\frac{E_a}{R}\left(\frac{1}{T_1}-\frac{1}{T_2}\right)\right]}$$

$$k_2 = k_1\,e^{-\left[\frac{E_a}{R}\left(\frac{1}{T_1}-\frac{1}{T_2}\right)\right]}$$

$$= (1.94\times10^{-4}\text{ L mol}^{-1}\text{s}^{-1})\,e^{-\left[\frac{161{,}000\text{ J mol}^{-1}}{8.3145\text{ J mol}^{-1}\text{ K}^{-1}}\left(\frac{1}{313.15\text{K}}-\frac{1}{303.15\text{K}}\right)\right]}$$

$$= (1.94\times10^{-4}\text{ L mol}^{-1}\text{s}^{-1})\,e^{+2.04} = \mathbf{1.49\times10^{-3}\ L\ mol^{-1}\ s^{-1}}$$

(b) We know that the reaction is second order because it is an elementary reaction with two components. The half life for a second-order reaction with both reactants present in equal amounts is: $t_{1/2} = \dfrac{1}{2k[X]_o}$ This will apply both at T_1 and T_2.

Dividing the expression for k at T_2 by the one for k at T_1 we get:

$$\frac{t_{1/2}(2)}{t_{1/2}(1)} = \left(\frac{1}{2k_2[X]_o}\right)\left(\frac{2k_1[X]_o}{1}\right) = \frac{k_1}{k_2}$$

$$t_{1/2}(2) = t_{1/2}(1)\frac{k_1}{k_2} = 1.00\times10^4\,\text{s}\frac{(1.94\times10^{-4}\text{L mol}^{-1}\text{ K}^{-1})}{(1.49\times10^{-3}\text{L mol}^{-1}\text{ K}^{-1})}$$

$$\mathbf{=1300\ s}$$

15-51. (a) $A = k\,e^{+E_a/RT} = (0.41\text{ s}^{-1})e^{\left[\left(\frac{161{,}000\text{ J mol}^{-1}}{8.3145\text{ J mol}^{-1}\text{K}^{-1}}\right)\left(\frac{1}{600\text{ K}}\right)\right]} = \mathbf{4.3\times10^{13}\ s^{-1}}$

(b) $k_2 = A\,e^{-\left[\frac{E_a}{R}\left(\frac{1}{T_2}\right)\right]} = 4.3\times10^{13}\text{ s}^{-1}e^{-\left[\frac{161{,}000\text{ J mol}^{-1}}{8.3145\text{J mol}^{-1}\text{ K}^{-1}}\left(\frac{1}{1000\text{ K}}\right)\right]}$

$= 1.7\times10^5\text{ s}^{-1}$

15-53. The height of the transition state complex on an energy plot is 3.5 kJ mol^{-1} above the energy of "OH *(g)* + HCl *(g)*" and these substances are 66.8 kJ higher in energy than "H_2O *(g)* + Cl *(g)*", then the barrier must be 66.8 + 3.5 = **70.3 kJ mol^{-1}** for the reaction H_2O *(g)* + Cl *(g)* → OH *(g)* + HCl *(g)*".

15-55. The substance CF_2Cl_2 is consumed in the second step and regenerated in the fourth. It is therefore an essential part of the reaction but is neither consumed nor produced over the whole mechanism. This means it plays a **catalytic** role.

15-57. We assume that the train slows at a constant rate. At the beginning of any given time interval, the average speed in miles per hour will be: 60 - x, where *x* is the number of minutes from the start of the hill. After *y* minutes later, the speed will be 60 - *x* - y. The average speed in an interval will be very close to:

$$\text{average speed} = \frac{(60-x)+(60-x-y)}{2} = 60 - x - \frac{y}{2}$$

We can then determine the average speed for any interval starting *x* minutes from the start of the hill and ending *y* minutes later.

Start time (*x*)	Interval length (*y*)	Average speed (mph)
0	1	$60-0-\frac{1}{2}$ = **59.5**
0	3	$60-0-\frac{3}{2}$ =**58.5**
3	3	$60-3-\frac{3}{2}$ =**55.5**
0	20	$60-0-\frac{20}{2}$ = **50.0**

15-59. rate = k [Hb][O_2] = $(4 \times 10^7\ \text{L mol}^{-1}\ \text{s}^{-1})(2 \times 10^{-9}\ \text{mol L}^{-1})(5 \times 10^{-5}\ \text{mol L}^{-1})$

$= \mathbf{4 \times 10^{-6}\ mol\ L^{-1}\ s^{-1}}$

15-61. (a) The data for the plot are as follows:

TIME	ln [In^+]
0	-4.80
240	-5.05
480	-5.29
720	-5.55
1000	-5.80
1200	-5.80
10000	-5.80

The last point is omitted from the graph.

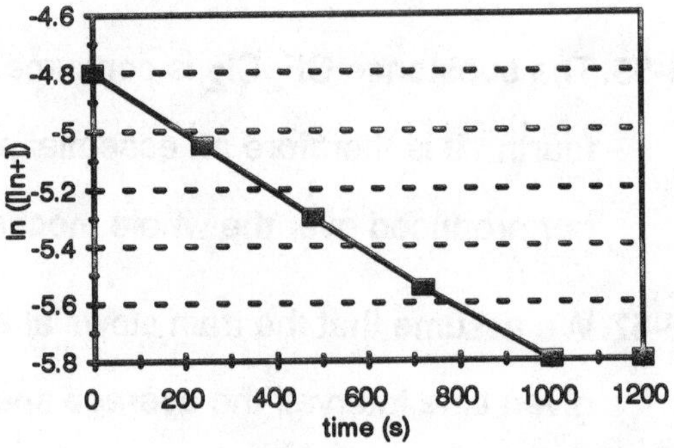

The data has two areas - a steady drop in ln[In^+] until about 1000 seconds, then a constant value because the reaction has reached equilibrium. The nature of dynamic equilibrium means that as soon as some In *(s)* and In^{3+} *(aq)* have formed, they will begin to react to give In^+ back. We must look at the very beginning of the data for the "pure" kinetics of the reaction of In^+ alone.

The In^+ reaction is first order in [In^+], so it will fit the equation with the point when t = 240 s:

$$\ln [In^+] = \ln [In^+]_o - kt$$

Rearranging:

$$k = -\frac{1}{t}\ln\left(\frac{[In^+]}{[In^+]_o}\right)$$

$$k = -\frac{1}{240\ \text{s}}\ln\left(\frac{0.00641\ \text{M}}{0.00823\ \text{M}}\right) = \mathbf{1.04 \times 10^{-3}\ s^{-1}}$$

(b) The half life for a first-order process is $t_{1/2} = \frac{0.6931}{k} = \frac{0.6931}{0.00104\ \text{s}^{-1}} = \mathbf{666\ s}$

(c) At equilibrium, we have 0.00303 M In^+ and have generated a concentration of In^{3+} equal to one-third the concentration of consumed In^+. Therefore,

$$[In^{3+}] = {}^1/_3(0.00823\ \text{M} - 0.00303\ \text{M}) = 0.00173\ \text{M}$$

15-61. (continued)

These concentrations are used to get the equilibrium constant:

$$K = \frac{[In^{3+}]}{[In^{+}]^3} = \frac{0.00173}{(0.00303)^3} = \mathbf{62{,}200}$$

15-63. The information in the problem gives us $k_f = 3.7 \times 10^9$ L mol^{-1} s^{-1} for the reaction of hydroxide and cyanide ions. The reaction in this case is best written:

$$OH^-\ (aq) + HCN\ (aq) \underset{k_f}{\overset{k_r}{\rightleftarrows}} CN^-\ (aq) + H_2O\ (l)$$

This reaction is the opposite of the reaction for hydrolysis of cyanide anion -- the "K_b" reaction. $K_b\,(CN^-) = \frac{K_w}{K_a(HCN)} = \frac{1.0 \times 10^{-14}}{4.93 \times 10^{-10}} = 2.03 \times 10^{-5}$

Given the general relation $K = {}^{\text{rate forward}}/_{\text{rate reverse}}$

we can solve for k_f: $k_f = K_b\, k_r = (2.03 \times 10^{-5})(3.7 \times 10^9 \text{ L mol}^{-1}\text{ s}^{-1})$

$= \mathbf{7.5 \times 10^4\ s^{-1}}$

15-65. **Initiation step:** $CH_3CHO \rightarrow CH_3 + CHO$

Propagation steps: $CH_3 + \mathbf{CH_3CHO} \rightarrow \mathbf{CH_4} + CH_2CHO$

(also form most of product) $CH_2CHO \rightarrow \mathbf{CO} + CH_3$

Termination steps: $CH_3 + CH_3 \rightarrow CH_3CH_3$

(may or may not form product) $CHO + CH_3 \rightarrow CH_4 + CO$

Most of the reactants undergo transformation to products in the propagation steps, as indicated in bold. The propagation steps regenerate the methyl radical intermediate, as they should in a true chain reaction.

The termination steps include one that merely terminates the chain, in this case making a small amount of ethane by product. The other actually forms product, but this is, it should be emphasized, *not* an important product forming step. It is most important as a chain-breaking step.

15-67. (a) The cooking of food is kinetically complex, but we will treat as if it is a process with a mechanism that does not change. The same relationship will hold for the rate constants. Then:

$$\ln\left(\frac{k_{373}}{k_{385}}\right) = -\frac{E_a}{R}\left(\frac{1}{373}-\frac{1}{385}\right)$$

$$\ln\left(\frac{1}{2}\right) = -\frac{E_a}{8.3145 \text{ J mol}^{-1}\text{ K}^{-1}}\left(2.6810\times10^{-3}\text{K}^{-1}-2.5974\times10^{-3}\text{K}^{-1}\right)$$

$$-0.6931 = -E_a \times (1.005 \times 10^{-5} \text{ mol J}^{-1})$$

$$E_a = \frac{0.6931}{1.005\times10^{-5}\text{ mol J}^{-1}} = \mathbf{69{,}000\ J\ mol^{-1}}$$

(b) This activation energy is all that is needed for the calculation of the relative rate at 94.4°C (367.55 K):

$$\ln\left(\frac{k_{373}}{k_{367.55}}\right) = -\frac{69000 \text{ J mol}^{-1}}{8.3145\text{J mol}^{-1}\text{ K}^{-1}}\left(\frac{1}{373\text{ K}}-\frac{1}{367.55\text{ K}}\right) = -0.3300$$

$$\left(\frac{k_{373}}{k_{367.55}}\right) = e^{+0.3399} = 1.391$$

SInce the average rate constant at 373 K is 1.391 times the rate at 267.55 K, the time required for cooking at 267.55 K is 1.391 times the time at 373 K:

time at 267.55 K = 10 min × 1.391 = **14 min**

15-69. The thermodynamic data from Appendix D (remember that I_2 is in the *gas* phase, so the enthalpy of formation for I_2 *(g)* is not zero) give: ΔH^o = -9.48 kJ and ΔS^o = 21.81 J K^{-1}. Then at 1000 K:

$$\Delta G^o_{1000} = -9{,}480 \text{ J} - 1000 \text{ K } (21.81 \text{ J K}^{-1})$$

$$= -31{,}290 \text{ J}$$

If we make the approximation that the change in enthalpy ΔH^o is equal to the change in energy ΔE^o (reasonable for a gas phase reaction with equal moles of gaseous products and reactants) then ΔE^o = - 9.48 kJ.

15-69. (continued)

This means that the energy of the products lies 9,480 J *below* the energy of the reactants. We know that the transition state energy is 165,000 J *above* the energy of the reactants. Therefore, the transition state energy is 165,000 + 9,480 = 177,480 J = 177 kJ above the energy of the products, for an activation energy for the reverse reaction of **177 kJ mol^{-1}**

We cannot use this E_a to determine k_r directly because we do not know the pre-exponential factor *A*. But the free energy change allows us to calculate the equilibrium constant for the reaction:

$$K = e^{-\Delta G^\circ/RT} = e^{-(-31{,}290 \text{ J mol}^{-1})/(8.3145 \text{ J mol}^{-1} \text{ K}^{-1})(1000 \text{ K})}$$

$$= 43.1$$

We can then use the relationship of forward and reverse rate constants and the equilibrium constant to get k_r:

$$K = 43.1 = \frac{k_f}{k_r}$$

Rearranging: $k_r = \dfrac{240 \text{ L mol}^{-1} \text{ s}^{-1}}{43.1} = \mathbf{5.56 \text{ L mol}^{-1} \text{ K}^{-1}}$

15-71. Such odd behavior indicates that something -- a catalyst since it is not among the continuously depleted reactants -- is forming in the course of the reaction that causes it to speed up, but then for some reason this species loses its effectiveness. There are two explanations. First, the catalyst may be an intermediate, whose rapid formation causes it to reach higher and higher concentrations until the rate of the initial reaction slows down as the reactants are depleted, and then the intermediate also declines in concentration. Second, the catalyst may be an intermediate or a product, but the step it catalyzes is dependent on relatively high concentrations of the reactants. As the reactants are depleted -- and, afterall, the reaction has to end sometime -- there is a change in the mechanism and the rate is no longer dependent on the catalyst or intermediate.

CHAPTER 16 - FUNDAMENTAL PARTICLES AND NUCLEAR CHEMISTRY

16-1. If $k = 1.2 \times 10^{-15}$ m, $\quad r = (1.2 \times 10^{-15}\text{ m})(127)^{1/3}$

$$= 6.0 \times 10^{-15}\text{ m} = 6.0 \times 10^{-13}\text{ cm}$$

$$V = {}^{4}/_{3}\,\pi\, r^{3} = 9.05 \times 10^{-37}\text{ cm}^{3}$$

If $k = 1.3 \times 10^{-15}$ m, $\quad r = 6.5 \times 10^{-15}$ m and $V = 1.15 \times 10^{-36}\text{ cm}^{3}$

The mass of one atom of ^{127}I is:

$$\left(\frac{126.9\text{ g }^{127}\text{I}}{1\text{ mol }^{127}\text{I}}\right)\left(\frac{1\text{ mol }^{127}\text{I}}{6.0221\times10^{23}\text{ atoms }^{127}\text{I}}\right) = 2.107 \times 10^{-22}\text{ g}$$

Density range:

$$\text{low: } \frac{2.107 \times 10^{-22}\text{ g}}{1.15 \times 10^{-36}\text{ cm}^{3}} = \mathbf{1.8 \times 10^{14}\text{ g cm}^{-3}}$$

$$\text{high: } \frac{2.107 \times 10^{-22}\text{ g}}{9.05 \times 10^{-37}\text{ cm}^{3}} = \mathbf{2.3 \times 10^{14}\text{ g cm}^{-3}}$$

16-3. Americium has atomic number 95. An ^{241}Am atom has 95 electrons, 95 protons, and 241 - 95 = 146 neutrons.

16-5. (a) Plutonium has atomic number 94. The ^{239}Pu nucleus has 94 protons and 239 - 94 = 145 neutrons. The $^{\text{proton}}/_{\text{neutron}}$ ratio is $^{145}/_{94}$ = 1.54.

(b) A Pu atom, which is neutral, has 94 electrons, so a Pu^{-} *anion* has 95 electrons.

16-7. We must add the mass of the separated components and compare it to the mass of the whole atom (in u). The difference in the masses is the mass defect.

(a) $^{40}_{20}$Ca	20 electrons:	20 × 0.00054858 =	0.01097160
	20 protons:	20 × 1.00727647 =	20.14552940
	20 neutrons:	20 × 1.00866490 =	20.17329800
		Sum of Parts:	40.32979900
		Observed Mass:	39.96258900
		Mass Defect:	0.36721000

16-7. (continued)

The mass defect represents the mass that "disappeared" (in fact, it was released as energy) when the atom was formed. It is equal to the binding energy of the nucleus. The relationship between mass and energy is given by Einstein's relation, from which we get a conversion factor: $\frac{931.494\ \text{MeV}}{1\ \text{u}}$. The relationship between the energy units MeV and kJ is $\frac{1.602177 \times 10^{-16}\ \text{kJ}}{1\ \text{MeV}}$.

For the ${}^{40}_{20}Ca$ nucleus, the binding energy for the whole nucleus is:

BE (nucleus) = 0.36721000 u × 931.494 MeV u^{-1} = 342.0539 MeV = **342.1 MeV**

BE (mole) = 342.0539 MeV × $\frac{1.602177 \times 10^{-16}\ \text{kJ}}{1\ \text{MeV}}$ × 6.0221 × 10^{23} atoms mol^{-1}

= **3.300 × 10^{10} kJ mol^{-1}**

There are 40 nucleons in this nucleus, so

BE (nucleon) = $^{342.0539\ \text{MeV}}/_{40\ \text{nucleons}}$ = **8.551 MeV nucleon^{-1}**.

For the other nuclei:

(b) ${}^{87}_{37}Rb$	37 electrons:	37 × 0.00054858 =	0.02029746
	37 protons:	37 × 1.00727647 =	37.26922939
	50 neutrons:	50 × 1.00866490 =	50.43324500
		Sum of Parts:	87.72277185
		Observed Mass:	86.90918400
		Mass Defect:	0.81358785
		BE(nucleus)	**757.8 MeV**
		BE(nucleon)	**8.711 MeV nucleon^{-1}**
		BE(mol)	**7.312 × 10^{10} kJ mol^{-1}**

(c) ${}^{238}_{92}U$ Sum of Parts: 239.98498000 u Observed Mass: 238.05078600 u

Mass Defect: 1.9341940 u BE(nucleon): **7.570 MeV nucleon^{-1}**

BE(nucleus): **1801.7 MeV** BE(mol): **1.738 × 10^{11} kJ mol^{-1}**

16-9. The mass of the ${}^{8}_{4}Be$ atom is 8.0053052 u, while that of two ${}^{4}_{2}He$ atoms is 8.0052065 u. The two helium atoms have less mass than a single ${}^{8}_{4}Be$ atom, by a difference of **0.0000987** u. Therefore, the **two helium atoms are more stable.**

16-11. Each particle has a mass equivalent to the energy of one of the photons. The Einstein relation indicates the mass equivalent to a given energy:

For each photon and each particle:

$$mc^2 = E \quad \Rightarrow \quad m = E/c^2 = \frac{8.1871\times10^{-14}\ \text{J}}{\left(2.99792\times10^{8}\ \text{m s}^{-1}\right)^2}$$

$$= \mathbf{9.1094 \times 10^{-31}\ kg}$$

Note the dimensional analysis for the J and $(\text{m s}^{-1})^2$:

$$(\text{J})\left(\frac{\text{s}}{\text{m}}\right)^2 = \left(\frac{\text{kg}-\text{m}^2}{\text{s}^2}\right)\left(\frac{\text{s}}{\text{m}}\right)^2 = \text{kg}$$

16-13. (a) $${}^{39}_{17}\text{Cl} \rightarrow {}^{39}_{18}\text{Ar} + {}^{0}_{-1}\beta + \tilde{\nu}$$

(b) $${}^{22}_{11}\text{Na} \rightarrow {}^{22}_{10}\text{Ne} + {}^{0}_{1}\beta + \nu$$

(c) $${}^{224}_{88}\text{Ra} \rightarrow {}^{220}_{86}\text{Rn} + {}^{4}_{2}\text{He}$$

(d) $${}^{82}_{38}\text{Sr} + {}^{0}_{-1}\beta \rightarrow {}^{82}_{37}\text{Rb} + \nu$$

Note the following rules for "balancing" nuclear chemical reactions:

i) The number of nucleons (the top number in the notation for a nuclide) must balance through the reactions.

ii) The number of nuclear charges + charges on positrons or electrons (the bottom number of the notation for a particle) must balance.

iii) The creation of an electron is always accompanied by the formation of an *anti*-neutrino.

iv) The creation of a positron is always accompanied by the formation of a neutrino.

16-15. Neutron activation: $${}^{30}_{14}\text{Si} + {}^{1}_{0}\text{n} \rightarrow {}^{31}_{14}\text{Si}$$

Decay to ^{31}P: $${}^{31}_{14}\text{Si} \rightarrow {}^{31}_{15}\text{P} + {}^{0}_{-1}\beta + \tilde{\nu}$$

16-17. α-particle emission: $${}^{210}_{84}\text{Po} \rightarrow {}^{206}_{82}\text{Pb} + {}^{4}_{2}\text{He}$$

neutron emission: $${}^{9}_{4}\text{Be} + {}^{4}_{2}\text{He} \rightarrow {}^{12}_{6}\text{C} + {}^{1}_{0}\text{n}$$

16-19. The kinetic energy of the products will come from the release of nuclear energy, which is indicated by the difference in mass of the products and reactants. As with other thermodynamic calculations, we take the

Σ (products) - Σ (reactants), where the quantities summed are the masses.

IMPORTANT NOTE: A beta particle formed in this reaction, but its mass is included in the mass of the product $^{40}_{20}Ca$ atom, so we do not list the mass of the electron separately:

PRODUCT MASSES	$^{40}_{20}Ca$ atom:	+39.962591
(all masses in u)	anti-neutrino:	+0.000000
-REACTANT MASSES	$^{40}_{19}K$ atom:	-:39.963999
	Δ(mass)	-0.001408 u

This decrease in mass results in a release of energy to the surroundings equal to $- (-0.001408\text{ u}) \times \left(\frac{931.494\text{ MeV}}{1\text{ u}}\right) =$ **1.312 MeV.** This energy appears initially as the kinetic energy of the emitted electron, and this energy is therefore the maximum kinetic energy the electron can have. Lower values for the kinetic energy of the emitted electrons mean some of the energy has been transferred to other places, for example, thermal energy.

16-21. The neutron decays to a proton and an **electron**:

$$^{1}_{0}n \rightarrow ^{1}_{1}p + ^{0}_{-1}\beta$$

PRODUCT MASSES	$^{0}_{-1}\beta$:	+0.000548799
(all masses in u)	$^{1}_{1}p$:	1.00727647
-REACTANT MASSES	$^{1}_{0}n$:	-:1.00866490
	Δ(mass)	-0.00083963 u

The kinetic energy of the products is then:

$$-(-0.00083963\text{ u}) \times \left(\frac{931.494\text{ MeV}}{1\text{ u}}\right) = \mathbf{+0.78\text{ MeV}}$$

16-23. In these and subsequent problems we will need to conveniently convert units of time. For long time spans, we take the length of the year as 365.25 days, to allow for leap years. Then we have:

1 year = 365.25 days = 8766 hrs = 5.2596×10^5 min = 3.15576×10^7 s

1 day = 24 hrs = 1440 min = 86,400 s

1 hour = 60 minutes = 3600 s

1 min = 60 s

The general relation for activity is:

$$A = kN$$

where N is the number of particles and k is the first-order rate constant. It is more convenient to express k in the form of the half-life $t_{1/2}$: $k = \dfrac{0.6931}{t_{1/2}}$.

Here, $$k = \frac{0.6931}{t_{1/2}} = \left(\frac{0.6931}{103\text{ yr}}\right)\left(\frac{1\text{ yr}}{5.260 \times 10^5\text{min}}\right) = 1.279 \times 10^{-8}\text{ min}^{-1}$$

And: $$N = \left(0.0010\text{ g }^{210}\text{Po}\right)\left(\frac{1\text{ mol }^{210}\text{Po}}{210\text{ g }^{210}\text{Po}}\right)\left(\frac{6.0221 \times 10^{23}\text{ atoms}^{210}\text{Po}}{1\text{ mol }^{210}\text{Po}}\right)$$

$$= 2.868 \times 10^{18}\text{ atoms }^{210}\text{Po}$$

Then: $$A = (1.279 \times 10^{-8}\text{ min}^{-1})(2.868 \times 10^{18}\text{ atoms})$$

$$= 3.7 \times 10^{10}\text{ atoms min}^{-1} = \mathbf{3.7 \times 10^{10}\ min^{-1}}.$$

16-25. (a) In this problem, we want to solve for N. Note that 1 Bq (one becquerel) is equal to 1 disintegration per second):

$$N = A\frac{t_{1/2}}{0.6931} = \left(2.5 \times 10^4\text{ s}^{-1}\right)\left(\frac{29\text{ s}}{0.6931}\right) = \mathbf{1.0 \times 10^6\ atoms\ {}^{19}O}.$$

(b) There will be a significant decay in two minutes. We must use the first order kinetic equation:

$$N = N_o\, e^{-(0.6931/t_{1/2})t} = 1.0 \times 10^6\, e^{-(0.6931/29\text{ s})120\text{ s}}$$

$$= 1.0 \times 10^6\, e^{-2.868} = \mathbf{5.9 \times 10^4\ atoms\ {}^{19}O}.$$

16-27. The number of atoms of ^{137}Cs is:

$$N = \left(0.00100 \text{ g } ^{137}\text{Cs}\right)\left(\frac{1 \text{ mol } ^{137}\text{Cs}}{137 \text{ g } ^{137}\text{Cs}}\right)\left(\frac{6.0221\times10^{23} \text{ atoms} ^{137}\text{Cs}}{1 \text{ mol } ^{137}\text{Cs}}\right)$$

$= 4.396 \times 10^{18}$ atoms ^{137}Cs

The initial activity is: $(3.19 \times 10^{9} \text{ s}^{-1})(3.156 \times 10^{7} \text{ s yr}^{-1}) = 1.01 \times 10^{17} \text{ yr}^{-1}$

$$t_{1/2} = \frac{0.6931N}{A} = \frac{(0.6931)(4.396\times10^{18})}{1.01\times10^{17} \text{ yr}^{-1}} = \mathbf{30.3 \text{ yr}}$$

16-29. We must apply the general formula for radioactive decay, for the decline of 1.00 mol of neutrons to 0.90 mol neutrons:

$$0.90 \text{ mol} = 1.00 \text{ mol } e^{-(0.6931/t_{1/2})t}$$

$$0.90 = e^{-(0.6931/t_{1/2})t}$$

$$\ln(0.90) = -(0.6931 / t_{1/2})\, t$$

$$-0.1054 = -(0.6931 / t_{1/2})\, t$$

$$t_{1/2} \times (0.1054/0.6931) = t = 0.152\, t_{1/2}$$

Based on old $t_{1/2}$: $t = (0.152)(1100 \text{ s}) = \mathbf{167 \text{ s}}$

Based on new $t_{1/2}$: $t = (0.152)(876 \text{ s}) = \mathbf{133 \text{ s}}$

16-31. The number of atoms of ^{219}At is:

$$N = \left(0.044 \text{ g } ^{219}\text{At}\right)\left(\frac{1 \text{ mol } ^{219}\text{At}}{219.01 \text{ g } ^{219}\text{At}}\right)\left(\frac{6.0221\times10^{23} \text{ atoms} ^{219}\text{At}}{1 \text{ mol } ^{219}\text{At}}\right)$$

$= 1.209 \times 10^{20}$ atoms ^{219}At

$$A = \left(\frac{0.6931}{54 \text{ s}}\right)(1.209\times10^{20} \text{ atoms}) = 1.5 \times 10^{18} \text{ s}^{-1} = \mathbf{1.5 \times 10^{18} \text{ Bq}}$$

16-33. As developed in Example 16-7:

$$\ln\left(\frac{A}{A_o}\right) = -\left(\frac{0.6931}{t_{1/2}}\right) t = -\left(\frac{0.6931}{5730 \text{ yr}}\right) t$$

$$\ln\left(\frac{0.153 \text{ Bq g}^{-1}}{0.255 \text{ Bq g}^{-1}}\right) = -(1.210 \times 10^{-4} \text{ yr}^{-1})\, t$$

$$0.5108 = (1.210 \times 10^{-4} \text{ yr}^{-1})\, t$$

$$t = \mathbf{4220 \text{ yr}}$$

16-35.

$$\ln\left(\frac{0.0005\ \text{Bq g}^{-1}}{0.255\ \text{Bq g}^{-1}}\right) = -\,(1.210 \times 10^{-4}\ \text{yr}^{-1})\ t$$

$$6.234 = (1.210 \times 10^{-4}\ \text{yr}^{-1})\ t$$

$$t = \mathbf{50{,}000\ yr}$$

16-37. (a) If there are 0.333 mol of ^{206}Pb for every 1.000 mol ^{238}U, then the number of mol of ^{238}U at the start was 1.333 mol ^{238}U. Thus, the fraction remaining from the original amount of ^{238}U is $(1.333 - 1.000)/_{1.333} = 0.750$. The fraction that has decayed is 1.000 - 0.750 = **0.250 (25.0%).**

(b) Rearranging the equation for a first-order decay we obtain (see the textbook immediately after Example 16-7):

$$\frac{N}{N_{\text{initial}}} = e^{-kt}$$

$$-\ln\left(\frac{N}{N_{\text{initial}}}\right) = kt = \left(\frac{0.6931}{t_{1/2}}\right) t$$

$$t = -\ln\left(\frac{N}{N_{\text{initial}}}\right)\left(\frac{t_{1/2}}{0.6931}\right)$$

Here, $\frac{N}{N_{\text{initial}}} = 0.750$, so: $t = -\ln(0.750)\left(\frac{4.468 \times 10^{9}\text{yr}}{0.6931}\right) = \mathbf{1.85 \times 10^{9}\ yr}$

16-39.

$$^{11}_{6}\text{C} \rightarrow {}^{11}_{5}\text{B} + {}^{0}_{+1}\beta + \nu$$

$$^{15}_{8}\text{O} \rightarrow {}^{15}_{7}\text{N} + {}^{0}_{+1}\beta + \nu$$

16-41. The dosage called the *rem* is approximately equal (for positron emission) to the rad, itself defined as that dosage that deposits 0.01 J of nuclear energy in 1 kg of tissue. The energy release is determined by the energy released by the radioactive nuclide over the time of the exposure:

Energy release = (# of disintegrations) × (ΔE per disintegration)

= activity × ΔE

In this problem we are concerned about the *ratio* of the dosage, assuming that all of the material decays in the body.

16-41. (continued)

Here: $$\frac{\text{dosage from } ^{15}\text{O}}{\text{dosage from } ^{11}\text{C}} = \frac{N(^{15}\text{O}) \times \Delta E(^{15}\text{O})}{N(^{11}\text{C}) \times \Delta E(^{11}\text{C})}$$

Note that the chemical amounts (N) are equal.

Then: $$\frac{\text{dosage from } ^{15}\text{O}}{\text{dosage from } ^{11}\text{C}} = \frac{\Delta E(^{15}\text{O})}{\Delta E(^{11}\text{C})} = \frac{1.72 \text{ MeV}}{0.99 \text{ MeV}} = \mathbf{1.74}$$

16-43. (a) The number of atoms of ^{131}I ingested is:

$$N = \left(5.0 \times 10^{-6} \text{ g } ^{131}\text{I}\right)\left(\frac{1 \text{ mol } ^{131}\text{I}}{131 \text{ g } ^{131}\text{I}}\right)\left(\frac{6.0221 \times 10^{23} \text{ atoms} ^{131}\text{I}}{1 \text{ mol } ^{131}\text{I}}\right)$$

$$= 2.3 \times 10^{16} \text{ atoms } ^{131}\text{I}$$

The half life in seconds is: 8.041 days × 86,400 s day^{-1} =6.947 × 10^{5} s

The activity is then: $A = N\,(0.6931 / t_{1/2}) = 2.3 \times 10^{16}\,(0.6931 / 6.947 \times 10^{5} \text{ s})$

$$= 2.3 \times 10^{10} \text{ s}^{-1} = \mathbf{2.3 \times 10^{10}\ Bq}$$

(b) The average energy deposited per disintegration is:

$$E = 0.40 \text{ MeV} \times \frac{1.6022 \times 10^{-13} \text{ J}}{1 \text{ MeV}} = 6.409 \times 10^{-14} \text{ J.}$$

The rate of dosage at the first moment of ingestion is:

$$6.409 \times 10^{-14} \text{ J} \times 2.3 \times 10^{10} \text{ s}^{-1} = 0.001474 \text{ J s}^{-1}$$

Per kilogram of body mass this equals:

$$0.001474 \text{ J s}^{-1} / 60 \text{ kg} = 2.5 \times 10^{-5} \text{ J kg}^{-1} \text{ s}^{-1}$$

Given 1 rad = 10^{-2} J kg^{-1} and 1 millirad = 0.01 rad, the dosage is

$$2.5 \times 10^{-5} \text{ J kg}^{-1} = \mathbf{2.5\ mrad\ s^{-1}}$$

(c) The rate of dosage is 2.45 mrad (0.00245 rad) per second. How long will it take to give a dose (500 rad) that exceeds the LD_{50}? If we assume a constant activity, then the time to deposit 500 rad of energy will be

$$500 \text{ rad} / 0.00245 \text{ rad s}^{-1} = 2.0 \times 10^{5} \text{ s} = 57 \text{ hours.}$$

This dose will **surely become lethal** in within two to three weeks. Of course, some of the nuclide will decay -- one-half in 8.04 days -- but not until a massive dose has been delivered.

16-45. Neutron activation: $^{238}_{92}U + ^{1}_{0}n \rightarrow ^{239}_{92}U$

Plutonium synthesis: $^{239}_{92}U \rightarrow ^{239}_{94}Pu + 2\,^{0}_{-1}\beta + 2\,\tilde{\nu}$

16-47. (a) First decay: $^{90}_{38}Sr \rightarrow ^{90}_{39}Y + ^{0}_{-1}\beta + \tilde{\nu}$

Second decay: $^{90}_{39}Y \rightarrow ^{90}_{40}Zr + ^{0}_{-1}\beta + \tilde{\nu}$

(b) Note (as in No. 19 earlier) that we can include the mass of the emitted electrons in the mass of the zirconium atom. The anti-neutrino is massless. Then the energy released is:

$$\Delta E = -(\text{mass } ^{90}_{40}Zr - \text{mass } ^{90}_{38}Sr) = (89.9043 \text{ u} - 89.9073) = 0.0030 \text{ u}$$

$$= 0.0030 \text{ u} \times 931.494 \text{ u MeV}^{-1}$$

$$= \mathbf{2.8\ MeV}$$

(c) A 1.00 g mass of $^{90}_{38}Sr$ corresponds to 6.698×10^{21} atoms. The half life in seconds is 28.1 yr × 3.156×10^{7} s yr^{-1} = 8.8677×10^{8} s.

Then the activity is: $A = \dfrac{0.6931}{t_{1/2}} N$

$$= \frac{0.6931}{8.8677 \times 10^{8}\ \text{s}}\ 6.698 \times 10^{21}$$

$$= 5.24 \times 10^{12}\ \text{s}^{-1} = \mathbf{5.24 \times 10^{12}\ Bq}$$

(d) $$A = A_0\, e^{-\left(\frac{0.6931}{t_{1/2}}\right)t}$$

$$= (5.24 \times 10^{12}\ \text{Bq})\, e^{-\left(\frac{0.6931}{28.1\ \text{yr}}\right)100\ \text{yr}} = \mathbf{4.45 \times 10^{11}\ Bq.}$$

16-49. Assuming that the uranium nuclides yield totally different elements (i.e., other than uranium) when they decay, the atomic mass of U should *increase* with time. This is because the lighter isotopes have shorter half-lives, so they will be depleted faster than ^{238}U.

16-51. We perform a products - reactants analysis again. Note that, although in a nuclear process it *is* important to indicate the presence of a neutron as a reactant, it is *not* important to the overall thermodynamics.

For this problem, we can write the reaction as:

$$^{235}_{92}U \rightarrow ^{94}_{36}Kr + ^{139}_{56}Ba + 2\ ^{1}_{0}n$$

PRODUCT PARTICLES	$1\ ^{94}_{36}Kr$	+ 93.919
	$1\ ^{139}_{56}Ba$	+ 138.909
	$2\ ^{1}_{0}n$	+ 2.0173
REACTANT PARTICLE	$-1\ ^{235}_{92}U$	- 235.0439
	Δm(total) =	-0.1986 u

This lost mass appears as energy released. It corresponds to

$(0.1986\ u)(931.494 MeV\ u^{-1})(1.602177 \times 10^{-13}\ J\ MeV^{-1}) = 2.964 \times 10^{-11}\ J$

This is the energy released *per disintegration*. The number of atoms of $^{235}_{92}U$ in 1 g of sample -- which all disintegrate under the conditions of this problem -- are:

$$\left(\frac{1\ mol\ ^{235}_{92}U}{235.05\ g\ ^{235}_{92}U}\right)\left(\frac{6.0221\times 10^{23}\ atoms\ ^{235}_{92}U}{1\ mol\ ^{235}_{92}U}\right) = 2.562 \times 10^{21}\ atoms\ g^{-1}$$

The energy released when this number of $^{235}_{92}U$ atoms react is:

$(2.562 \times 10^{21}\ atoms\ g^{-1})(2.964 \times 10^{-11}\ J\ atom^{-1})$

$= 7.59 \times 10^{10}\ J\ g^{-1} = \mathbf{7.59 \times 10^{7}\ kJ\ g^{-1}}$

16-53. As suggested in the hint, a good approach to this problem is to look at *differences* in charge. So, ranking the droplets from least to most charge, we also note the amount the charge differs from the charge on the previous droplet in the list.

16-53. (continued)

DROP	CHARGE (all × 10^{-19} C)	DIFFERENCE (all × 10^{-19} C)	UNITS OF CHARGE (CHARGE/1.63×10^{-19} C)
1	6.563	-	**4**
2	8.204	1.641	**5**
3	11.50	3.296	**7**
4	13.13	1.63	**8**
5	16.48	3.35	**10**
6	18.08	1.60	**11**
7	19.71	1.63	**12**
8	22.89	3.28	**14**
9	26.18	3.29	**16**

The data all differ from the adjacent values in the list by either 1.63×10^{-19} C or twice that value. This suggests that there is a fundamental unit of charge equal to 1.63×10^{-19} C. Dividing this quantity into the observed charges gives the number of electrons on each droplet.

(b) If we divide each observed charge by the integral charge the droplet seems to have, we get these values for the electron charge:

1.6407×10^{-19} C	1.640×10^{-19} C	1.6425×10^{-19} C
1.6408×10^{-19} C	1.648×10^{-19} C	1.635×10^{-19} C
1.643×10^{-19} C	1.6436×10^{-19} C	1.636×10^{-19} C

The average of all of these values is **1.641×10^{-19} C.**

(c) We have chosen the least possible charge to fit the data. The data could be any fraction (1/2, 1/3, 1/4, etc.) of the value suggested. One could only check the result by a thorough search for droplets with fractional charge.

16-55. Chemists and physicists before Moseley lacked an understanding of what made the elements unique in a fundamental way. By developing an independent way to measure a fundamental characteristic of the atom -- the atomic number Z -- Moseley was able to predict exactly which elements should occur where.

16-57. (a) From Appendix D:

$$\Delta H^o = 2 \times \Delta H_f^o(H_2O,\ (g)) - \Delta H_f^o(N_2H_4,\ (l))$$

$$= (2 \text{ mol} \times -241.82 \text{ kJ mol}^{-1}) - (1 \text{ mol} \times 50.63 \text{ kJ mol}^{-1}) = \mathbf{-534.27\ kJ}$$

(b) As we saw in Chapter 11:

$$\Delta E^o = \Delta H^o - RT\Delta n_g$$

Where Δn_g = change in No. of moles of gas...in this case, +2.

So: $\Delta E^o = -534{,}270 \text{ J} - (8.3145 \text{ J mol}^{-1} \text{ K}^{-1})(298 \text{ K})(2 \text{ mol}) = \mathbf{-539{,}230\ J}$

(c) $$\Delta m = \frac{\Delta E}{c^2} = \frac{-539{,}230 \text{ J}}{\left(2.9980 \times 10^8 \text{ m s}^{-1}\right)^2} = 5.9998 \times 10^{-12} \text{ J} \frac{s^2}{m^2}$$

$$= 5.8888 \times 10^{-12} \frac{\text{kg-m}^2}{s^2}\frac{s^2}{m^2} = \mathbf{5.9998 \times 10^{-12}\ kg}$$

16-59. Decay by positron emission leaves behind a negatively charged atom, and the electron that is typically ejected, though it comes from the electrons of the atom, not from the nucleus, must be accounted for among the products.

$$^{64}_{29}\text{Cu} \rightarrow {}^{64}_{28}\text{Ni} + {}^{0}_{+1}\beta + {}^{0}_{-1}e$$

PRODUCTS	$1\ {}^{0}_{+1}\beta$	+ 0.00054858
	$1\ {}^{0}_{-1}e$	+ 0.00054858
	$1\ {}^{64}_{28}\text{Ni}$	+ 63.92796
REACTANTS	$1\ {}^{64}_{29}\text{Cu}$	- 63.92976
	Net mass change:	0.000703 u

This corresponds to (0.000703 u) × (931.494 MeV u^{-1}) = **-0.655 MeV**

16-61. For positron emission the reaction will be: $^{231}_{92}U \rightarrow ^{231}_{91}Pa + ^{0}_{+1}\beta$

For electron capture the reaction will be: $^{231}_{92}U + ^{0}_{-1}e \rightarrow ^{231}_{91}Pa$

(b) As we saw above, the mass change in positron emission involves the mass of the emitted positron and an ejected "normal" electron:

$$\Delta m = \text{mass}(^{231}_{91}Pa) + \text{mass}(^{0}_{+1}\beta) + \text{mass}(^{0}_{-1}e) - \text{mass}(^{231}_{92}U)$$

$$= 231.035880 + 2\,(0.00054858) - 231.0363 = +\,0.00068\text{ u}$$

There is an *increase* in the mass of the system, indicating **a non-spontaneous process.**

For the electron capture the mass balance is

$$\Delta m = \text{mass}(^{231}_{91}Pa) - \text{mass}(^{0}_{-1}\beta) - \text{mass}(^{231}_{92}U)$$

$$= 231.035880 - 0.00054858 - 231.0363 = \mathbf{-\,0.00097\text{ u}}$$

There is a net decrease in the mass of the system, indicating **spontaneity.** The critical difference about positron emission is that the mass change includes the production of a positron from the nucleus and an electron from the atom's electron cloud. These work *against* spontaneity. Electron capture, on the other hand, effects the same change from U to Pa, but it also "uses" the mass in one of the uranium electrons.

16-63. The numbers in the problem are more useful if we note that

$$0.255\text{ Bq g}^{-1} = 0.255\text{ s}^{-1}\text{ g}^{-1}$$

and $t_{1/2} = 5730\text{ yr} \times 3.1558 \times 10^{7}\text{ s yr}^{-1} = 1.808 \times 10^{11}\text{ s}$

The equation relating activity and number of ^{14}C nuclei is the basis for determining *N*: $A = kN$

$$N = \frac{A}{k} = \frac{At_{1/2}}{0.6931} = \frac{(0.255\text{ s}^{-1}\text{ g}^{-1})(1.808 \times 10^{11}\text{ s})}{0.6931}$$

$$= \mathbf{6.653 \times 10^{10}\text{ atoms}\,^{14}C\text{ g}^{-1}}$$

16-63. (continued)

(b) The total number of atoms of all types of carbon is, per gram:

$$N_{total} = (1\text{ g C})\left(\frac{1\text{ mol C}}{12.011\text{ g C}}\right)\left(\frac{6.0221\times10^{23}\text{ atoms C}}{1\text{ mol C}}\right)$$

$$= 5.014 \times 10^{22}\text{ atoms C g}^{-1}$$

The ratio is: $$\frac{N}{N_{total}} = \frac{6.653\times10^{10}\text{ atoms }^{14}\text{C g}^{-1}}{5.014\times10^{22}\text{ atoms C g}^{-1}} = \mathbf{1.33 \times 10^{-12}}$$

Put another way, there are $$\frac{5.014\times10^{22}\text{ atoms C g}^{-1}}{6.665\times10^{10}\text{ atoms }^{14}\text{C g}^{-1}} = 7.5 \times 10^{11}\text{ atoms}$$

(or 750 billion atoms) of non-radioactive carbon for every atom of ^{14}C.

16-65. In this problem, since we are everywhere concerned with *ratios* of atoms, we may work in moles. The amount of helium tells us how many ^{238}U nuclei *used* to be in the rock, but which have decayed. There are 8 mol of He for every mol of decayed ^{238}U, and the number of moles of He is determined by recalling that one mole of He gas occupies 22.4 L at STP:

$$\text{decayed }^{238}\text{U} = \left(9.0\times10^{-5}\text{cm}^3\text{He}\right)\left(\frac{1\text{ L He}}{1000\text{ cm}^3\text{ He}}\right)\left(\frac{1\text{ mol He}}{22.4\text{ L He}}\right)\left(\frac{1\text{ mol }^{238}\text{U}}{8\text{ mol He}}\right)$$

$$= 5.022 \times 10^{-10}\text{ mol }^{238}\text{U}$$

The number of moles of ^{238} U remaining is determined directly:

$$\text{remaining }^{238}\text{U} = \left(2.0\times10^{-7}\text{ g }^{238}\text{U}\right)\left(\frac{1\text{mol }^{238}\text{U}}{238.01\text{ g }^{238}\text{U}}\right) = 8.403 \times 10^{-10}\text{ mol}$$

$$N = 8.403 \times 10^{-10}\text{ mol}$$

The amount of ^{238}U originally in the rock, per gram, is:

$$N_o = \text{remaining }^{238}\text{U} + \text{decayed }^{238}\text{U} = 13.425 \times 10^{-10}\text{ mol}$$

For the decay of any nuclide, the kinetics indicate:

$$-\frac{0.6931\,t}{t_{1/2}} = ln\left(\frac{N}{N_o}\right) = ln\left(\frac{8.401\times10^{-10}\text{mol }^{238}\text{U}}{13.425\times10^{-10}\text{ mol }^{238}\text{U}}\right) = -0.4688$$

$$t = \frac{(4.47\times10^{9}\text{ yr})(0.4688)}{(0.6931)} = \mathbf{3.0 \times 10^{9}\text{ yr (3 billion years)}}$$

16-67. (a) As we saw in problem No. 41 earlier, under the assumption that

1 rem = 1 rad and that *all* of the nuclide decays in the body:

$$\frac{\text{dosage from } ^{60}\text{Co}}{\text{dosage from } ^{131}\text{I}} = \frac{\Delta E(^{60}\text{Co})}{\Delta E(^{131}\text{I})} = \frac{0.32 \text{ MeV}}{0.60 \text{ MeV}} = \mathbf{0.53}$$

(b) If we must consider only a limited time of the decay, then the radiation dosage will also be proportional to the rate constant for the decay. Note also that the rate constant is *inversely* proportional to the half life, and that the half-life for ^{60}Co = 5.27 yr = 1924.6 days. Then:

$$\frac{\text{dosage from } ^{60}\text{Co}}{\text{dosage from } ^{131}\text{I}} = \frac{k(^{60}\text{Co}) \times \Delta E(^{60}\text{Co})}{k(^{131}\text{I}) \times \Delta E(^{131}\text{I})} = \frac{t_{1/2}(^{131}\text{I}) \times \Delta E(^{60}\text{Co})}{t_{1/2}(^{60}\text{Co}) \times \Delta E(^{131}\text{I})}$$

$$= \frac{(8.041 \text{ days})(0.32 \text{ MeV})}{(1924.6 \text{ days})(0.60 \text{ MeV})} = \mathbf{0.023}$$

16-69. $$^{10}_{5}\text{B} + ^{1}_{0}\text{n} \rightarrow ^{4}_{2}\text{He} + ^{7}_{3}\text{Li}$$

16-71. Note that we are not told the mass number of the actinium, and indeed that doesn't matter if all we want is the atomic number of the unknown nucleus. In working a problem like this, it is sometimes best to use a backwards approach: "What element would result if actinium combined with an electron or with a helium nucleus?" Then we can determine the atomic number and mass number of the unknown element directly:

β decay (backwards): $_{89}\text{Ac} + {}_{-1}\beta \rightarrow {}_{88}\text{Ra}$

(forwards): $_{88}\text{Ra} \rightarrow {}_{89}\text{Ac} + {}_{-1}\beta$

α decay (backwards): $_{89}\text{Ac} + {}_{2}\text{He} \rightarrow {}_{91}\text{Pa}$

(forwards): $_{91}\text{Pa} \rightarrow {}_{89}\text{Ac} + {}_{2}\text{He}$

Since radium was already known, and no radium isotopes decay by β emission, the logical source of actinium was indeed element 91, suitably named "proto-actinium" = protactinium.

16-73.(a) The energy output of the sun is much greater than the amount absorbed by the earth, specifically:

$$\text{total output} = \frac{3.4 \times 10^{17}\ \text{J s}^{-1}}{4.5 \times 10^{-10}} = 7.56 \times 10^{26}\ \text{J s}^{-1}$$

This energy is coming from the conversion of some mass of the sun into energy, specifically, by Einstein's relation:

$$\Delta m = \frac{\Delta E}{c^2} = -\frac{7.56 \times 10^{26}\ \text{J s}^{-1}}{\left(2.998 \times 10^{8}\text{m s}^{-1}\right)^2} = -8.4 \times 10^{9}\text{J}\frac{\text{s}}{\text{m}^2}$$

Converting J: $$= -8.4 \times 10^{9}\frac{\text{kg m}^2}{\text{s}^2}\frac{\text{s}}{\text{m}^2} = \mathbf{-8.4 \times 10^{9}\ kg\ s^{-1}}$$

The decrease in the mass of the sun is due to the reaction "hydrogen burning" first suggested by Bethe and van Weizsäcker. The individual steps, involving helium-3 intermediates, are discussed in the text. The *overall* nuclear reaction is (massless γ rays and neutrinos are also formed): $4\ {}^{1}_{1}\text{H} \rightarrow {}^{4}_{2}\text{He} + 2\ {}^{0}_{+1}\beta$

The corresponding mass change is :

$$\Delta m = \text{mass}\ {}^{4}_{2}\text{He} + 2\ \text{mass}\ {}^{0}_{+1}\beta - 4 \times \text{mass}\ {}^{1}_{1}\text{H}$$

$$= 4.0026034\ \text{u} + (2 \times 0.0054858\ \text{u}) + (4 \times 1.00782504\ \text{u}) = -0.0275815\ \text{u}$$

In kg: $\Delta m = -0.0275815\ \text{u} \times 1.6606 \times 10^{-24}\ \text{g u}^{-1}$

$$= -4.580 \times 10^{-26}\ \text{g} = \mathbf{-4.580 \times 10^{-29}\ kg}$$

How many times is this reaction proceeding per second? We relate the mass change per reaction and the sun's mass change per second to find out:

$$\text{Reactions per second} = \frac{-8.4 \times 10^{9}\ \text{kg s}^{-1}}{-4.580 \times 10^{-29}\ \text{kg}} = 1.835 \times 10^{38}\ \text{s}^{-1}$$

Four hydrogen atoms, which together have a mass of 6.69×10^{-27} kg, are involved in each reaction. The mass of the reacting hydrogen is, per second:

$$\text{mass}\ {}^{1}_{1}\text{H} = 1.835 \times 10^{38}\ \text{s}^{-1} \times 6.69 \times 10^{-27}\ \text{kg}$$

$$= \mathbf{1.22 \times 10^{12}\ kg\ {}^{1}_{1}H\ s^{-1}}$$

CHAPTER 17 - QUANTUM MECHANICS AND THE HYDROGEN ATOM

17-1. The frequency of the waves is once every 3.2 s, or $\nu = \frac{1}{3.2}\text{sec}^{-1} = 0.312\ \text{s}^{-1}$.

The wavelength--the crest-to-crest distance--is $\lambda = 2.1$ m. So the velocity is:

$v = \nu\lambda = (0.312\ \text{s}^{-1})\ (2.1\ \text{m}) = \mathbf{0.66\ m\ s^{-1}}$.

17-3. For light: $c = \nu\lambda \quad \Rightarrow \lambda = \frac{c}{\nu} = \frac{2.998 \times 10^{8}\ \text{m s}^{-1}}{9.86 \times 10^{7}\ \text{s}^{-1}} = \mathbf{3.04\ m}$

17-5. (a) $\nu = \frac{c}{\lambda} = \frac{2.998 \times 10^{8}\ \text{ms}^{-1}}{6.00 \times 10^{2}\ \text{m}} = \mathbf{5.00 \times 10^{5}\ s^{-1}}$

(b) $\text{time} = \frac{\text{distance}}{\text{velocity}} = \frac{8.0 \times 10^{10}\ \text{m}}{2.998 \times 10^{8}\ \text{m s}^{-1}} = 267\ \text{s} = \mathbf{4.4\ min}$

17-7. $\lambda = \frac{\text{speed}}{\text{frequency}} = \frac{343.3\ \text{m s}^{-1}}{261.6\ \text{s}^{-1}} = \mathbf{1.313\ m}$

$\text{time} = \frac{\text{distance}}{\text{velocity}} = \frac{30.0\ \text{m}}{343.3\ \text{m s}^{-1}} = \mathbf{0.0873\ s}$

17-9. Blue light has a shorter wavelength than green light, and therefore more energy per photon. It will give the electrons more energy than green light.

17-11. A wavelength of 671 nm corresponds to **red** light.

17-13. The Planck relation is: $E = h\nu = \frac{hc}{\lambda}$

Rearranging: $\lambda = \frac{hc}{E} = \frac{(6.6261 \times 10^{-34}\ \text{J s})(2.998 \times 10^{8}\ \text{m s}^{-1})}{3.6 \times 10^{-19}\ \text{J}}$

$= 5.52 \times 10^{-7}\ \text{m} = \mathbf{550\ nm}$

This corresponds to **green** light.

17-15. When handling wavelengths in nm, it is useful (and perfectly accurate) to merely tack "$\times 10^{-9}$ m" onto the number instead of "nm." You can even put the number into your calculator that way. Thus, we can write:

"589.3 nm = 589.3×10^{-9} m."

17-15. (continued)

(a) $E = \dfrac{hc}{\lambda} = \dfrac{(6.6261 \times 10^{-34}\ \text{J s})(2.998 \times 10^{8}\ \text{m s}^{-1})}{589.3 \times 10^{-9}\ \text{m}} = \mathbf{3.371 \times 10^{-19}\ J}$

(b) $\left(3.371 \times 10^{-19}\ \dfrac{\text{J}}{\text{photon}}\right)\left(6.0221 \times 10^{23}\ \dfrac{\text{photon}}{\text{mol}}\right) = 203{,}000\ \text{J mol}^{-1}$

$= \mathbf{203.0\ kJ\ mol^{-1}}$

(c) We know that one mole of sodium atoms emits 203,000 J of energy. To produce 1000 J of energy, we will need:

$$\frac{1000\ \text{J}}{203{,}000\ \text{J mol}^{-1}} = 4.296 \times 10^{-3}\ \text{mol}.$$

If this energy is emitted in one second, then the rate of sodium atom emission is **4.296×10^{-3} mol s^{-1}**.

17-17. The minimum photon energy required to eject electrons from cesium is the energy of the work function, 3.43×10^{-19} J. This corresponds to:

$$\lambda = \frac{hc}{E} = \frac{(6.6261 \times 10^{-34}\ \text{J-s})(2.998 \times 10^{8}\ \text{m s}^{-1})}{3.43 \times 10^{-19}\ \text{J}}$$

$$= 5.79 \times 10^{-7}\ \text{m} = 579\ \text{nm}$$

Light with wavelength below this wavelength--all blue, green, and part of the yellow regions--will eject electrons from Cs. For Se, the maximum wavelength is 209 nm. This lies below the visible region. No visible light will eject electrons from a Se surface.

17-19. (a) $E_{kinetic,max} = E_{light} - \Phi$

$$E_{light} = \frac{hc}{\lambda} = \frac{(6.6261 \times 10^{-34}\ \text{J s})(2.998 \times 10^{8}\ \text{m s}^{-1})}{2.50 \times 10^{-7}\ \text{m}}$$

$$= 7.95 \times 10^{-19}\ \text{J}$$

$$\Phi = 7.21 \times 10^{-19}\ \text{J}$$

$$E_{kinetic,max} = 7.95 \times 10^{-19}\ \text{J} - 7.21 \times 10^{-19}\ \text{J}$$

$$= 0.74 \times 10^{-19}\ \text{J} = \mathbf{7.4 \times 10^{-20}\ J}$$

17-19. (continued)

(b) $E_{\text{kinetic,}} = \frac{1}{2}m_e v^2$ Note 1 J = kg m^2 s^{-2}

$$v = \sqrt{\frac{2E}{m_e}} = \sqrt{\frac{2\left(7.4 \times 10^{-20}\ \text{kg m}^2\ \text{s}^{-2}\right)}{9.1093 \times 10^{-31}\ \text{kg}}}$$

$$= \sqrt{1.625 \times 10^{-11}\ \frac{\text{m}^2}{\text{s}^2}} = \mathbf{4.0 \times 10^5\ m\ s^{-1}}$$

17-21. For clarity, the answers to (a) and (b) are given in a common table. The energy in Rydbergs is calculated directly from Z and n while the energy in J is calculated from : E_n (J) = E_n (Ry) × 2.18 × 10^{-18} J Ry^{-1}.

The radius in units of a_o is determined from n^2/Z (with Z = 1 for hydrogen) and in units of meters by substitution of a_o = 0.529 × 10^{-10} m. The largest atom is the one with n = 8.

n	$E_n = -\frac{Z^2}{n^2}$ Ry	E_n (J)	$r_o = \frac{n^2}{Z}a_o$	r_o (m)
3	- 0.111 Ry	-2.42 × 10^{-19} J	9 a_o	4.76 × 10^{-10} m
6	- 0.0278 Ry	-6.06 × 10^{-20} J	36 a_o	19.0 × 10^{-10} m
8	-0.0156 Ry	-3.41 × 10^{-20} J	64 a_o	33.9 × 10^{-10} m

17-23. For the energy change, we use the equation derived in Section 17-3 of the textbook.

	n_{initial}	n_{final}	$\Delta E = \left(\frac{1}{n^2_{\text{final}}} - \frac{1}{n^2_{\text{initial}}}\right)$ Ry	ΔE (J)
(a)	7	4	+0.0421 Ry	9.18 × 10^{-20} J
(b)	4	3	+0.0486 Ry	1.06 × 10^{-19} J
(c)	3	4	-0.0486 Ry	-1.06 × 10^{-19} J

17-25. (a) The photon is emitted in this case. It has wavelength

$$\lambda = \frac{hc}{\Delta E} = \frac{(6.62621\times10^{-34}\,\text{J s})(2.998\times10^{8}\,\text{m s}^{-1})}{9.18\times10^{-20}\,\text{J}}$$

$$= \mathbf{2.16\times10^{-6}\ m} = 2{,}160\ \text{nm}$$

(b) Again, a photon is emitted. Its wavelength, determined as in (a), is

1.87×10^{-6} m (= 1870 nm).

(c) Here, the photon must be absorbed. It has the same wavelength as (b),

1.87×10^{-6} m.

17-27. The B^{4+} ion has one electron, so we may use the Bohr model with $Z = 5$.

$$E_3 = -\frac{Z^2}{n^2}\text{Ry} = -\frac{25}{9}\,2.18\times10^{-18}\,\text{J} = \mathbf{-6.06\times10^{-18}\ J}$$

$$r_3 = \frac{n^2}{Z}a_o = \frac{9}{5}\,5.29\times10^{-11}\ \text{m} = 9.52\times10^{-11}\ \text{m} = \mathbf{0.0952\ nm}$$

$$E_3\ (\text{mole}) = (6.06\times10^{-18}\ \text{J})\ (6.0221\times10^{23}\ \text{mol}^{-1}) = \mathbf{3{,}650\ kJ\ mol^{-1}}$$

The energy of an atom in the $n = 2$ state will be:

$$E_2 = -\frac{25}{4}\,2.18\times10^{-18}\,\text{J} = -13.62\times10^{-18}\ \text{J}$$

For the 3 → 2 transition,

$$\Delta E = E_2 - E_3 = -13.62\times10^{-18} - (-6.06\times10^{-18}) = 7.56\times10^{-18}\ \text{J}$$

For the frequency of the emitted light:

$$\nu = \frac{h}{\Delta E} = \frac{7.56\times10^{-18}\ \text{J}}{6.6261\times10^{-34}\ \text{J s}} = \mathbf{1.14\times10^{16}\ s^{-1}}$$

For wavelength: $$\lambda = \frac{c}{\nu} = \frac{2.998\times10^{8}\ \text{m s}^{-1}}{1.14\times10^{16}\ \text{s}^{-1}} = \mathbf{2.63\times10^{-8}\ m = 26.3\ nm}$$

17-29. Since $\Delta E = -Z^2\left(\frac{1}{n_{\text{final}}^2} - \frac{1}{n_{\text{initial}}^2}\right)$ Ry and in this problem n_{final} and n_{initial} is the same in both cases: $$\frac{\Delta E_H}{\Delta E_{Li}} = \frac{Z_H^2}{Z_{Li}^2} = \frac{hc/\lambda_H}{hc/\lambda_{Li}} = \frac{\lambda_{Li}}{\lambda_H}$$

Therefore: $$\lambda_{Li} = \lambda_H\frac{Z_H^2}{Z_{Li}^2} = (656.1\ \text{nm})\left(\frac{1^2}{3^2}\right) = \mathbf{72.90\ nm.}$$

This lies in the **ultraviolet** region of the spectrum.

17-31. (a) The equation relating the number of the harmonic, the wavelength, and length is $n\frac{\lambda}{2} = L$. Rearranging, we get: $\lambda = \frac{2L}{n}$.

For $n = 1$ $\lambda = 2L =$ **100 cm** and for $n = 3$ $\lambda = \frac{2L}{n} =$ **33 cm**

(b) The third harmonic has $n - 1 = 3 - 1 =$ **2 nodes.**

17-33. (a) $$\lambda = \frac{h}{mv} = \frac{6.6261 \times 10^{-34}\ \text{J s}}{(9.109 \times 10^{-31}\ \text{kg})(1.00 \times 10^{3}\ \text{m s}^{-1})}$$

$$= 7.27 \times 10^{-7}\ \text{J}\frac{\text{s}^2}{\text{kg-m}} = \mathbf{7.27 \times 10^{-7}\ m}$$

Note: $\text{J} = \frac{\text{kg m}^2}{\text{s}^2}$, so $(\text{J})\left(\frac{\text{s}^2}{\text{kg m}}\right) = \left(\frac{\text{kg m}^2}{\text{s}^2}\right)\left(\frac{\text{s}^2}{\text{kg m}}\right) = \text{m}$

(b) $$\lambda = \frac{6.6261 \times 10^{-34}\ \text{J s}}{(1.6726 \times 10^{-27}\ \text{kg})(1.00 \times 10^{3}\ \text{m s}^{-1})} = \mathbf{3.96 \times 10^{-10}\ m}$$

(c) Note: 170.0 g = 0.1700 kg; 95 km hr $^{-1}$ = 26.4 m s^{-1}.

$$\lambda = \frac{6.6261 \times 10^{-34}\ \text{J s}}{(0.1700\ \text{kg})(26.4\ \text{m s}^{-1})} = \mathbf{1.48 \times 10^{-34}\ m}$$

17-35. (a) $$(\Delta p\, \Delta x) \geq \frac{h}{4\pi}$$

$$m\Delta v \geq \frac{h}{4\pi \Delta x}$$

$$\Delta v \geq \frac{h}{m 4\pi \Delta x} = \frac{6.6261 \times 10^{-34}\ \text{J s}}{(9.1094 \times 10^{-31}\ \text{kg})\, 4\pi(1.0 \times 10^{-9}\text{m})}$$

$\Delta v \geq 58{,}000$ m s^{-1} Hence $\Delta v_{min} =$ **58,000 m s^{-1}**

(b) $$(\Delta p\, \Delta x) \geq \frac{h}{4\pi}$$

$$m\Delta v \geq \frac{h}{4\pi \Delta x}$$

$$\Delta v \geq \frac{h}{m 4\pi \Delta x} = \frac{6.6261 \times 10^{-34}\ \text{J s}}{(6.64 \times 10^{-27}\ \text{kg})\, 4\pi(1.0 \times 10^{-9}\text{m})}$$

$\Delta v \geq 7.93$ m s^{-1}. Hence $\Delta v_{min} =$ **7.9 m s^{-1}**

17-37. (a) 4p (b) 2s (c) 6f

17-39.

	(a)	(b)	(c)
nodes = n - 1	3	1	5
angular nodes = ℓ	1	0	3
radial nodes: $n - \ell - 1$	2	1	2

17-41. An electron in the $3p_y$ orbital is most likely to be found along the y-axis. The probability of finding the electron in the x-z plane equals zero. The wave-function also has one radial node, which is a spherical surface. The probability of finding the electron there is also zero.

17-43. A quantum number defines some quantized physical quantity. For the Cl^{16+} ion, which is hydrogen-like, there are three electronic quantum numbers.

17-45. Answers are written in bold

n	ℓ	label	number of orbitals
2	1	**2p**	**3**
3	**2**	3d	5
4	**3**	**4f**	7

17-47. Allowed: (b) only.

(a): ℓ must be less than or equal to n-1.

(c) $|m_\ell|$ must be less than or equal to ℓ.

(d) ℓ must be greater than or equal to zero.

17-49.

$$\lambda = \frac{speed}{\nu} = \frac{343 \text{ m s}^{-1}}{440 \text{ s}^{-1}} = \mathbf{0.780 \text{ m}}$$

$$time = \frac{distance}{speed} = \frac{10.0 \text{ m}}{343 \text{ m s}^{-1}} = \mathbf{0.0292 \text{ s}}$$

17-51. The observed colors appear from a combination of wavelengths, which extend from the red region through the yellow, then the green, and finally the blue. A green appearance would require emission a narrow band of wavelengths in the center of the visible region of the electromagnetic spectrum. This is inconsistent with the continuous nature of black-body radiation. Emission of green light does occur from a black body, but always in combination with light of longer wavelengths, and sometimes with light of shorter wavelengths, too.

17-53.

$$\text{x-ray: } E\,(\text{photon}) = \frac{hc}{\lambda} = \frac{(6.6261\times10^{-34}\,\text{J s})(2.998\times10^{8}\,\text{m s}^{-1})}{0.20\times10^{-9}\,\text{m}}$$

$$= \mathbf{9.9\times10^{-16}\ J\ photon^{-1}}$$

$$E\,(\text{mole}) = 9.9\times10^{-16}\,\text{J}\times6.0221\times10^{23}\,\text{mol}^{-1}$$

$$= \mathbf{6.0\times10^{8}\ J\ mol^{-1}}$$

$$\text{AM radio: } E\,(\text{photon}) = \frac{h\nu}{\lambda} = \frac{(6.6261\times10^{-34}\,\text{J s})(2.998\times10^{8}\,\text{m s}^{-1})}{200\,\text{m}}$$

$$= 9.9\times10^{-28}\,\text{J}$$

$$E\,(\text{mol}) = 9.9\times10^{-28}\,\text{J}\times6.0221\times10^{23}\,\text{photon mol}^{-1}$$

$$= \mathbf{6.0\times10^{-4}\ J\ mol^{-1}}$$

The x-ray radiation carries about 600 million joules per mole. The radio radiation only 0.6 thousandths. The x-ray photon can easily crack bonds. The radio photon is much weaker.

17-55. The Lyman series involves transitions to n_{final} = 1. With Z= 1, this corresponds to transitions to an energy level of E_H = - 1.0 Ry.

Such an energy level *is* encountered with He^+-- for Z = 2, and n = 2,

E_{He^+} = -1 Ry also.

Therefore, a He^+ atom in the n = 2 state could absorb light emitted in a Lyman transition of hydrogen.

17-55. (continued)

One specific example of a match in energy of a He^+ energy level and a H atom energy level is:

$H_{n=2} \rightarrow H_{n=1}$ $\quad \Delta E = \left(\frac{1}{4} - 1\right) \text{Ry} = -\frac{3}{4} \text{Ry}$

$He^+_{n=2} \rightarrow He^+_{n=4}$ $\quad \Delta E = \left(1 - \frac{2^2}{4^2}\right) \text{Ry} = +\frac{3}{4} \text{Ry}$

17-57. Each photon must provide half the energy needed for ionization. For He^+, $n = 2$ (other quantum numbers do not matter in this hydrogenic orbital) the energy for ionization is:

$$\Delta E_{ionization} = E_2 = +\frac{(2)^2}{(2)^2} 2.18 \times 10^{-18} \text{ J} = 2.18 \times 10^{-18} \text{ J}$$

Each photon must have an energy of 1.09×10^{-18} J. The wavelength will be:

$$\lambda = \frac{hc}{\Delta E} = 1.82 \times 10^{-7} \text{ m} = \mathbf{182\ nm.}$$

17-59. The Bohr quantization of angular momentum is:

$$\text{angular momentum} = mvr = n\frac{h}{2\pi}$$

Rearranging:

$$n = \frac{2\pi mvr}{h} = \left(\frac{2\pi(1.5 \times 10^{11} \text{ m})(6.0 \times 10^{24} \text{ kg})(3.0 \times 10^{4} \text{ m s}^{-1})}{(6.626 \times 10^{-34} \text{ J - s})}\right)$$

$$= \mathbf{2.6 \times 10^{74}}$$

If n increases by 1 in the angular momentum mvr--currently equal to 2.7×10^{40} J-s--will increase by $\frac{h}{2\pi}$, or 2.1×10^{-34} J-s, less than one part in 10^{76}. No one would notice.

17-61. (a) The energy is specified to $\Delta E_{kinetic} = 0.02 \times 10^{-19}$ J = 2×10^{-21} J. If we equate this with kinetic energy then the uncertainty in velocity can be derived

$$\frac{1}{2}m(\Delta v)^2 = E_{kinetic}$$

$$\Delta v = \sqrt{\frac{2\Delta E_{kinetic}}{m}} = \sqrt{\frac{2\left(2\times10^{-21}\right)\text{ J}}{9.1\times10^{-31}\text{ kg}}} = 6.6\times10^{4}\text{ m s}^{-1}$$

Then, by Heisenberg's relation (see Problem No. 35)

$$\Delta mv\Delta x = m\Delta v\Delta x \geq \frac{h}{4\pi}$$

$$\Delta x \geq \frac{h}{(m)\ \Delta v\, 4\pi} = \frac{6.6261\times10^{-34}\text{ J-s}}{\left(9.1\times10^{-31}\text{ kg}\right)\left(6.6\times10^{4}\text{ m s}^{-1}\right)4\pi}$$

$\Delta x \geq 9 \times 10^{-10}$ m = 0.9 nm = smallest distance for location

(b) For helium, with mass = 6.65×10^{-27} kg, we get:

$$\Delta v = \sqrt{\frac{2\left(2\times10^{-21}\text{ J}\right)}{6.65\times10^{-27}\text{ kg}}} = 775\text{ m s}^{-1}$$

$$\Delta x \geq \frac{6.6261\times10^{-34}\text{ J-s}}{\left(6.65\times10^{-27}\text{ kg}\right)\left(775\text{ m s}^{-1}\right)4\pi}$$

$\Delta x \geq 1 \times 10^{-11}$ m

17-63. They *look* the same--with nodal planes bisecting the *xy* planes. But the orbital on oxygen will be almost 50 times smaller.

CHAPTER 18 - MANY ELECTRON ATOMS AND CHEMICAL BONDING

18-1. (a) $1s^2\ 2s^2\ 2p^2$

(b) $1s^2\ 2s^2\ 2p^6\ 3s^2\ 3p^6\ 3d^{10}\ 4s^2\ 4p^4$ = [Ar] $3d^{10}\ 4s^2\ 4p^4$

(c) $1s^2\ 2s^2\ 2p^6\ 3s^2\ 3p^6\ 3d^6\ 4s^2$ = [Ar] $3d^6\ 4s^2$

18-3.

Be^+	$1s^2\ 2s^1$	paramagnetic
C^-	$1s^2\ 2s^2\ 2p^3$	paramagnetic
Ne^{2+}	$1s^2\ 2s^2\ 2p^4$	paramagnetic
Mg^+	$1s^2\ 2s^2\ 2p^6\ 3s^1$ = [Ne] $3s^1$	paramagnetic
P^{2+}	$1s^2\ 2s^2\ 2p^6\ 3s^2\ 3p^1$ = [Ne] $3s^2\ 3p^1$	paramagnetic
Cl^-	$1s^2\ 2s^2\ 2p^6\ 3s^2\ 3p^6$ = [Ne] $3s^2\ 3p^6$	not paramagnetic
As^+	$1s^2\ 2s^2\ 2p^6\ 3s^2\ 3p^6\ 3d^{10}\ 4s^2\ 4p^2$ = [Ar] $3d^{10}\ 4s^2\ 4p^2$	paramagnetic
I^-	$1s^2\ 2s^2\ 2p^6\ 3s^2\ 3p^6\ 3d^{10}\ 4s^2\ 4p^6\ 4d^{10}\ 5s^2\ 5p^5$ = [Kr] $4d^{10}\ 5s^2\ 5p^5$	not paramagnetic

18-5, (a) In (b) S^{2-}

(c) Mn^{4+} (note that when ions are formed from transition element atoms, the *s* electrons are removed first!)

18-7. Elements are currently being discovered in the seventh row of the periodic table, and they have atomic numbers that are 32 greater than the atomic numbers of the corresponding elements in the sixth row of the periodic table. This reflects the filling of *7s*, *7p*, *6d*, and *5f* subshells. Assuming that the *5g* subshell does not get filled, the atomic number of the next halogen will be 32 greater than the atomic number for At, so we expect: 85 + 32 = 117.

18-9. A closed shell is the main feature of the electronic configuration of the noble gases. Without the spin quantum number, closed shells would occur for the following configurations:

$1s^1$: atomic **#1** $1s^1\,2s^1\,2p^3$: atomic **#5** $1s^1\,2s^1\,2p^3\,3s^1\,3p^3$ atomic **#9**

18-11. (a) Sr - it is just to the right of Rb in a row.

(b) Rn - it is two elements to the right of Po in a row.

(c) Xe - is a noble gas while Cs is an alkali metal.

(d) Sr - it is higher in a group than Ba.

18-13. (a) Cs - Xe is a noble gas with a closed electron shell.

(b) F - it is at the top right of the periodic table.

(c) K - it can attain a filled *s* subshell.

(d) At - it is to the right within a row.

18-15..

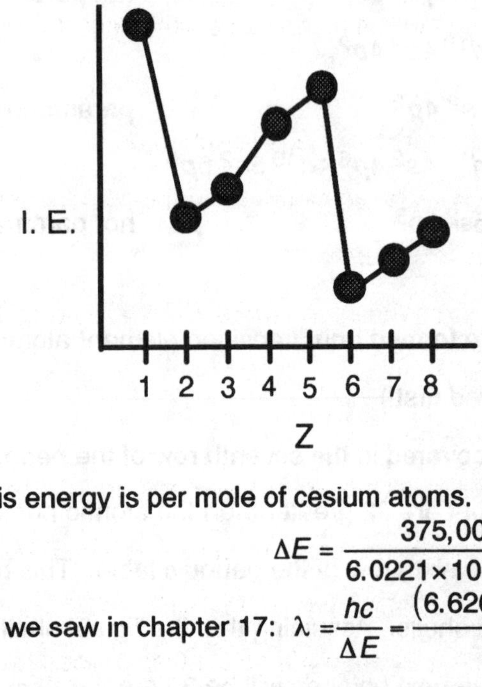

18-17. This energy is per mole of cesium atoms. We need the value per individual atom.

$$\Delta E = \frac{375{,}000 \text{ J mol}^{-1}}{6.0221 \times 10^{23} \text{ atom mol}^{-1}} = 6.227 \times 10^{-19} \text{ J atom}^{-1}$$

As we saw in chapter 17: $\lambda = \dfrac{hc}{\Delta E} = \dfrac{(6.6261 \times 10^{-34} \text{ J s})(2.998 \times 10^{8} \text{ m s}^{-1})}{6.227 \times 10^{-19} \text{ J atom}^{-1}}$

$$= 3.19 \times 10^{-7} \text{ m} = \mathbf{319\ nm}$$

18-19. The radii increase from top to bottom because more electrons must be accommodated within the atom. Because electron shells of smaller principal quantum number *n* are already filled, shells of higher quantum number must be used. These have a larger radius that shells of smaller quantum number. Pauli repulsion -- whereby electrons may not occupy the same region of space -- also causes electrons added later to stay away from the core of the atom's electron cloud.

18-21. (a) K - it is lower than Na in the same group.

(b) Cs - a cation of an element is always smaller than a neutral atom.

(c) Kr - with an identical electron configuration, the species with the smaller nuclear charge is larger.

(d) K - both of these atoms have valence electrons in the *3s* subshell, so the atom with the smaller nuclear charge is larger.

(e) Cl^- with an identical electron configuration, the less positively charged species is larger.

18-23. (a) S^{2-} - it is lower in the group *and* has two negative charges

(b) Ti^{2+} - both of these atoms have valence electrons in the *3d* subshell, so the atom with the smaller nuclear charge is larger

(c) Mn^{2+} - for a given element, the size of ions always decreases with increasing positive charge.

(d) Sr^{2+} - it is lower in the same group

18-25. If we keep one element constant and let it bond to the members of a group, then the bond will be longer for the lower members of the group, as atoms increase in size down a column. Bonds will weaken as they get longer, so the bonds from the element to the lower members of a group will be weaker. Exceptions occur rarely, and only with certain exceptional elements, for example F, which forms a weaker bond to O than Cl does (see Chapter 11).

18-27. We expect bonds to arsenic to lie in between the lengths of comparable bonds to phosphorus and antimony. This would place the As-H bond at about 1.5-1.6 Å. The weakest bond will be the longest bond: SbH_3.

18-29. (a) CI_4, a molecule with mostly covalent C-I bonds and weak intermolecular attractions should have the higher vapor pressure.

(b) OF_2 contains bonds between two elements of similar electronegativity. It should have more covalent bonding and higher vapor pressure.

(c) SiH_4 should have the higher vapor pressure; NaH, though formed of two elements from the same group (Group I) is a "saline hydride," indicating its significant salt-like (ionic) character.

18-31. (a) K *(g)* + Cl *(g)* → K^+ *(g)* + Cl^- *(g)*

I.E. (K) - E.A.(Cl) = +419 kJ mol^{-1} - +349 kJ mol^{-1} = **+70 kJ mol^{-1}**

K *(g)* + Cl *(g)* → K^- *(g)* + Cl^+ *(g)*

I.E. (Cl) - E.A.(K) = +1251 kJ mol^{-1} - +48 kJ mol^{-1} = **+1203 kJ mol^{-1}**

(a) Na *(g)* + Cl *(g)* → Na^+ *(g)* + Cl^- *(g)*

I.E. (Na) - E.A.(Cl) = +496 kJ mol^{-1} - +349 kJ mol^{-1} = **+147 kJ mol^{-1}**

Na *(g)* + Cl *(g)* → Na^- *(g)* + Cl^+ *(g)*

I.E. (Cl) - E.A.(Na) = +1251 kJ mol^{-1} - +53 kJ mol^{-1} = **+1198 kJ mol^{-1}**

18-33.

MOLECULE	E.N.(A)	E.N. (X)	ΔE.N.	% IONIC (Calc)	% IONIC (Observed))
HF	2.20	3.98	1.78	40	41
HCl	2.20	3.16	0.96	19	18
HBr	2.20	2.96	0.76	14	12
HI	2.20	2.66	0.46	8	6
CsF	0.79	3.98	3.19	87	70

18-33. (continued)

The quality of the agreement is good. This strongly suggests that electronegativity is a "real" parameter that accurately depicts some fundamental characteristics of the elements.

18-35. (a) The problem does not distinguish the direction of the polarity, so bonds are listed in order of decreasing absolute value for Δ E.N. :

N-**P** (ΔE.N= 0.85) > N-**C** (ΔE.N.= 0.49) > **N**-O (ΔE.N.= 0.40) > N-N (ΔE.N.= 0)

(b) For the heteronuclear species, a positive charge will be located on the atom with the lower electronegativity. These are indicated in **bold** in part (a).

18-37. (a) 4 (b) 3 (c) 6

(d) 4 (includes a lone pair) (e) 5 (includes two lone pairs)

18-39. Lone pairs on the outer atoms are omitted; the outer atoms all have a complete octet.

(a)
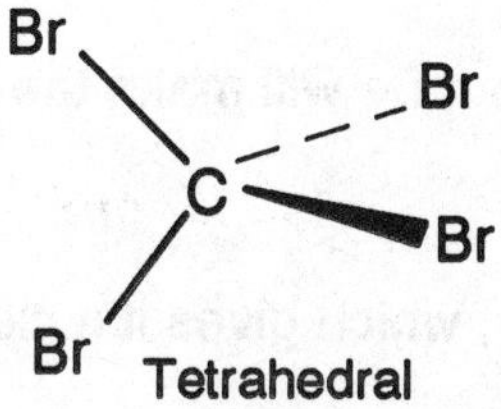

Tetrahedral

(b)
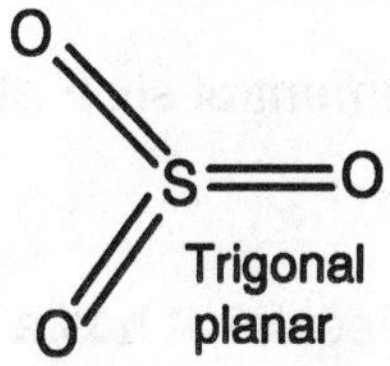

Trigonal planar

(c)
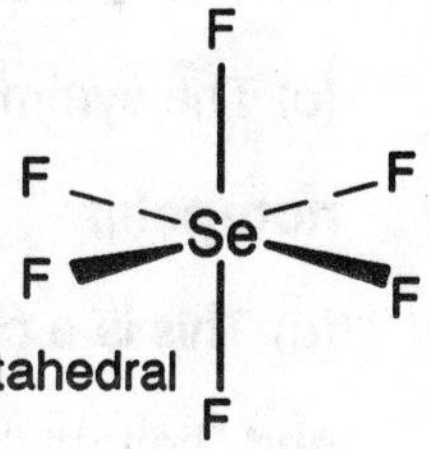

Octahedral

(d)

Pyramidal

(e)
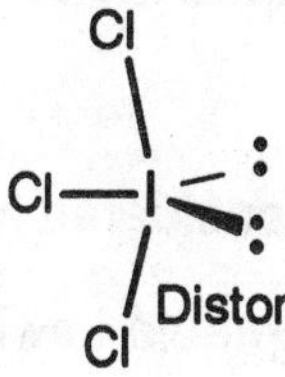

Distorted "T"

18-41. (a)

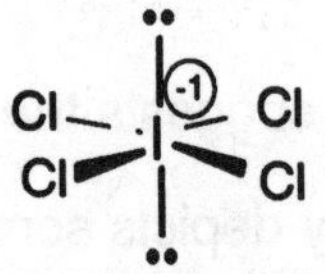

SN = 6; Square planar
Derived from octahedron

(b)

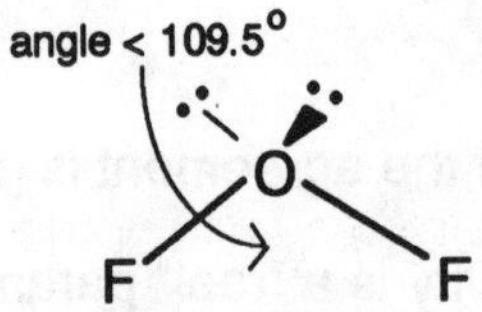

SN = 4; Bent -
derived from tetrahedron

(c)

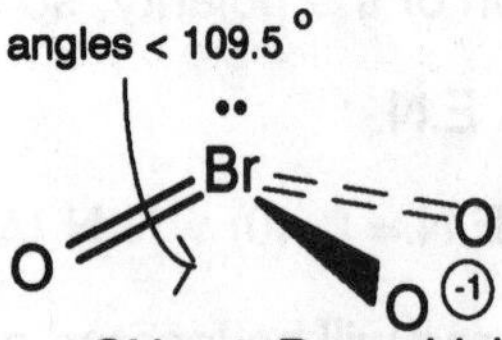

SN = 4; Pyramidal
derived from tetrahedron

(d) $S{=}C{=}S$

SN = 2; Linear

18-43. (a) Planar AB_3: BF_3 or SO_3 (b) Pyramidal AB_3: NF_3 or PCl_3

(c) Bent AB_2^-: NO_2^- or NH_2^- (d) Planar AB_3^{2-}: CO_3^{2-}

18-45. (a) The symmetric arrangement of four Br atoms about carbon will make the molecule **non-polar**.

(b) The O atoms are symmetric about the S. This molecule is **non-polar**.

(c) The symmetric arrangement of six F atoms about Se will make the molecule **non-polar**.

(d) This is a pyramidal molecule. It has a lone pair, which gives it a clear "top" and "bottom." The molecule will be **polar**.

(e) This distorted "T" shaped molecule has two adjacent lone pairs. It will be **polar**.

18-47. These molecules were considered from a Lewis-dot structure standpoint back in Problem No. 3-49. Acceptable Lewis-dot structures that like this:

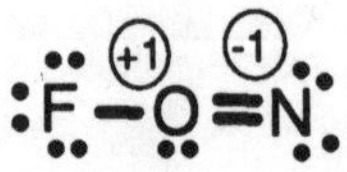

Both have a central atom with *S.N.* = 3. Both structures are expected to be bent, and therefore both should be polar. The information about why the molecule is bent does not resolve the question of the structure.

18-49. (a) The Lewis dot structure is: 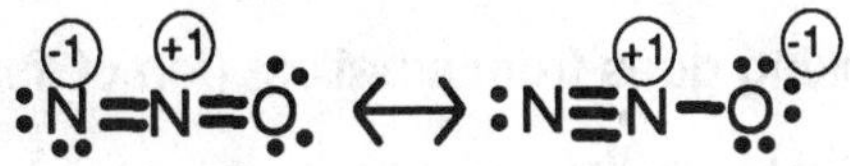

There are two reasonable resonance structures; both have no lone pairs on the central N; we expect the central N to have *S.N.* = 2 and the molecule to have a linear structure.

(b) The Lewis structures are no help in deciding the molecule's polarity. But because nitrogen is less electronegative than oxygen we can predict that the nitrogen end of the molecule is the positive end.

18-51. All of these element should reach the top oxidation state available to their group: V^{5+}; P^{5+}; I^{7+}; Sr^{2+}.

18-53. Formic acid can be considered in the group of "$XO(OH)_m$" acids in Table 18-5. It should lie towards the bottom of the range, because carbon is not very electronegative. A K_a in the neighborhood of 1×10^{-4} to 1×10^{-3} is expected. This compares well with the experimental value of 1.77×10^{-4}. At pH 14, well above the pK_a of formic acid (3.75) $HCOO^-$ should predominate.

18-55. We predict that higher (No. lone O atoms) : (No. B atoms) ratios will correlate with greater acid strength. The number of lone O atoms can be determined by assuming that all H's are bound to an O. Then the number of lone O's becomes:

No. O atoms - No. H atoms = No. lone O atoms.

We expect acidity to increase (the ratio is given in parentheses)

$H_3B_3O_3$ (0 : 3) < $H_5B_3O_7$ (2 : 3) < $H_6B_4O_9$ (3 : 4) < $H_2B_4O_7$ (5 : 4).

18-57. The ground state of a sodium atom is [Ne] **3** s^1. The **6** s^1 configuration is an excited electronic state.

18-59. The ground state of a transition metal ion has *3d* electrons not *4s*. The Cr^{4+} ion has two valence electrons. Thus, the configuration should be [Ar]$3d^2$.

18-61. The ranking goes from smallest (top of list) to largest (bottom)

Co^{25+}: Such a highly charged ion must be very, very small

F^+: F is a small atom to begin with. It's cation will be very small

F: F is among the smallest neutral atoms

Br: This is in the same row as K. Br will be smaller

K: This is smaller than its heavier group-mate Rb

Rb: An alkali metal low in the periodic table will be large

Rb^-: Adding an electron to a large atom will make it very large

18-63. The difference in electronegativity for the elements in LiCl is 2.18, and that for the elements in HF is 1.78. We are not surprised that LiCl exhibits the high melting and boiling points typical of an ionic compound, while HF exhibits covalent properties.

18-65. As the text indicates, electronegativity should be larger when the electrons of an atom are tightly held. This is true literally in the sense that smaller atoms should have higher electronegativity and figuratively in that atoms where the principal quantum number of the valence shell electrons is smaller -- atoms higher in a group -- will spend more time "in close" to the nucleus. The elements that don't fit the expected trend of decreasing electronegativity down the group are germanium and lead. Germanium appears right after the first transition series and its valence electrons are not well shielded by the newly filled *4d* shell. This makes the element both smaller and more electronegative than expected. Supporting this analysis, a similar anomaly appears when the electronegativities and atomic radii of aluminum and gallium are compared.

In the case of lead, size arguments (atomic radius of Pb is 1.75 Å; that of Sn is 1.40Å) and poorly shielding shells are probably not good arguments for the unexpectedly high electronegativity of Pb. The effects are probably more subtle,

18-65. (continued)

and may be due to the fact that the huge charge of the Pb nucleus is inducing relativistic effects on the core electrons (*J. Chem. Educ.* ***1991***, *68*, 110).

18-67. The "mechanism" of bond formation in both cases is electrons going to the lowest energy position in a compound. For ionic bonds, this means they largely transfer from the less to the more electronegative element. For covalent bonds, this means they occupy regions of space between the elements, with significant attachment to both elements. By all means, both mechanisms can contribute to bond strength, as in the formation of strongly polar covalent bonds in the hydrogen halides.

18-69. (a)

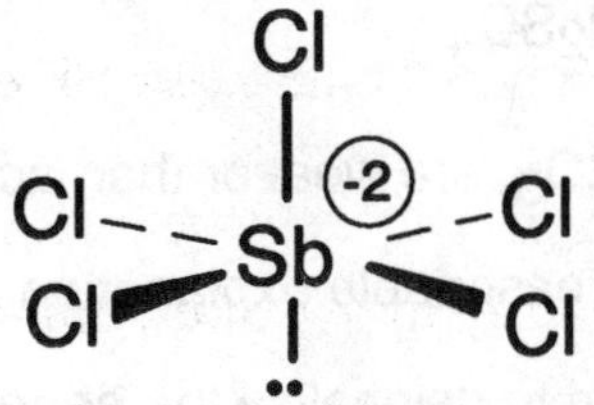

SN of S = 6; square pyramid

(b)

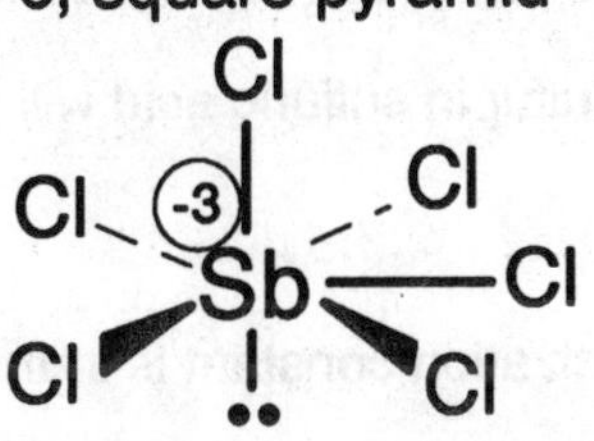

SN = 7 for Sb; pentagonal pyramid derived from a bi-pyramid

In this case, the basic structure for *SN* = 7 is not known to us. A reasonable structure is presented, based on minimizing electron pair repulsion.

18-71.

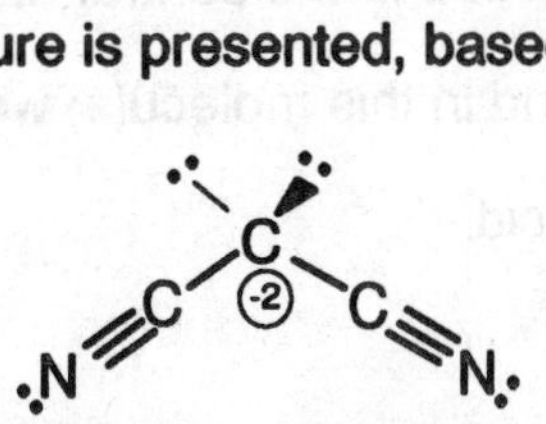

SN = 4 for C; Bent - derived from tetrahedron

The structure is derived from a tetrahedron, but the presence of two lone pairs on the carbon mean that the C-C-C angle is contracted to something *less* than 109.5^{o}

18-73. Element 114 will probably be a super-heavy member of the carbon group -- right under lead. The maximum oxidation state of the element should be 4, but the trend to lower stability of higher oxidation states at the bottom of the representative elements means that the +2 oxidation state may dominate the chemistry of this element.

18-75.

SN = 4 for S; Pyramidal derived from tetrahedron
H_2SO_3

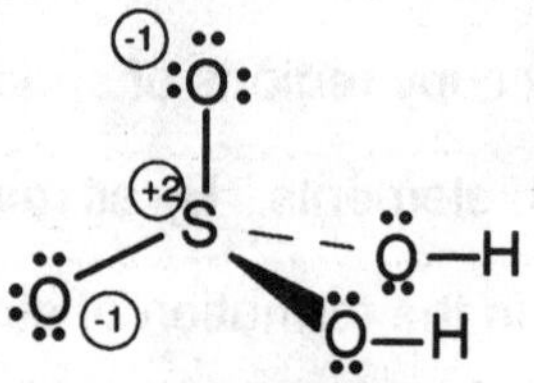

SN = 4 for S; Tetrahedral
H_2SO_4

Acids are of the "$XO(OH)_m$" type, like H_2SO_3, are weaker than acids of the "$XO_2(OH)_m$" type, like sulfuric acid. Two reasonable explanation are that the extra oxygen atom in sulfuric acid will serve to delocalize the negative charge that results when a hydrogen ion is removed. The second observation is that the higher oxidation state on the sulfur in sulfuric acid will stablize the negative charge better.

18-77

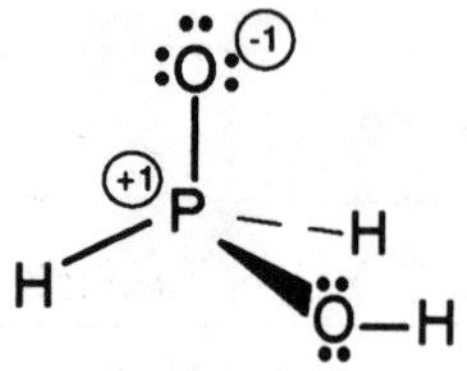

The acid ionization constant is in the range for oxyacids of the "$XO(OH)_m$" type, except here there are only two oxygens for three hydrogens. Still, recall that the critical factor in determining acid strength is actually the *number of lone oxygen atoms bonded to the central atom.* There is a single O-H bond in this molecule; we expect it to act as a *mono* protic acid.

CHAPTER 19 - MOLECULAR ORBITALS AND SPECTROSCOPY

19-1. **The same principles are used in determining the configuration of homonuclear diatomic ions as were used in the text with neutral species. One must remember, though, that the dication has two fewer electrons than a neutral molecule.**

ION	CONFIGURATION	bond order
He_2^{2+}	$(\sigma_{1s})^2$	1
Li_2^{2+}	$(\sigma_{1s})^2(\sigma^*_{1s})^2$	0
Be_2^{2+}	$(\sigma_{1s})^2(\sigma^*_{1s})^2(\sigma_{2s})^2$	1
B_2^{2+}	$(\sigma_{1s})^2(\sigma^*_{1s})^2(\sigma_{2s})^2(\sigma^*_{2s})^2$	0
C_2^{2+}	$(\sigma_{1s})^2(\sigma^*_{1s})^2(\sigma_{2s})^2(\sigma^*_{2s})^2(\pi_{2p})^2$	1
N_2^{2+}	$(\sigma_{1s})^2(\sigma^*_{1s})^2(\sigma_{2s})^2(\sigma^*_{2s})^2(\pi_{2p})^4$	2
O_2^{2+}	$(\sigma_{1s})^2(\sigma^*_{1s})^2(\sigma_{2s})^2(\sigma^*_{2s})^2(\sigma_{2p})^2(\pi_{2p})^4$	3
F_2^{2+}	$(\sigma_{1s})^2(\sigma^*_{1s})^2(\sigma_{2s})^2(\sigma^*_{2s})^2(\sigma_{2p})^2(\pi_{2p})^4(\pi^*_{2p})^2$	2
Ne_2^{2+}	$(\sigma_{1s})^2(\sigma^*_{1s})^2(\sigma_{2s})^2(\sigma^*_{2s})^2(\sigma_{2p})^2(\pi_{2p})^4(\pi^*_{2p})^4$	1

19-3. **We consider only the molecular orbitals derived from $n = 2$ atomic orbitals.**

(a) F_2: $(\sigma_{2s})^2(\sigma^*_{2s})^2(\sigma_{2p})^2(\pi_{2p})^4(\pi^*_{2p})^4$

F_2^+: $(\sigma_{2s})^2(\sigma^*_{2s})^2(\sigma_{2p})^2(\pi_{2p})^4(\pi^*_{2p})^3$

(b) The bond order for F_2 is 1. The bond order for F_2^+ is $^3/_2$.

(c) Only F_2^+ is expected to be paramagnetic.

(d) The F_2^+ molecule should have a stronger bond.

19-5. The electronic configuration should resemble that of O_2, except for sulfur the n = 3 orbitals are the valence orbitals. We will only focus on the molecular orbitals derived from n = 3 atomic orbitals.

Configuration: $(\sigma_{3s})^2(\sigma^*_{3s})^2(\sigma_{3p})^2(\pi_{3p})^4(\pi^*_{3p})^2$ Bond Order: $^1/_2$ (8 - 4) = **2.**

Partial occupancy of the π^*_{3p} orbitals will make S_2, like O_2, **paramagnetic.**

19-7. All of these molecules are in the second row of the periodic table with the n = 2 shell used to form molecular orbitals.

(a) 14 valence electrons in a neutral homonuclear diatomic molecule -- **F**

(b) 9 valence electrons in a homonuclear diatomic molecule with +1 charge -- **N**

(c) 13 valence electrons in a homonuclear diatomic molecule with -1 charge -- **O**

19-9. (a) $^1/_2$ (8 bonding electrons - 6 anti-bonding electrons) = **1.**

(b) $^1/_2$ (7 bonding electrons - 2 anti-bonding electrons) = **2 $^1/_2$.**

(a) $^1/_2$ (8 bonding electrons - 5 anti-bonding electrons) = **1$^1/_2$**

19-11. (a) Even number of electrons with no partially filled orbitals: **diamagnetic**

(b) Odd number of electrons: **paramagnetic**

(c) Odd number of electrons: **paramagnetic**

19-13.

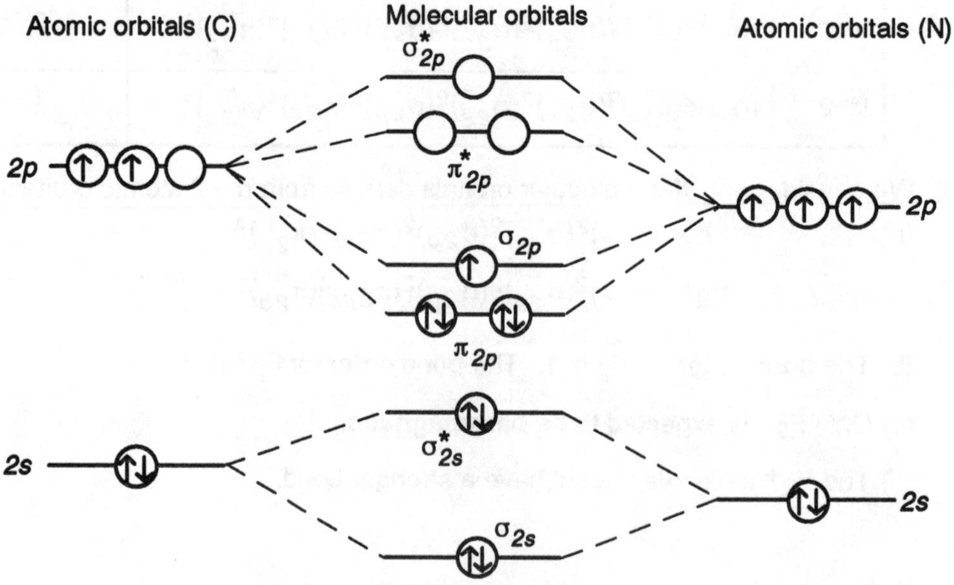

19-13. (continued)

There are seven bonding and two anti-bonding electrons, so the bond order is $2^1/_2$. The unpaired electron will make the molecule **paramagnetic.**

19-15.

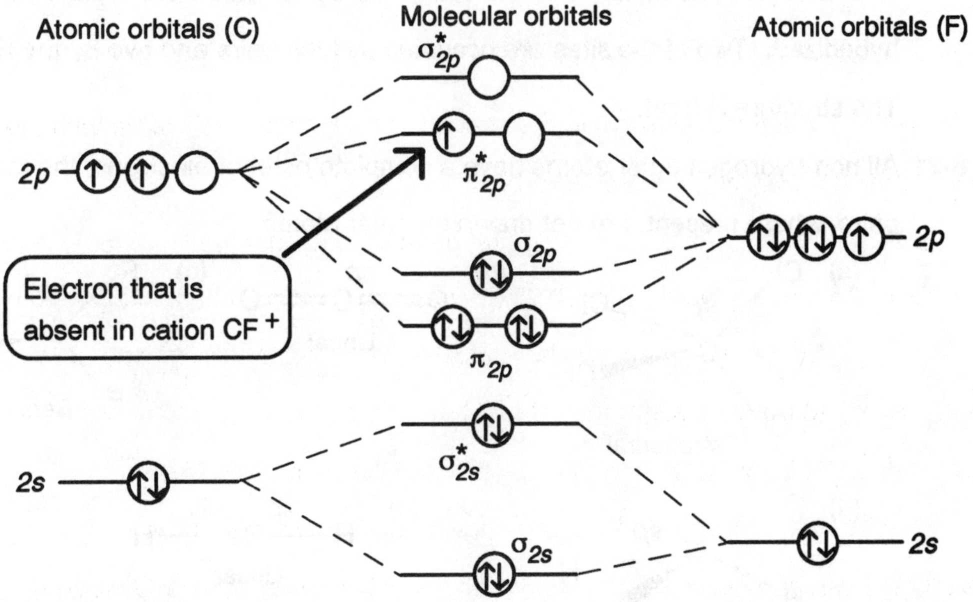

The appropriate molecular orbital diagram for CF shows an unpaired electron in an antibonding orbital. This is the electron removed in forming CF^+. The bond order in CF is **2 $^1/_2$**. The bond order in CF^+ is 3.

19-17.

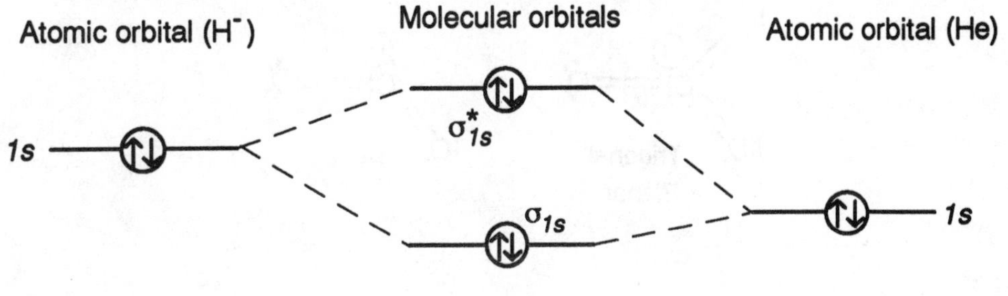

Both the bonding and the antibonding orbitals are fully occupied in HeH^-. The electronic configuration is $(\sigma_{1s})^2(\sigma^*_{1s})^2$, so the bond order is zero and the species should not be stable.

19-19. The Lewis dot structure for NH_2^- is: 

The molecule has *S.N.* = 4 on the central nitrogen, which is therefore sp^3 hybridized. Two of the sites are occupied by lone pairs and two by the H's. The structure is bent.

19-21. All non-hydrogen outer atoms have a complete octet of electrons; the lone pairs, where present, are not drawn on outer atoms.

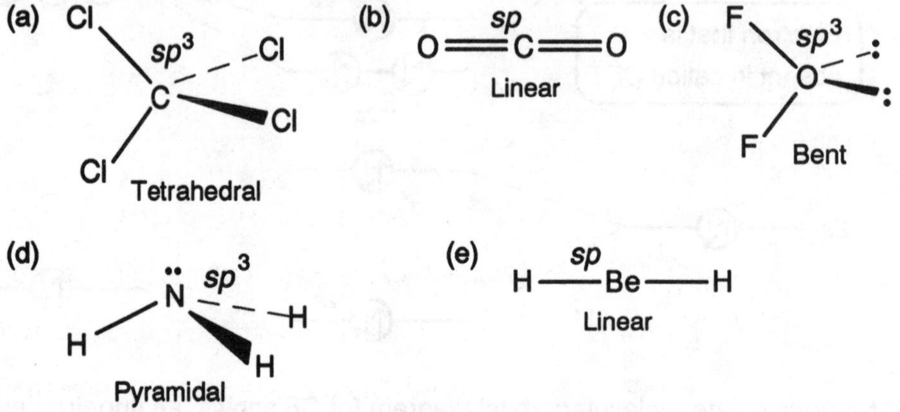

19-23. Both compounds have an sp^2-hybridized central chlorine atom with *S.N.* = 3. These Lewis structures also show the shapes.

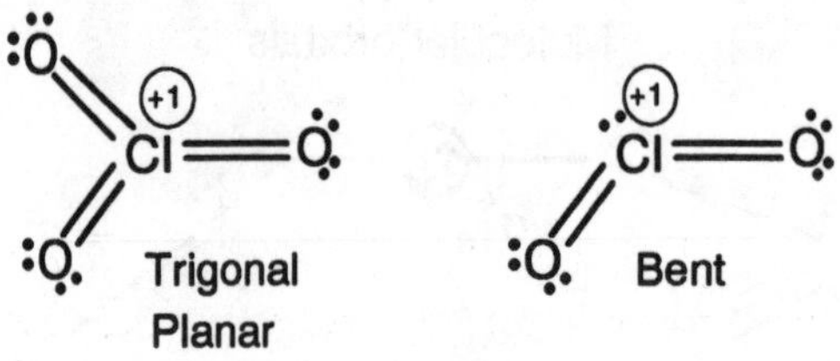

19-25. Based on the most reasonable Lewis structure, shown below, orthonitrate will have sp^3 hybridization on the nitrogen and a tetrahedral geometry.

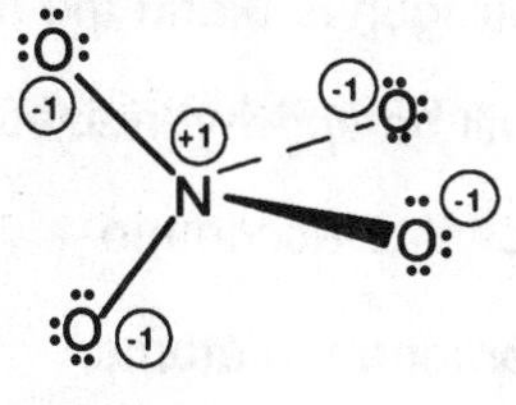

19-27. (a) Ethylene: 5-σ bonds, 1-π bond

(b) Fluorine: 1-σ bond. Note that, though the MO diagram for F_2 has π electrons, there are no *net* π bonds.

(c) Propane has 10 σ bonds and 0 π bonds. It can be written $H_3C\text{-}CH_2\text{-}CH_3$.

(d) Carbon tetrachloride has 4 σ bonds and 0 π bonds.

19-29.

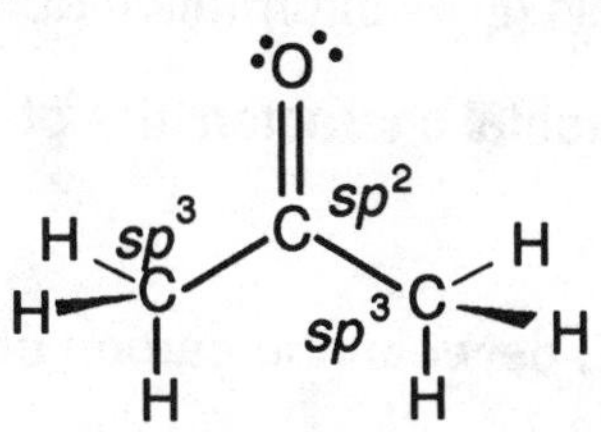

The geometry about the central C is trigonal with 120° bond angles. The geometry about the other C's is tetrahedral with approximately 109.5° bond angles. There is one π bond, between the oxygen and the central carbon.

19-31.

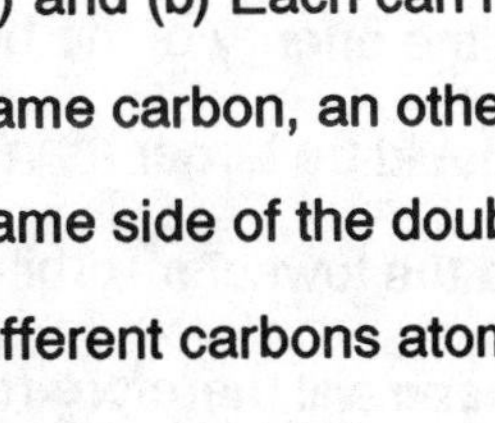

The geometry and bonding are essentially the same as for acetone in #19-29 above.

19-33.(a) and (b) Each can have three isomers, one with the two halogens on the same carbon, an other with the halogens on different carbon atoms but on the same side of the double bond ("*cis*") and the third with the halogens on different carbons atoms and on the opposite side of the double bond from one another ("*trans*").

19-35. The Lewis dot structure for nitrite ion is: 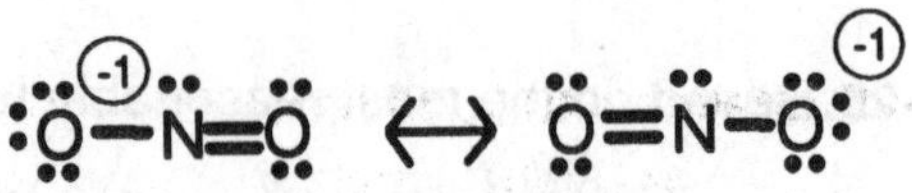

The steric number of the nitrogen is **3** and the molecule is expected to be **bent**. The nitrogen atom will be *sp*^{2} hybridized.

We can draw a single π orbital to accommodate the multiple bonding among the atoms, shown at right. In this case, the single π orbital is split among the two N-O bonds, giving each N-O bond an order of **1 $^1/_2$**.

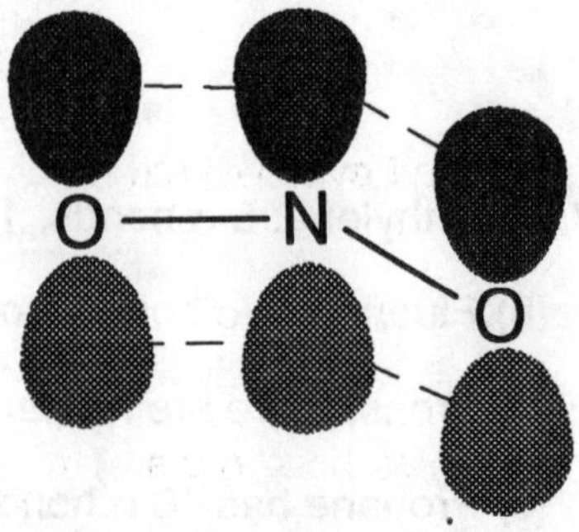

19-37. As indicated in Table 19-3, microwave radiation affects the *rotational* energy a molecule. Knowledge of rotational energy levels gives information about bond lengths and angles, which are the fundamental characteristics of molecular structure.

19-39. Ethylene has a single, doubly occupied π-orbital between the carbon atoms. It will also have a single, unoccupied π^*-orbital. The added electron in $C_2H_4^-$ will go into this π^* orbital, weakening the C-C bond. The bond order will **decrease** from 2 to 1 $^1/_2$.

19-41. The color that is complementary to orange is blue; indanthrene is expected to absorb blue light, around **400-475 nm**, strongly.

19-43. There is one localized π bond in cyclohexene, compared to the three delocalized π bonds in benzene. The gap between the energy of the highest π-orbital and the lowest π^*-orbital in cyclohexene should be larger than the gap between the energy of the highest π-orbital and the lowest π^*-orbital in benzene. The promotion of an electron in cyclohexene will therefore require light of higher energy -- which means light of shorter wavelength.

19-45. It takes 440 kJ to break one mole of C-F bonds, which means it takes

$$\frac{440{,}000 \text{ J mol}^{-1}}{6.022 \times 10^{23} \text{ atoms mol}^{-1}} = 7.31 \times 10^{-19} \text{ J atom}^{-1}.$$ The light for this has

wavelength: $$\lambda = \frac{hc}{\Delta E} = \frac{(6.6261 \times 10^{-34} \text{ J s})(2.998 \times 10^{8} \text{ m s}^{-1})}{7.31 \times 10^{-19} \text{ J}} = 2.7 \times 10^{-7} \text{ m}$$

= **270 nm**; This is in the UV region ofv the spectrum.

19-47. (a) The Lewis dot structure is:

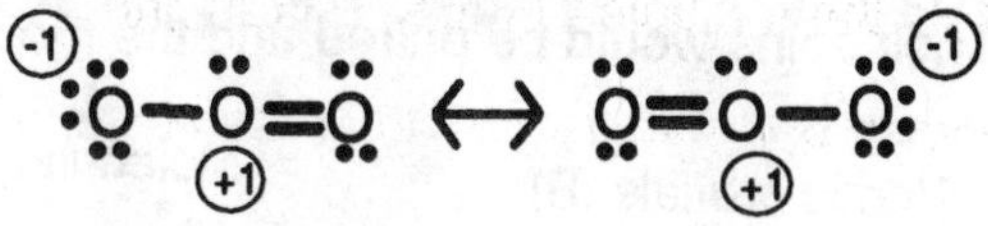

This is essentially the same as for NO_2^- in problem No. 35. We can describe ozone as having a single delocalized π orbital and net bond order of $^3/_2$ between the oxygens. The steric number of the central O is **3** and the molecule is expected to be **bent**. The central oxygen atom will be ***sp*²** hybridized.

19-49.

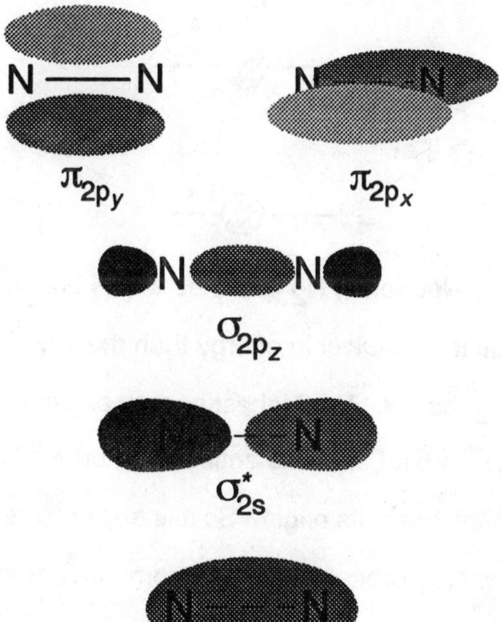

All the orbitals but the σ^*_{2s} orbital are bonding

19-51. The molecular orbital diagram for B_2 is given below. Paramagnetism results from the partial occupancy of the π_{2p} orbital with one electron in each of the two orbitals. By Hund's rule, this means the electrons have parallel spins, and therefore the molecule is paramagnetic. If the ordering of the σ_{2p} and the π_{2p} orbitals were reversed, then the two electrons could occupy a single orbital. Their spins would be paired and the molecule would be diamagnetic.

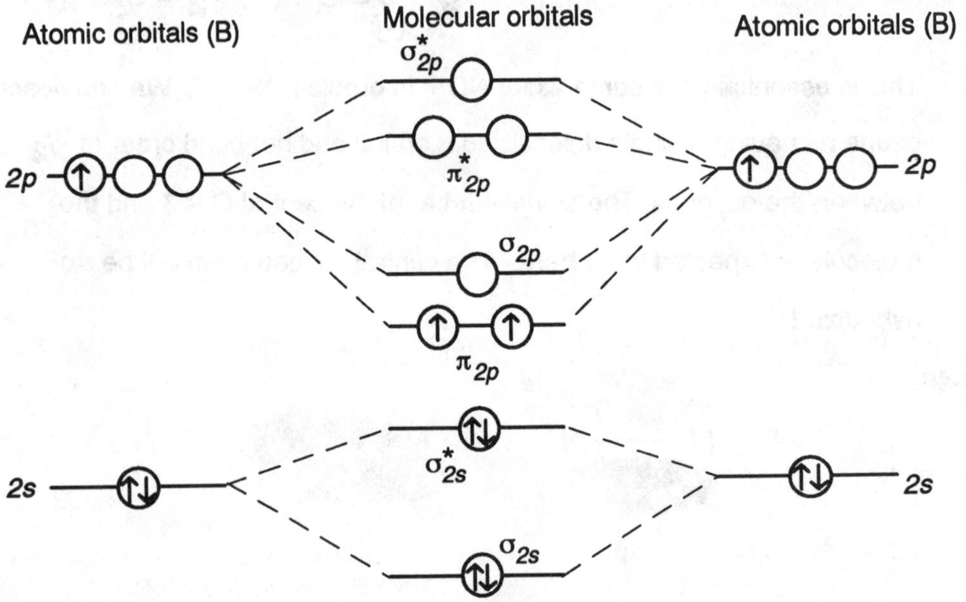

19-53. The highest energy electron in H_2 occupies a H-H bonding orbital, by definition an orbital that is *lower* in energy than the lone H 1*s* orbital. So it is harder to ionize H_2 than H. The highest energy electron in O_2, on the other hand, occupies a π^* orbital, and this antibonding orbital is *higher* in energy than the O 2*p* orbital that is its origin. So it is easier to remove an electron from the highest energy orbital in O_2 than from an O atom.

19-55. The two structures have very different Lewis structures:

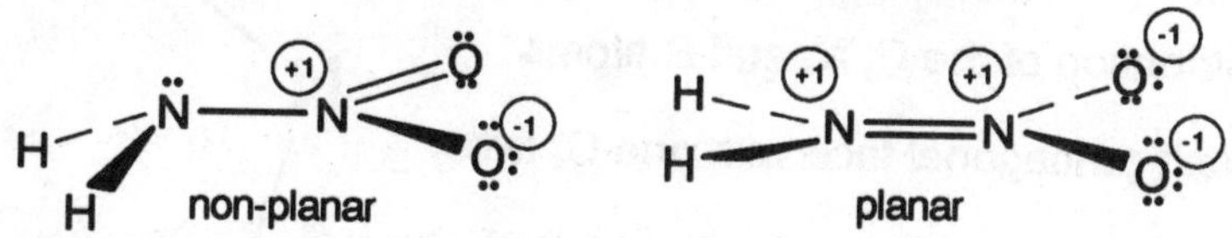

(a) In the non-planar structure, the nitrogen with the hydrogens has *S.N.* = 4 and sp^3 hybridization. It has has a lone pair and the N-N bond order is 1.

(b) In the planar structure both N's have *S.N.*= 3 and sp^2 hybridization. There are no lone pairs on nitrogen, and there *is* a π bond between the nitrogens, for a N-N bond order of 2.

19-57. For formic acid, there is only a single Lewis structure, with a planar, sp^2 hybridized carbon with SN = 3 and a trigonal planar geometry. There is one C-O single bond to the OH group and one C=O double bond to the lone oxygen. It is not surprising that the single bond is longer and the double bond is shorter.

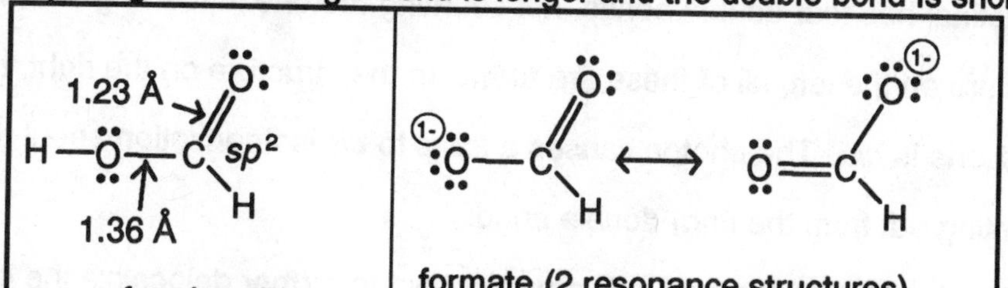

formic acid

formate (2 resonance structures)

The hybridization, steric number, and geometry about the carbon in formate ion is the same as for formic acid. But in formate ion there are two resonance structures as the double bond can be drawn to *either* of the oxygens. We expect that the C-O bond distance will be intermediate between 1.23 Å and 1.36 Å -- about 1.30 Å.

19-59. (a) The number of valence electrons in C_{60} is 4 × 60 = 240. For $C_{12}B_{24}N_{24}$, there are (4 × 12) + (3 × 24) + (5 × 24) = 240 valence electrons, also with 60 atoms. An equal number of valence electrons and atoms suggests likely similarities in electronic and molecular structure.

19-59 (b) The structure of C_{60} has 12 pentagonal faces. A symmetric distribution of the C, N, and B atoms would have each pentagonal face with one C, two B's and two N's. They could be arranged so that, within a face, there were no B-B or N-N bonds. This structure can be repeated around the sphere to give a completely symmetric structure. One face is shown at right.

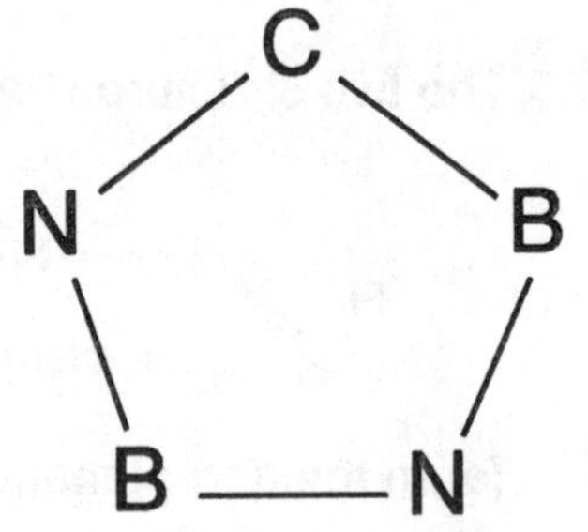

19-61. If a light appears green because of the transmission of just green light, then a prism will leave the light the same color. But if a light appears green to the eye because of a mixing of yellow and blue light, then these will be separated by the prism.

19-63. (a) Retinal has four double bonds, not counting the one in the ring. In the structure on the left, all of these are *trans*. In the structure on the right, three are *trans*, one is *cis*. The photon causes a *trans* to *cis* isomerization about the third (counting out from the ring) double bond.

(b) The double bond in the CHO group will act to further delocalize the electrons in the π-orbitals of retinal, so it will *lower* the energy required for promotion of an electron, compared to a CH_3 group at the same position. This means the replacement of CHO by CH_3 will cause the absorption to shift to higher energy, and *lower* wavelength.

19-65. As the text discusses, both nitrogen dioxide and ozone are important elements in the photochemistry of the stratosphere and the troposphere. In the stratosphere, ozone acts as a very effective absorber of ultraviolet radiation from the sun, in the process forming O_2 + O. Eventually, many of the O atoms recombine to give ozone back, unless there are other molecules to react with them. NO_2 in particular can react with O atoms to give NO and O_2, effectively removing a

19-65. (continued)

source of ozone from the stratosphere. Hence, ozone has beneficial properties in the stratosphere but NO_2 is a pollutant.

In the troposphere, ozone is important for its toxicity, as is NO_2. Hence both are pollutants in the troposphere. But NO_2, because it is photochemically active at visible wavelengths, also acts as an intermediate for the *formation* of ozone in the troposphere, acting in a completely opposite way from its role in the stratosphere.

19-67. Relatively little infrared radiation reaches the earth from the sun, but the earth is an excellent source of this radiation. Part of the cosmic energy budget for the planet, then, is absorption of visible wavelength radiation and re-emission of energy into space by infrared radiation. The greenhouse effect describes the problems associated with the disruption of this budget by molecules that do a very good job at absorbing infrared radiation and converting it into thermal energy. Hence such molecules, which include CO_2, act to make the earth retain energy as thermal energy, possibly inducing global warming. Any process that adds a net amount of CO_2 to the atmosphere adds to the greenhouse effect. An example is the combustion of fossil fuels (coal, oil, and natural gas). Three energy sources that do not act as a net source of CO_2 are nuclear power, hydropower, and the direct conversion of solar energy into either electrical or chemical energy (for example, hydrogen gas). A fourth source of power is the burning of *recently grown* biomass (including derived fuels like ethanol from corn). While the process does give off CO_2, the carbon in, say, corn, was only recently converted from CO_2 by the plant. A cycle

$$CO_2 + \text{sunlight} \rightarrow \text{biomass} \rightarrow CO_2 + \text{energy}$$

does *not* increase the amount of CO_2 in the atmosphere.

CHAPTER 20 - COORDINATION COMPLEXES

20-1. (a) $[Fe(CN)_6]^{3-}$ (b) $[Mn(NH_3)(H_2O)_2(Cl)_3]$ (c) $[Pt(H_2O)Br(en)]^+$

20-3. **Methylamine is a monodendate ligand. It binds through the nitrogen atom, the only site of a lone pair on the molecule.**

20-5. **The first acid ionization reaction is:**

$$[Pt(en)_3]^{4+}\ (aq) + H_2O\ (l) \rightarrow [Pt(en)_2(NH_2CH_2CH_2NH)]^{3+}\ (aq) + H_3O^+\ (aq)$$

We can neglect the second ionization for this calculation. At this concentration of such a weak acid the extent of the reaction is small,

Then, with $[H_3O^+] = [Pt(en)_2(NH_2CH_2CH_2NH)]^{3+} = x$

and $[Pt(en)_3]^{4+} \sim 0.124$ M:

$$x = \sqrt{[Pt(en)_3]^{4+}K_a} = \sqrt{(0.124)(4.5\times10^{-6})} = 7.47 \times 10^{-4}$$

$[H_3O^+] = 7.467 \times 10^{-4}$ M; **pH = 3.13**

20-7. **To get the oxidation state of the metal, we only need to consider the charged ligands and the net charge on the complex.**

V (**+2**) + 2 Cl^- = zero charge 2 Mo (**+2**) + 8 Cl^- = - 4 charge

Co (**+2**) + 3 Cl^- = -1 charge Ni (**0**) + no charged ligands = zero charge

20-9. (a) tetrahydrox0 = 4 OH^- groups; zincate(II) = Zn^{2+}: overall charge of -2

Formula: **$Na_2[Zn(OH)_4]$**

(b) dichloro = 2 Cl^- groups; cobalt(III) = Co^{3+}: overall charge of +1

bis(ethylenediamine) = 2 en groups nitrate = NO_3^- counterion

Formula: **$[Co(Cl_2(en)_2]NO_3$**

20-9. (continued)

(c) <u>bromo</u> = Br group *on* Pt; <u>platinum(II)</u> = Pt^{2+}: overall charge of +1

<u>triaqua</u> = three H_2O groups; <u>chloride:</u> Cl^- ion *not* bound to Pt.

Formula: **$[Pt(H_2O)_3Br]Cl$**

(d) <u>dinitro</u> = 2 NO_2^- groups; <u>platinum(IV)</u> = Pt^{4+}: overall charge of +2

<u>tetraammine</u> = 4 NH_3 groups; <u>bromide</u> = Br^- ions *not* bound to Pt.

Formula: **$[Pt(NH_3)_4(NO_2)_2]Br_2$**

20-11. (a) Ammonium diamminetetraisothiocyanatochromate(III)

(b) Pentacarbonyliodotechnetium(I)

(c) Potassium pentacyanomanganate(IV)

(d) Tetraammineaquachlorocobalt(III) bromide

20-13. A thermodynamically stable complex will not react to give a complex of a different formula. It can still be kinetically labile, which means it will exchange bound ligands for other ligands that are the same -- ammonia for ammonia, for example. This can be detected through isotopic labeling.

20-15. In *basic* aqueous solution, the ammonia will come off the copper(II) as NH_3:

$$[Cu(NH_3)_4]^{2+}\ (aq) \rightarrow Cu^{2+}\ (aq) + 4\ NH_3\ (aq)$$

$$\Delta G^o = 4\ \Delta G_f^o\ (NH_3,\ aq) + \Delta G_f^o\ (Cu^{2+},\ aq) - \Delta G_f^o\ (Cu(NH_3)_4^{2+},\ aq)$$

$$= \left(4\ \text{mol} \times -26.50 \frac{\text{kJ}}{\text{mol}}\right) + \left(1\ \text{mol} \times 65.49 \frac{\text{kJ}}{\text{mol}}\right) - \left(1\ \text{mol} \times -111.07 \frac{\text{kJ}}{\text{mol}}\right)$$

$$= \mathbf{+\ 70.56\ kJ}$$

The reaction is non-spontaneous; **$Cu(NH_3)_4^{2+}$ is stable.**

In pH = 0 solution $[H_3O^+]$ = 1 M; ammonia will gain an H^+ ion as it comes off the copper the reaction then is:

$$4\ H_3O^+\ (aq) + [Cu(NH_3)_4]^{2+}\ (aq) \rightarrow Cu^{2+}\ (aq) + 4\ NH_4^+\ (aq) + 4\ H_2O\ (l)$$

The thermodynamics indicate that ΔG^o = **-140.68 kJ**, so the **dissociation is spontaneous** in acidic solution.

20-17. The number of ions per formula is determined by the number of anions that will *not* remain bound to the metal when the complex dissolves

	$Cu(NH_3)_2Cl_2$ <	KNO_3 <	$Na_2[PtCl_6]$ <	$[Co(NH_3)_6]Cl_3$
ions per formula:	0	2	3	4

20-19. (a)

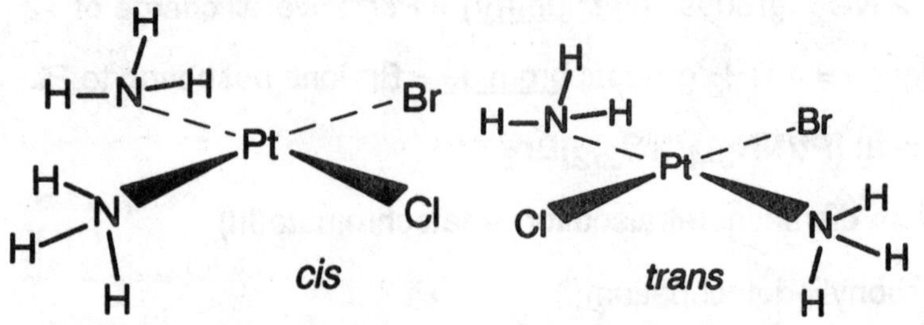

(b)

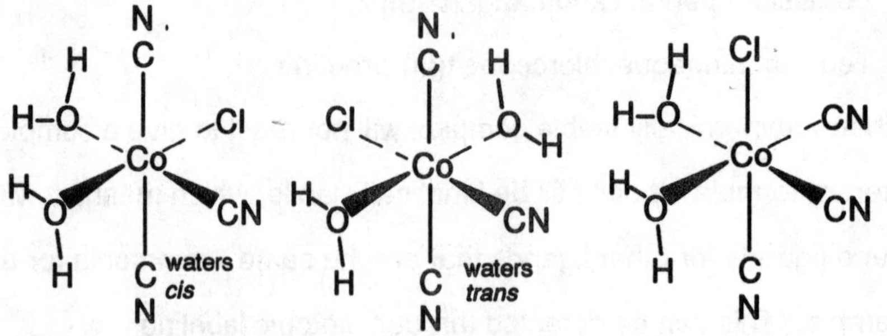

meridional *facial*

The *meridional* isomers each have a mirror plane perpendicular to the NC-Co-CN axis, and hence they are achiral. The *facial* isomer has a mirror plane bisecting the O-Co-O angle, and hence is achiral.

20-19. (c)

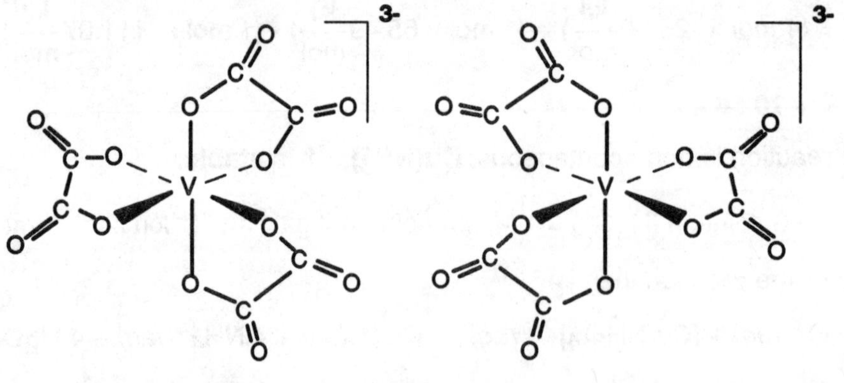

These enantiomers are the only isomers

20-21.

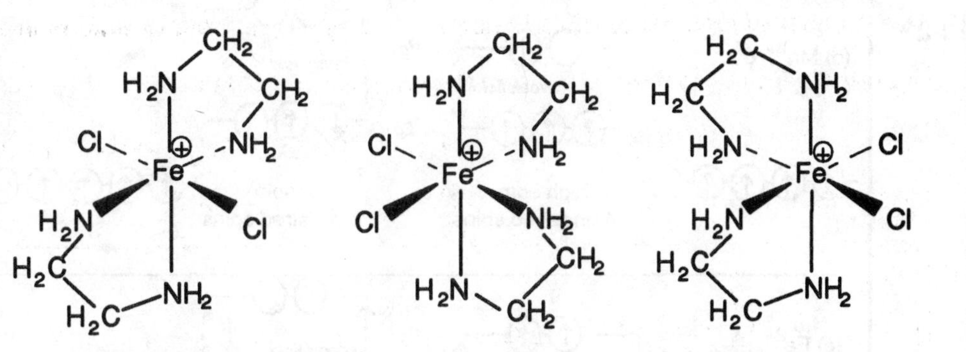

There is a single *trans* isomer

There are two *cis* isomers, and they are enantiomers of one another

20-23.

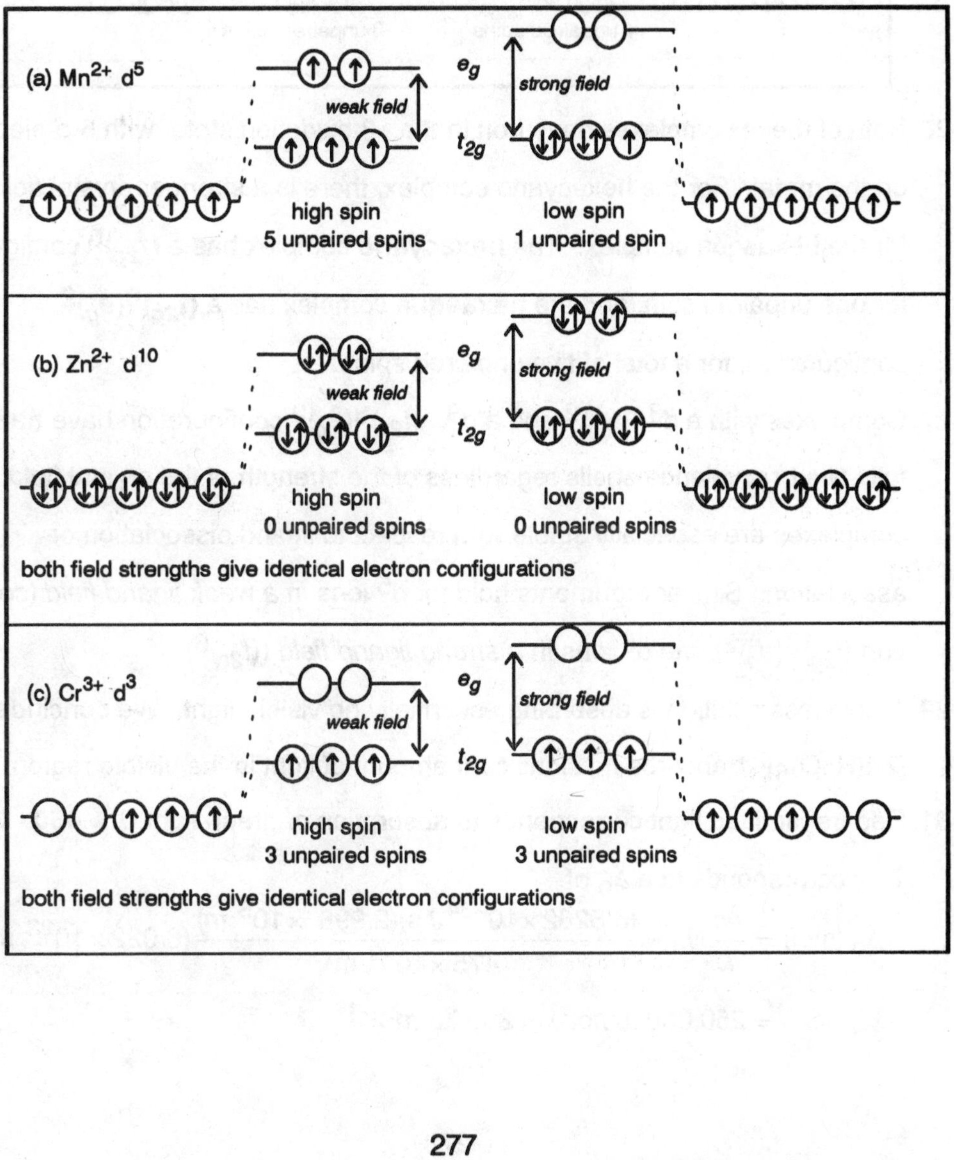

20-23

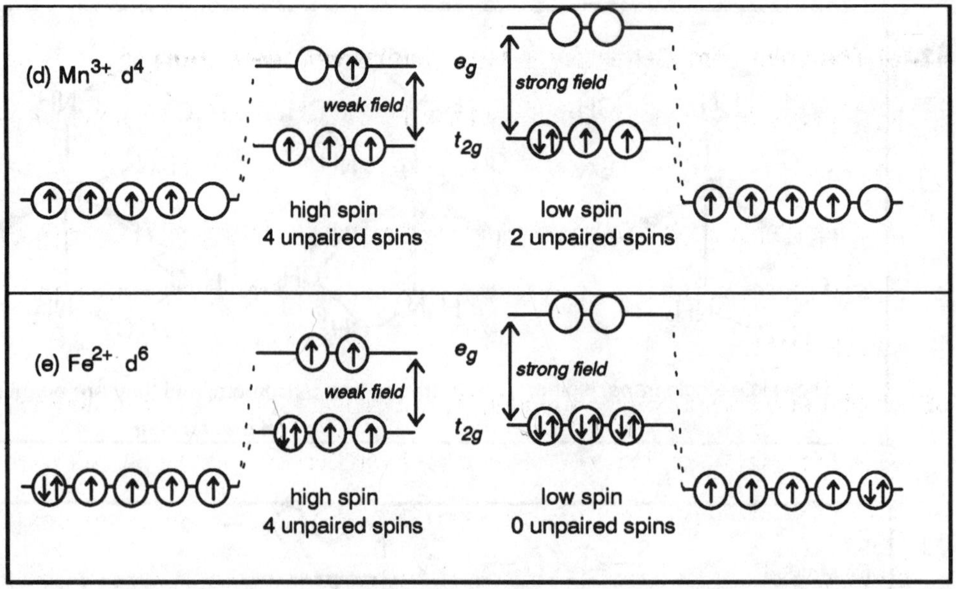

20-25. Both of these complexes have iron in the +3 oxidation state, with 5 *d*-electrons on the metal. For the hexacyano complex, there is a stronger crystal field than for the hexaaqua complex. The **hexacyano** complex has a $\mathbf{(t_{2g})^5}$ configuration, for one unpaired spin, and the **hexaaqua** complex has a $\mathbf{(t_{2g})^3(e_g)^2}$ configuration, for a total of five unpaired spins.

20-27. Complexes with a d^3, $(t_{2g})^3$ and a d^8, $(t_{2g})^6(e_g)^2$ configuration have half-filled or fully-filled t_{2g} valence shells regardless of the strength of the crystal field. These complexes are especially stable with respect to ligand dissociation or association. Similar arguments hold for d^5 ions *in a weak ligand field* (configuration $(t_{2g})^3(e_g)^2$) and d^6 ions in a *strong ligand field* ($(t_{2g})^6$).

20-29. A colorless solution is absorbing essentially no visible light. We conclude that $[Zn(H_2O)_6]^{2+}$ absorbs no significant amount of light in the visible region.

20-31. Red transmitted light corresponds to absorption of green light, $\lambda \sim$ **450 - 500** nm. This corresponds to a Δ_o of:

$$\Delta_o\,(\text{mol}) = \frac{hc}{\lambda}N_o = \frac{(6.6262\times10^{-34}\text{ J s})(2.998\times10^{8}\text{ m})}{475\times10^{-9}\text{ m}}(6.022\times10^{23}\text{ mol}^{-1})$$

$$= 250{,}000\text{ J mol}^{-1} = \mathbf{250\ kJ\ mol^{-1}}$$

20-33. (a) The color complementary to blue-violet is **yellow-orange.**

(b) The maximum absorbance is at the border of yellow and orange, at about **600 nm.**

(c) The introduction of cyano ligands will make the crystal field stronger; this should *increase* the t_{2g} - e_g gap and shift the absorbance maximum to **shorter** wavelengths.

20-35. All of these complexes contain Fe^{3+}, but they differ in the ligand environment. Note the relative crystal field strengths, based on the spectrochemical series: $[Fe(H_2O)_6]^{3+} < [Fe(CN)_6]^{3-}$. The first complex has a weak crystal field, the second a strong crystal field. The hexaaquo complex will have a $(t_{2g})^3(e_g)^2$ configuration, and this configuration, with five unpaired spins and half-filled subshells, should absorb light weakly. The hexacyano complex, with no unpaired spins and a completely vacant e_g level, should absorb light relatively well. Note that these are indications of how readily light is absorbed, not the energy of the transition. The hexafluoro complex $[FeF_6]^{3-}$ should have a ligand field even weaker than that for the hexaaquo complex. Its solutions should also be pale.

20-37. The percentage indicates that there are 4.43 g of Co for 100.00 g of the vitamin. Therefore:

$$\text{molar mass } B_{12} = \frac{\text{g } B_{12}}{\text{mol } B_{12}} = \left(\frac{100 \text{ g } B_{12}}{4.43 \text{ g Co}}\right)\left(\frac{58.93 \text{ g Co}}{1 \text{ mol Co}}\right)\left(\frac{1 \text{ mol Co}}{1 \text{ mol } B_{12}}\right)$$

$$= \mathbf{1330 \text{ g mol}^{-1}}$$

20-39. Ligands typically act as Lewis bases. It makes sense that ligands are often ready sources of lone pairs, which is more likely to happen with neutral or anionic species, species some chemists call "electron rich."

20-41. The diruthenium complex has an overall charge of +2 (note the two perchlorate counterions). The complex also has three anionic ligands with three negative charges. Therefore:

charge on Ru's + charge on anionic ligands = total charge

charge on Ru's = total charge - charge on anions

= +2 - (-3) = 5

The charge *per Ru atom* is half of this value, or **Ru(+2$^1/_2$)**. There is no problem with a fractional oxidation number *provided it is shared among enough atoms to make the fraction disappear.*

20-43. Among the non-metal containing species in this problem, the most important molecule to figuring out this puzzle is HCl. This is a strong acid and cannot have been present as a molecule in the original formula. Hence, there must have been some base that held the hydrogen ion in HCl -- and the logical candidate for this is the ammonia that is produced. Thus, we can imagine that the original complex also had one more ammonium and one more chloro group. The last thing to consider is that the two moles of water were probably present as ligands, not just waters of solvation. We then have:

ORIGINAL COMPOUND: **$[NH_4]_2[IrCl_5(H_2O)]$**

NAME: **Ammonium aquopentachloroiridium(III)**

20-45. The experiments give us the number of water molecules available for removal, which we presume are the water of *solvation* not waters of *ligation*. Therefore:

Compound 1 two H_2O available on heating.......... $[Cr(H_2O)_4Cl_2]Cl{\bullet}2H_2O$

Compound 2 one H_2O available on heating............ $[Cr(H_2O)_5Cl]Cl_2{\bullet}H_2O$

Compound 3 no H_2O available on heating....................... $[Cr(H_2O)_6]Cl_3$

20-45. (continued)

All three compounds have identical empirical formulas and molar masses -- 248.35 g mol^{-1}. Therefore, 100.0 g of each will contain 0.40266 mol of compound. The amount of silver chloride that will precipitate will depend on the number of free chloride ions in the formula, not on the bound chloro ligands. Note: the molar mass of AgCl is 143.34 g mol^{-1}

COMPOUND	Chloride ions per formula	Moles of free Cl^- in 100 g	Moles of AgCl	Mass of AgCl
$[Cr(H_2O)_4Cl_2]Cl{\cdot}2\ H_2O$	1	0.40266	0.40266	**57.72 g**
$[Cr(H_2O)_5Cl]Cl_2{\cdot}\ H_2O$	2	0.80532	0.80532	**115.4 g**
$[Cr(H_2O)_6]Cl_3$	3	1.20798	1.20798	**173.2g**

20-47. The two structures under consideration are:

Both exist as a single structure with at least one mirror plane perpendicular to the N-Co-N plane. There is no isomerism possible with either complex, unless one considers any folding or puckering of the five membered ring.

20-49.

$[Mn(CN)_6]^{5-}$	Mn(I)	d^6	$(t_{2g})^6$
$[Mn(CN)_6]^{4-}$	Mn(II)	d^5	$(t_{2g})^5$
$[Mn(CN)_6]^{3-}$	Mn(III)	d^4	$(t_{2g})^4$

20-51. The empirical formula $[Pt(SCN)_2Br(en)]$ suggests molecular units with the Pt in the 3+ oxidation state, which gives the Pt a d^7 configuration. This odd electron count makes the formula almost certainly incompatible with the observed diamagnetism. In the alternative formulation, half of the Pt atoms occur in $[Pt(SCN)_2(en)_2]^{2+}$ units, which makes them Pt(IV, d^6 and the other half occur in $[Pt(SCN)_2Br_2]^{2-}$ units, which makes them Pt(II), d^8 Both metal sites have an even number of electrons, so the diamagnetism is reasonable.

20-53. The anion in this compound is $CuF_6{}^{2-}$, so the oxidation state of copper is +4. This gives the copper a $\mathbf{d^7}$ configuration. The geometry of the coordination around copper will presumably be **octahedral**. Fluoride is a weak field ligand, so we expect the complex to have a high spin configuration for the electrons -- $\mathbf{(t_{2g})^5(e_g)^2}$. The corresponding low spin complex would have a configuration of $(t_{2g})^6(e_g)^1$

20-55. We presume that nitrogen remains uncharged when it is a ligand, as is true of the isoelectronic molecule CO. Then, at low temperature the $[V(N_2)_6]$ complex will have V(0) and a d^5 configuration. It must be paramagnetic. The corresponding CO complex is $V(CO)_6$.

CHAPTER 21 - STRUCTURE AND BONDING IN SOLIDS

21-1. "Second-order" means $n = 2$ for this reflection. Given an experimental angle $2\theta = 54.70^{\circ}$, then $\theta = 27.35^{\circ}$. Therefore:

$$2d \sin\theta = n\lambda \quad \Rightarrow \quad d = \frac{n\lambda}{2\sin\theta} = \frac{(2)\left(1.660\ \text{Å}\right)}{2\sin\left(27.35^{\circ}\right)} = \mathbf{3.613\ Å}$$

21-3. "Fourth-order" means $n = 4$.

$$2d\sin\theta = n\lambda$$

$$\theta = \sin^{-1}\left(\frac{n\lambda}{2d}\right) = \sin^{-1}\left(\frac{(4)\left(1.936\ \text{Å}\right)}{2\left(4.950\ \text{Å}\right)}\right) = \sin^{-1}(0.7822) = 51.46^{\circ}$$

$$\mathbf{2\theta = 102.92^{\circ}}$$

21-5. The maximum possible value for the argument in the $\sin^{-1}$ function is 1.00, because the sine of any angle cannot exceed 1. We insert values of n into the Bragg formula to determine when this maximum value is reached. The equation that we need is: $\frac{n\lambda}{2d} = n\frac{\left(2.167\ \text{Å}\right)}{2\left(2.570\ \text{Å}\right)} = (0.4216)\,n$

n	$\frac{n\lambda}{2d}$	$\theta = \sin^{-1}\left(\frac{n\lambda}{2d}\right)$	2θ
1	0.4216	24.935	49.87°
2	0.8432	57.48	115.0°
3	1.265	Not Reasonable	

21-7. The Bragg Law is not restricted to any particular wavelength or type of radiation. It works with visible wavelengths as well. "First order" means $n = 1$, and here $\theta = 42.5^{\circ}$. $\lambda = \left(\frac{2d}{n}\right)\sin\theta = \left(\frac{2\,(500\ \text{nm})}{(1)}\right)\sin\left(42.5^{\circ}\right) = \mathbf{680\ nm}$.

This is **red** light.

21-9. A single crystal will give diffraction as *spots*. As an analogy, think of a mirror lying at a fixed angle reflecting a beam of light from a single source. The reflection will be a point of light. If there are many micro-crystals present, the Bragg relationship is satisfied for each and every micro-crystal. But there is no unique crystal orientation. One obtains a *ring* of diffracted radiation. It is all at the angle 2θ, but spread around in a circle.

21-11. (a) This does not have three fold symmetry. Three-fold symmetry requires all corners to be identical. In an isosceles triangle, two angles (corners) are identical but the third is not.

(b) Yes, this has three-fold symmetry. The equilateral triangle has identical corners.

(c) Yes, this has three-fold symmetry. The *face* of a tetrahedron is an equilateral triangle.

(d) Yes, this has three-fold symmetry The *corner* of a cube has three equal edges coming out of it. This is on an axis of three-fold symmetry.

21-13. (a) Yes, the number 1881 has **two** mirror planes, one vertical and lying in between the 8's and the other horizontal and bisecting the 1's and 8's. But the written image of the number 1881 may or may not have mirror symmetry, depending on whether there are little wiggles on the "ones," which remove mirror symmetry.

(b) Yes. The ideal box has two mirror planes perpendicular to all its faces.

(c) Yes, but the mirror plane is in the plane of the hook.

21-15. As noted in Table 21-1, the tetragonal system must possess ***one*** **4-fold rotation** element.

21-17. For an orthorhombic crystal with $\alpha = \beta = \gamma = 90^o$:

$$V = abc = (8.06\ \text{Å})\ (9.12\ \text{Å})\ (10.06\ \text{Å}) = 739\ \text{Å}^3$$

Note that Å = 10^{-10} m, so $V = (739\ \text{Å}^3)\left(\frac{10^{-10}\ \text{m}}{1\ \text{Å}}\right)^3 = \mathbf{7.39 \times 10^{-28}\ m^3}$

21-19. (a) Volume of C = $45.385\ \text{Å}^3\ \text{cell}^{-1} \times \left(\frac{1\ \text{cell}}{8\ \text{C atoms}}\right) = \mathbf{5.6731\ Å^3}$ per C atom

(b) The average C atom weighs 12.011 u, or 1.9945×10^{-23} g. We need density in grams cm^{-3}. Therefore:

$$\left(\frac{1.9945 \times 10^{-23}\ \text{g}}{5.6731\ \text{Å}^3}\right)\left(\frac{1\ \text{Å}}{10^{-8}\ \text{cm}}\right)^3 = \mathbf{3.5157\ g\ cm^{-3}}$$

21-21. (a) With a cubic unit cell, $\alpha = \beta = \gamma = 90^o$ and $a = b = c = 5.431$ Å. Therefore, noting that 1 Å = 10^{-8} cm:

$$V = (5.431\ \text{Å})^3 \left(\frac{10^{-8}\ \text{cm}}{1\ \text{Å}}\right)^3 = \mathbf{1.602 \times 10^{-22}\ cm^3}$$

(b)

$$\text{Mass} = \text{volume} \times \text{density}$$
$$= (1.6019 \times 10^{-22}\ \text{cm}^3) \times (2.328\ \text{g cm}^{-3})$$
$$= \mathbf{3.729 \times 10^{-22}\ g}$$

(c) $(3.729 \times 10^{-22}\ \text{g unit cell}^{-1})\left(\frac{1\ \text{unit cell}}{8\ \text{Si atoms}}\right) = 4.6616 \times 10^{-23}\ \text{g (Si atom)}^{-1}$

$$= \mathbf{4.662 \times 10^{-23}\ g\ (Si\ atom)^{-1}}$$

(d) This corresponds to a mass in u of $(4.6616 \times 10^{-23})\ (N_o) = 28.0855$ u

$$N_o = \frac{28.0855}{4.6616 \times 10^{-23}} = \mathbf{6.025 \times 10^{23}}$$

This is 0.003×10^{23} away from the correct number, an error of 0.05%

21-23. We begin by noting the general relation of density, mass, and volume will apply to any sample size large enough to reflect the entire crystal's properties. The smallest such unit is the unit cell.

21-23. (continued)

$$\frac{\text{density }(\beta\text{ - quartz})}{\text{density }(\alpha-\text{quartz})} = \frac{\left(\text{mass }(\beta\text{ - quartz})\Big/ V\ (\beta\text{ - quartz})\right)}{\left(\text{mass }(\alpha\text{ - quartz})\Big/ V\ (\alpha\text{ - quartz})\right)}$$

Since the contents of the unit cells are the same, the masses of the unit cells are the same, so we may simplify the above equation:

$$\frac{\text{density }(\beta\text{ - quartz})}{\text{density }(\alpha-\text{quartz})} = \frac{V(\alpha-\text{quartz})}{V(\beta-\text{quartz})}$$

$$\text{density }(\beta\text{-quartz}) = \frac{V(\alpha-\text{quartz})}{V(\beta-\text{quartz})}\text{density }(\alpha\text{ - quartz})$$

$$= \frac{113.01\ \text{Å}^3}{118.15\ \text{Å}^3} 2.648\ \text{ g cm}^{-3} = \mathbf{2.533\ g\ cm^{-3}}$$

21-25. With a single non-90° angle the unit cell must be monoclinic, so $\alpha = \gamma = 90^{o}$ and $\beta = 97.07^{o}$. Then, in the general volume formula (neglecting terms in $\cos\alpha$ or $\cos\gamma$, which are zero):

$$V = abc\sqrt{1-\cos^2\beta}$$

$$= (21.021\ \text{Å})\ (4.014\ \text{Å})\ (18.989\ \text{Å})\ \sqrt{1-\cos^2\left(97.07^{o}\right)}$$

$$= 1582.46\ \text{Å}^3 = 1.5825 \times 10^{-21}\ \text{cm}^3$$

The molar mass of $Pb_4In_3B_{17}S_{18}$ is 1934.2 g mol^{-1}, which means one formula unit weighs $\dfrac{1934.2\ \text{g mol}^{-1}}{6.0221\times10^{-23}\ \text{molecules mol}^{-1}} = 3.2119 \times 10^{-21}$ g.

Each unit cell contains two formula units, so each cell has a mass of 6.4237×10^{-21} g.

The density is: $\dfrac{6.4237\times10^{-21}\ \text{g}}{1.5825\times10^{-21}\ \text{cm}^3} = \mathbf{4.059\ g\ cm^{-3}}$.

21-27. The volume of a unit cell is: $V = abc = (5.863\ \text{Å})\ (12.304\ \text{Å})\ (9.821\ \text{Å})$

$$= 708.47\ \text{Å}^3 = 7.0847 \times 10^{-22}\ \text{cm}^3$$

The mass of the contents of one unit cell is:

$$\text{mass} = (7.08427 \times 10^{-22}\ \text{cm}^3)\ (2.663\ \text{g cm}^{-3}) = 1.8867 \times 10^{-21}\ \text{g}$$

21-27. (continued)

In atomic mass units this is:

$$\text{mass} = (1.88627 \times 10^{-21}\ \text{g})\ (6.0221 \times 10^{23}\ \text{u g}^{-1}) = 1136.16\ \text{u}$$

The formula mass for Na_2SO_4 is 142.04 u, so the unit cell contains

$$\frac{1136.160\ \text{u}}{142.04\ \text{u}} = \textbf{8 formula units.}$$

21-29. (a) $V_{\text{unit cell}} = a^3 = (5.6402 \times 10^{-10}\ \text{m})^3 = \mathbf{1.7943 \times 10^{-28}\ m^3}$

(b) The crystal itself has a volume of $(1.00 \times 10^{-3}\ \text{m})^3 = 1.00 \times 10^{-9}$ m

$$\text{unit cells in crystal} = \frac{1.00 \times 10^{-9}\ \text{m}^3 - \text{crystal}^{-1}}{1.79423 \times 10^{-28}\ \text{m}^3 - (\text{unit cell})^{-1}}$$

$$= 5.5734 \times 10^{18} = \mathbf{5.57 \times 10^{18}}\ \frac{\text{unit cell}}{\text{crystal}}$$

(c) The area of the crystal face is $1.00 \times 10^{-6}\ \text{m}^2$.

The area of the unit cell face is $(5.6402 \times 10^{-10}\ \text{m})^2 = 3.1812 \times 10^{-19}\ \text{m}^2$.

$$\text{unit cells on surface} = \frac{1.00 \times 10^{-6}\ \text{m}^2 - (\text{crystal face}^{-1})}{3.1812 \times 10^{-19}\ \text{m}^2 - (\text{unit cell})^{-1}}$$

$$= 3.143 \times 10^{-12}\ \frac{\text{unit cell}}{\text{crystal face}}$$

With 6 faces (and neglecting the fact that we are counting cells on the edges and corners more than once), there are $(3.143 \times 10^{12}) \times 6 = \mathbf{1.89 \times 10^{13}}$ unit cells on all the faces.

This represents $\dfrac{1.886 \times 10^{13}}{5.5734 \times 10^{18}} = 3.38 \times 10^{-6} = \mathbf{0.000338\%}$ of all the unit cells

(or one out of every 300,000 unit cells).

21-31. The magnitude of the difference in the electronegativities of the two elements in a binary compound indicates the major form of bonding.

(a) $BaCl_2$	ΔEN = 2.27	Ionic	(b) SiC	ΔEN = 0.65	Covalent
(c) CO	Molecular		(d) Co	Metallic	

21-33. The only ambiguity in predicting the melting points is removed by the data given in the problem.

m.p (CO) < m.p. ($BaCl_2$) < m.p. (Co) < m.p. (SiC)

21-35. Since antimony is a semi-metal, copper is a metal, and oxygen is a non-metal, the conductivity should go as: O_2 < Sb < Cu

21-37. There are **eight** nearest neighbors--the eight Cl's bound to each Cs. There are **six** Cs atoms that then bridge these Cl's. They are the second-nearest neighbors.

21-39.

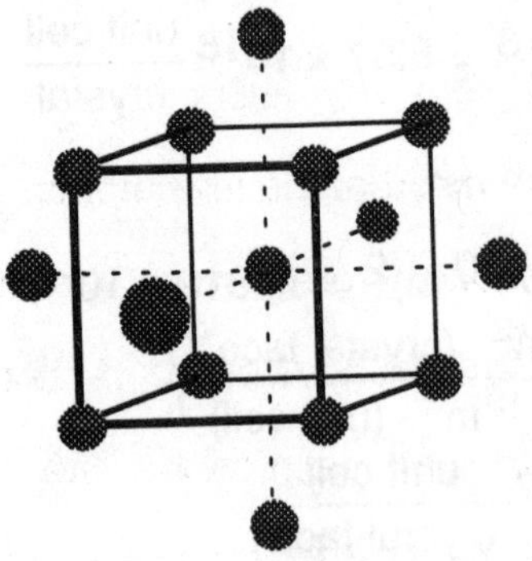

There are **eight** nearest neighbors in this structure. For a sodium atom in the center of the unit cell body, these are the eight sodium atoms at the corners of the cell. Beyond each face of the unit cell lies the second nearest neighbors -- and there are **six** of these, to go with the six faces of a cube.

21-41. Frenkel defects are *displacement* defects. Ions do not leave the crystal. They move where they don't (in a perfect crystal) belong--to an interstitial site. Thus the crystal has as many of each ion as it should. There will be no effect on density.

21-43. Based on the assumption of a 100 g sample (See Chapter 2):

(a) $$\frac{76.55\text{ g Fe}}{55.847\text{ g mol}^{-1}} = 1.3707\text{ mol Fe}$$

$$\frac{23.45\text{ g O}}{15.9994\text{ g mol}^{-1}} = 1.4657\text{ mol O}$$

We set the stoichiometric coefficient of O to 1.000 and determine Fe by division: $$Fe_{\frac{1.3707}{1.4657}}O_{1.000} = \mathbf{Fe_{0.9352}O}$$

21-43. (continued)

(b) The non-stoichiometric nature of the material is due to the fact that a certain fraction of the iron is Fe^{3+}. We can denote the formula as "$(Fe^{2+})_{x-y}(Fe^{3+})_y$"O, where x= 0.9352 here. The variable y represents the stoichiometric coefficient for Fe^{3+}. Then (as developed in part (b) to example 21-9) we solve for y in:

$$3y + 2(x - y) = 2$$

or:

$$y = 2 - 2x$$

where x = the stoichiometric coefficient for Fe.

Here:

$$y = 2 - 2(0.9352) = 0.1296$$

This represents a fraction $^{0.1296}/_{0.9352}$ = **0.1356** of the iron atoms.

21-45. The liquid phase will have rapid molecular motion (rotational and transitional) for all molecules. The plastic crystalline phase will have some fraction of the molecules tumbling in their places, but no translational motion. The plastic phase will have lower enthalpy (you must heat it to melt it to the liquid phase) and lower entropy than the liquid phase.

21-47. *Scattering* refers to the diffraction of x-rays by a sample. *Interference* occurs when this scattering is coherent--in phase--and this requires crystalline material.

21-49. The conditions for this problem are the same as for Bragg diffraction.

$$2d \sin\theta = n\lambda$$

For first order, n = 1, so:

$$\sin\theta = \frac{\lambda}{2d}$$

$$\theta = \sin^{-1}\left(\frac{\lambda}{2d}\right) = \sin^{-1}\left(\frac{3.0 \text{ m}}{2(5.0 \text{ m})}\right)$$

$$= 17.46^{o} \text{ and } \mathbf{2\theta = 35^{o}}$$

21-51. Neglecting questions about type-faces:

(a) 10801 has two mirror planes and a two-fold rotation axis.

(b) 86198 has a two-fold rotation axis.

(c) A teacup, exclusive of decoration, has a mirror plane.

21-53. (a) Unit cell volume: $V = a^3 = (5.6402\ \text{Å})^3 = \mathbf{179.43\ Å^3}$

(b) The primitive unit cell has the volume associated with one lattice point:

$$\frac{179.43\ \text{Å}^3}{4} = \mathbf{44.86\ Å^3}$$

(c) $\#\ \text{beams} = \frac{4}{3}\pi\left(\frac{2}{2.2896\ \text{Å}}\right)^3 44.86\ \text{Å}^3 = 125.24 = \mathbf{125\ beams}\ \text{observable}$

Note that there is no such thing as a fraction of a diffracted beam--hence we round the answer down.

(d) $\#\ \text{beams} = \frac{4}{3}\pi\left(\frac{2}{0.7093\ \text{Å}}\right)^3 44.86\ \text{Å}^3 = \mathbf{4212\ beams}\ \text{observable}$

21-55. As in problem No. 25, in this monoclinic structure we may neglect terms in α and γ because their cosines are 0.

Then:

$$V = abc\sqrt{1 - \cos^2\beta}$$
$$= (11.04\ \text{Å})\ (10.98\ \text{Å})\ (10.92\ \text{Å})\ \sqrt{1 - \cos^2(96.73)}$$
$$= 1314\ \text{Å}^3 = 1.314 \times 10^{-21}\ \text{cm}^3$$

This is the volume of 48 S atoms. Their mass will be:

$$48\ \text{S atoms} \times \left(\frac{32.066\ \text{u}}{1\ \text{S atom}}\right)\left(\frac{1\ \text{g}}{6.0221 \times 10^{23}\ \text{u}}\right) = 2.5559 \times 10^{-21}\ \text{g}$$

The density is then:

$$d = \frac{2.5559 \times 10^{-21}\ \text{g}}{1.314 \times 10^{-21}\ \text{cm}^3} = \mathbf{1.945\ g\ cm^{-3}}$$

21-57. (a) With $\alpha = \gamma = 90^o$ and $\beta \neq 90^o$, the system is **monoclinic.**

(b) $(HgNO_2)_4$ is the contents of the unit cell. It has a mass of 986.62 u, or 1.6379×10^{-21} g. We can then compare the data.

21-57. (continued)

Report	Mass per cell	V_{cell}	Density = Mass/V
1	1.6379×10^{-21} g	271.02 Å^3 = 2.7102×10^{-22} cm^3	6.0435 g cm^{-3}
2	1.6379×10^{-21} g	273.74 Å^3 = 2.7374×10^{-22} cm^3	5.983 g cm^{-3}

(c) The unit cell contents must contain a whole-number multiple of the formula unit. Hence, each Hg(I) must be matched by one NO_2^-.

(d) The second report contains less precise data for the axis lengths, suggesting a precision to ±0.001 Å. The first report is more precise, judging by significant figures. Clearly, however, the variation in the data--by 1% in the volume--is greater than that suggested by the significant figures.

21-59. (a) The wavelength of the neutrons is determined by the de Broglie relation:

$$\lambda = \frac{h}{mv} = \frac{\left(6.6261 10^{-34}\text{ J s}\right)}{\left(1.6749 \times 10^{-27}\text{ kg}\right)\left(2.639 \times 10^{3}\text{ m s}^{-1}\right)}$$

$$= \mathbf{1.499 \times 10^{-10}\ m = 1.499\ Å}$$

(b) "Scattered in second order" means $n = 2$ in the Bragg equation. We have $2\theta = 36.26^{o}$, so $\theta = 18.13^{o}$. Then: $d = \dfrac{n\lambda}{2\sin\theta} = \dfrac{(2)\left(1.499\text{ Å}\right)}{2\sin\left(18.13^{o}\right)} = \mathbf{4.817\ Å}$.

(c) If the crystal has a rock salt structure, then there are Na^+ ions at the unit cell corners with H^- ions lying half-way between them. Thus, the Na-H distance is one-half the unit cell edge length, or **2.408 Å**.

(d) The Na-H distance is the sum of the ionic radii. Therefore, the H^- radius is 2.408 Å - 0.98 Å = **1.43 Å**.

21-61. (a) In a hypothetical 100 g sample, there will be 28.31 g O (= 1.7694 mol O) and 71.69 g Ti (= 1.4973 mol Ti), so we get: $Ti_{\frac{1.4973}{1.7694}}O = Ti_{0.8462}O$

(b) The defect here is the same as in problem 21-43 -- M(III) ions in place of some M(II) ions. We may use the same equation as in problem No. 43 to determine the stoichiometric coefficient for the ions in the +3 oxidation state.

$y = 2 - 2x = 2 - 2(0.8462) = 0.3076.$

This gives a modified formula "$Ti(II)_{0.5386}Ti(III)_{0.3076}O$".

The fraction of sites occupied by Ti(III) is 0.3076. The fraction of vacant sites is 1 - 0.8462 = **0.1538.**

21-63. Mineralogical orpiment had the opportunity to grow over geological time spans -- perhaps millions of years -- and this may be absolutely required for growth of large single crystals. Also, in nature the material may have been subject to countless cycles of heating and cooling that enabled it to anneal to a low energy form. Neither of these conditions are easily matched in the laboratory.

CHAPTER 22 - SILICON AND SOLID-STATE MATERIALS

22-1. As we have seen, most particularly in Chapter 17, there is a simple relationship between light energy and wavelength:

$$E = \frac{hc}{\lambda} = \frac{(6.626 \times 10^{-34}\ \mathrm{J\ s})(2.998 \times 10^{8}\ \mathrm{m\ s^{-1}})}{920 \times 10^{-9}\ \mathrm{m}} = \mathbf{2.16 \times 10^{-19}\ J}$$

This is the *minimum* energy that will cause an electron to move from the valence to the conduction band of the semiconductor. Light of higher energy will also move electrons accross the band gap.

22-3. We will have: $E\,(\text{mole}) = E\,(\text{band-gap width}) \times N_O$

$$= (8.7 \times 10^{-19}\ \mathrm{J})(6.0221 \times 10^{23}\ \mathrm{mol^{-1}})$$

$$= 524{,}000\ \mathrm{J\ mol^{-1}}$$

$$n_O = (4.80 \times 10^{15}\ \mathrm{cm^{-3}}K^{-3/2})(300\ \mathrm{K})^{3/2} e^{-\left[524{,}000\ \mathrm{J\ mol^{-1}}/(2 \times 8.3145\ \mathrm{J\ mol\ K^{-1}} \times 300\ \mathrm{K})\right]}$$

$$= \mathbf{6.1 \times 10^{-27}\ cm^{-3}}$$

This is considerably less -- about 50 orders of magnitude less -- than the number of *atoms* per cubic centimeter. There will be essentially no electrons in diamond's conduction band at 300 K.

22-5. The starting point of this class of semiconductors is the number of electrons in a pure group IV element -- four per atom. If we dope Si with P, then we are adding an element with five valence electrons in place of one with four. There will be extra electrons and the conduction will be of the ***n***-type to indicate the negative charge carriers. If we dope InSb, a III-V semiconductor, with Zn, then we are adding an element with fewer than 4 electrons. There will be electrons missing from the structure relative to pure InSb. Conduction will be of the ***p***-type, to indicate the positive charge carriers, also known as holes.

22-7. This is the reverse of the calculation in No. 1 above:

$$\lambda = \frac{hc}{E} = \frac{(6.626 \times 10^{-34}\ \text{J s})(2.998 \times 10^{8}\ \text{m s}^{-1})}{2.9 \times 10^{-19}\ \text{J}} = 6.85 \times 10^{-7}\ \text{m} = \mathbf{680\ nm}$$

Light of this or shorter wavelengths will have enough energy to promote electrons from the valence to the conduction band.

22-9. White room temperature ZnO absorbs no visible light. When heated, it appears yellow because it absorbs purple light (complementary to yellow). We can explain this by envisioning light of longer and longer wavelengths becoming capable of promoting electrons across a band gap that is **decreasing** with temperature.

22-11.

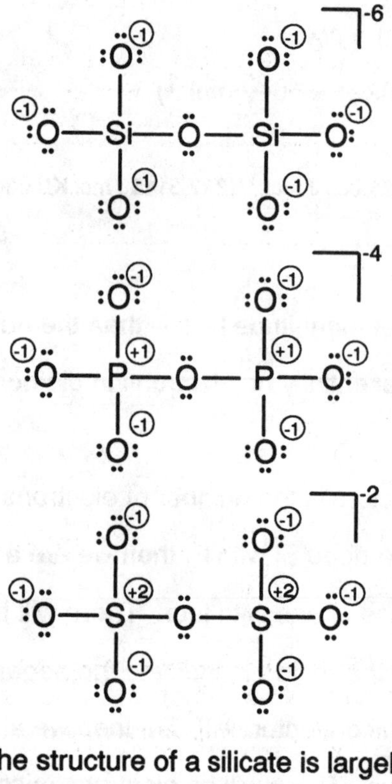

If we went to P and then S as the central atom, we would be introducing elements with additional valence electrons *when neutral.* They would form structures of the same overall shape and electron distribution, but with two fewer total charges on the "O_3ZOZO_3" unit. Charge neutrality would be maintained by the placement of positive formal charges on the "Z" atoms -- +1 on P, +2 on S. Taking this process one step further, with Cl there would be the same structure and electron distribution on the *neutral* molecule Cl_2O_7.

22-13. The structure of a silicate is largely set by the Si : 0 ratio. The ratio is determined by the number of lone O's only. Hydroxide anions are operating as counterions in the structure, as in talc (Figure 22-4f in the textbook). In all of these structures O and Si will be in their most geochemically stable oxidation

22-13. (continued)

states, O(-2) and Si(+4). The other oxidation states are determined either by prior knowledge (e.g., Na is always Na(1+) in compounds) or by the need for overall charge neutrality.

	Si : O ratio	Structure type	Other oxidation numbers
(a)	1 : 4	discrete tetrahedral SiO_4^{4-} anions	Ca(+2), Fe(+3)
(b)	1 : 2$^1/_2$	infinite sheets	Na(+1), Zr(+2)
(c)	1 : 3$^1/_2$	pairs of tetrahedra	Ca(+2), Zn(+2)
(d)	1 : 2$^1/_2$	infinite sheets	Mg(+2), H(+1)

22-15. For these compounds, it is the ratio of the (Al + Si) : O that determines the structure. The oxidation number of Al is +3, of Si is +4, and of O is -2 in all.

	(Al +Si) : O ratio	Structure type	Other oxidation numbers
(a)	1 : 2	infinite network	Li(+1)
(b)	1 : 2$^1/_2$	infinite sheets	K(+1), H(+1)
(c)	1 : 3	closed rings or infinite single chains	Mg(+2)

22-17. (a) Quartz is a form of SiO_2. The reaction then is:

$$CaCO_3\,(s) + SiO_2\,(s) \rightarrow CaSiO_3\,(s) + CO_2\,(g)$$

(b) For this reaction we will have:

$$\Delta H^o = \Delta H_f^o\,(CaSiO_3\,(s)) + \Delta H_f^o\,(CO_2\,(g)) - \Delta H_f^o\,(CaCO_3\,(s)) - \Delta H_f^o\,(SiO_2\,(s))$$

$$= (1\text{ mol} \times -1634.94\frac{\text{kJ}}{\text{mol}}) + (1\text{ mol} \times -393.51\frac{\text{kJ}}{\text{mol}})$$

$$- (1\text{ mol} \times -1206.92\frac{\text{kJ}}{\text{mol}}) - (1\text{ mol} \times -910.94\frac{\text{kJ}}{\text{mol}}) = \mathbf{+\,89.41\ kJ}$$

$$\Delta S^o = S^o(CaSiO_3\,(s)) + S^o(CO_2\,(g)) - S^o(CaCO_3\,(s)) - S^o(SiO_2\,(s))$$

$$= (1\text{ mol} \times 81.92\frac{\text{J}}{\text{mol-K}}) + (1\text{ mol} \times 213.63\frac{\text{J}}{\text{mol-K}})$$

$$- (1\text{ mol} \times 92.9\frac{\text{J}}{\text{mol-K}}) - (1\text{ mol} \times 41.84\frac{\text{J}}{\text{mol-K}}) = \mathbf{+\,160.8\ J\ K^{-1}}$$

22-17. (continued)

(c) As in Chapter 12, for equilibrium we evaluate the point where ΔG is zero:

$$T = \frac{\Delta H}{\Delta S} = \frac{89,410 \text{ J}}{160.8 \text{ J K}^{-1}} = 556 \text{ K}$$

Because ΔH and ΔS are both greater than zero, the reaction will be spontaneous at temperatures above this point: **T > 556 K**

22-19. Ceramics have tremendous strength in resisting deformation, but they are very vulnerable to catastrophic cracking. Metals are ductile, which makes them flexible enough to withstand repeated stresses but also vulnerable to bending under intense stress.

22-21. Ceramics are shaped either by setting a precursor in a certain form followed by heating or by grinding. Metals can be shaped by casting molten metal, but they can also be bent to a final shape after they are produced.

22-23. The SiO_2 and $MgSiO_3$ are generated as a grainy network within the product. Still, though the product is heterogeneous, each microcrystal is pure SiO_2 or $MgSiO_3$, so we write those substance as products of the reaction.

$$Mg_3Si_4O_{10}(OH)_2 \, (s) \rightarrow 3 \, MgSiO_3 \, (s) + SiO_2 \, (s) + H_2O \, (g)$$

22-25. The molar mass of this sample of glass, which corresponds to the "soda-lime glass" discussed in the text, is 478.57 g mol^{-1}. Thus, 2.50 kg (=2500 g) of glass contains $^{2500 \text{ g}}/_{478.57 \text{ g mol}^{-1}}$ = 5.224 mol of glass.

Carbon dioxide is produced in the manufacture of glass because of the use of sodium carbonate and calcium carbonate as the ultimate sources of the sodium and calcium ions in the glass. In this case, the overall process is:

$$6 \, SiO_2 + Na_2CO_3 + CaCO_3 \rightarrow Na_2O{\bullet}CaO{\bullet}(SiO_2)_6 + 2 \, CO_2.$$

Thus we have a 2 : 1 ratio of CO_2 to glass, and for the manufacture of 5.224 mol of glass we will generate 2 × 5.224 mol = 10.448 mol of CO_2. This will occupy a volume of 10.448 mol × 22.4 L mol^{-1} = **234 L of CO_2** at STP.

22-27. We can make our old reliable assumption of a 100.00 g working sample for this analysis. We must then determine the masses of each of the elements from the percentage composition of the glass and the composition of the oxides.

Oxide	Fraction of glass	Mass fraction of M in oxide	Mass of M in 100 g of glass	Moles of M in 100 g of glass
SiO_2	0.724	$\frac{28.086}{60.085}=0.4674$	33.840 g	1.2049 mol
Na_2O	0.181	$\frac{45.980}{61.979}=0.7419$	13.428 g	0.5841 mol
CaO	0.081	$\frac{40.078}{56.077}=0.7147$	5.789 g	0.1444 mol
Al_2O_3	0.010	$\frac{53.964}{101.962}=0.5293$	0.529 g	0.0196 mol
MgO	0.002	$\frac{24.305}{40.304}=0.6030$	0.121 g	0.0050 mol
BaO	0.002	$\frac{137.33}{153.33}=0.8956$	0.179 g	0.0013 mol

The total mass of all the metal in this sample is 53.886 g, which means the mass of oxygen is 100.000 - 58.886 = 46.114 g. This corresponds to 2.882 mol of O. We conclude the problem by relating the number of moles of the metal atoms to one mole of O. To do this, we divide the mole amounts in the 100 g sample by 2.882. We then obtain, per mol of O:

Si: **0.418 mol** Na: **0.203 mol** Ca: **0.050 mol**

Al: **0.0068 mol** Mg: **0.002 mol** Ba: **0.0005 mol**

22-29. For this reaction we will have:

$$\Delta H^o = \Delta H_f^o\,((CaO)_3SiO_2\ (s)) - 3\,\Delta H_f^o\,(CaO\ (s)) - \Delta H_f^o\,(SiO_2\ (s))$$

$$= (1\ \text{mol} \times -2929.2\frac{\text{kJ}}{\text{mol}}) - (3\ \text{mol} \times -635.09\ \frac{\text{kJ}}{\text{mol}}) - (1\ \text{mol} \times -910.94\frac{\text{kJ}}{\text{mol}})$$

$$= -\ \mathbf{113.0\ kJ}$$

22-31. (a) $SiO_2\ (s) + 3\ C\ (s) \rightarrow SiC\ (s) + 2\ CO\ (g)$

(b) $\Delta H^o = \Delta H_f^o\ (SiC\ (s)) + 2\ \Delta H_f^o\ (CO\ (g)) - 3\ \Delta H_f^o\ (C\ (s)) - \Delta H_f^o\ (SiO_2\ (s))$

$$= (1\ \text{mol} \times -65.3\frac{\text{kJ}}{\text{mol}}) + (2\ \text{mol} \times -110.52\ \frac{\text{kJ}}{\text{mol}})$$

$$- (3\ \text{mol} \times 0.00\frac{\text{kJ}}{\text{mol}}) - (1\ \text{mol} \times -910.94\frac{\text{kJ}}{\text{mol}}) = \mathbf{+\ 624.6\ kJ}$$

(c) Because silicon carbide is an extended three dimensionald structure formed from elements of similar electronegativity, it will have a high melting point, great hardness, and poor conductivity.

22-33. The reaction is: $SiC\ (s) + 2\ O_2\ (g) \rightarrow SiO_2\ (s) + CO_2\ (g)$

$\Delta G^o = \Delta G_f^o\ (SiO_2\ (s)) + \Delta G_f^o\ (CO_2\ (g)) - 2\ \Delta G_f^o\ (O_2\ (g)) - \Delta G_f^o\ (SiC\ (s))$

$$= (1\ \text{mol} \times -856.67\frac{\text{kJ}}{\text{mol}}) + (1\ \text{mol} \times -394.36\ \frac{\text{kJ}}{\text{mol}})$$

$$- (2\ \text{mol} \times 0.00\frac{\text{kJ}}{\text{mol}}) - (1\ \text{mol} \times -62.8\frac{\text{kJ}}{\text{mol}}) = \mathbf{-1188.2\ kJ}$$

Because this process has a negative standard free energy change, we expect that silicon carbide is **unstable** with respect combustion with oxygen.

22-35. The sum of the charges on the elements must add to zero. We already have:

2 Ba (+2) + 1 Y (+3) + 7 O(-2) = 7- charges

The copper ions must counter these charges with +7 charges overall. The charge per copper -- and their oxidation number -- is $+^7/_3$.

22-37. The silicon atoms in solid silicon are sp^3 hybridized while the carbon atoms in graphite are sp^2 hybridized. If silicon adopted a graphite structure, then it would be more conducting than in the normal silicon structure. However, conduction in the graphite structure occurs through an almost infinite π-bonding system formed by the p orbitals. π-bonding is strong with carbon *2p* orbitals but it is much weaker with silicon (and other atoms with a 3*p* valence shell). Silicon in the graphite structure would probably be a poorer conductor than carbon in the graphite structure.

22-39. It is easy to focus on the actions of the people in this problem. After all, it is they, not the empty seat, that move. But the *unique* thing is the empty seat that appears to move one position to the right every 5 minutes, with a velocity of 0.2 positions min^{-1}. The same situation applies for the holes in a *p*-type semiconductor. A hole is, well, nothing. The particles that move are the electrons. But there are so many electrons that watching them move and interact with the environment (an external electric field, for example) is difficult. It is easier to get an exact description of the electronic properties of a *p*-type semiconductor by watching the positions and interactions of the holes.

22-41. (a) This problem asks for a standard state calculation for the reaction:

$$SiO_2\ (quartz) \rightarrow SiO_2\ (cristobalite)$$

$$\Delta H^o = \Delta H_f^o\ (SiO_2,\ \text{cristobalite}) - \Delta H_f^o\ (SiO_2,\ \text{quartz})$$
$$= (1\ \text{mol} \times -909.48 \frac{\text{kJ}}{\text{mol}}) - (1\ \text{mol} \times -910.94 \frac{\text{kJ}}{\text{mol}}) = \mathbf{+1.46\ kJ}$$

$$\Delta S^o = S^o(SiO_2,\ \text{cristobalite}) - S^o(SiO_2,\ \text{quartz})$$
$$= (1\ \text{mol} \times 42.68 \frac{\text{J}}{\text{mol-K}}) - (1\ \text{mol} \times -856.67 \frac{\text{J}}{\text{mol-K}}) = \mathbf{+0.84\ J\ K^{-1}}$$

$$\Delta G^o = \Delta G_f^o\ (SiO_2,\ \text{cristobalite}) - \Delta G_f^o\ (SiO_2,\ \text{quartz})$$
$$(1\ \text{mol} \times -855.43 \frac{\text{kJ}}{\text{mol}}) - (1\ \text{mol} \times -856.67 \frac{\text{kJ}}{\text{mol}}) = \mathbf{+1.24\ kJ}$$

(b) The quartz form is more stable under standard state conditions.

(c) With a positive entropy of reaction, there may be a temperature where cristobalite becomes more stable than quartz.

22-43. This silicate has a Si : O ratio in the silicate network of 12 : 30 = 1 : $2^1/_2$. We expect it to be built of **infinite sheets** of $Si_2O_5^{2-}$ units. The oxidation numbers of the "invariant" elements are: Si(+4), H(+1), Mg(+2), O(-2) and Cl(-1). These elements have a total charge of -26. This must be balanced by positive charges on the 13 transition metal ions. Average oxidation states of **Mn(+2)** and **Fe(+2)** are expected.

22-45. (a) The reaction is a simple dehydration reaction:

$Mg_3Si_4O_{10}(OH)_2$ *(s)*+ Mg_2SiO_4 *(s)* → 5 $MgSiO_3$ *(s)*+ H_2O *(g)*

(b) The only substance in this reaction that is not a pure condensed phase is water vapor. Therefore, $K = P_{H_2O}$. Increasing the pressure of the system at equilibrium will cause P_{H_2O} to rise above K and the reaction will shift **right to left** as a result.

22-47. The difference between the reactant anorthite and the product kaolinite is the exchange of one Ca^{2+} ion in anorthite for two hydrogen ions and a water molecule in kaolinite. This reaction is promoted by carbonic acid:

$CaAl_2Si_2O_8$ *(s)*+ H_2CO_3 *(aq)* + H_2O *(l)* → $CaCO_3$ *(s)* + $Al_2Si_2O_5(OH)_4$ *(s)*

As the pH is lowered, the relative amount of carbonic acid compared to carbonate and hydrogen carbonate will increase. This will **favor** the weathering of anorthite.

22-49. Air-rich kilns will have a relatively large amount of O_2 present, compared to the amount needed for fuel combustion. That oxygen will maintain the iron in a high oxidation state, so an **air rich kiln will favor red colors**. Conversely, the presence of a smoky atmosphere suggests soot formed by incomplete oxidation of a fossil fuel. A smoky kiln will have a relatively small amount of oxygen present, so low oxidation states of iron will be favored. **A smoky kiln will favor black colors.**

22-51. The composition of leaded glass in Table 22-2 includes 56% of "SiO_2" and 29% of "PbO" *by mass.* To obtain relative chemical amounts, we must convert these to moles. For convenience, let us assume a 100 g sample size containing 56 g of SiO_2 and 29 g of PbO.

22-51. (continued)

$$\text{mol Si} = (56\text{ g SiO}_2)\times\left(\frac{28.086\text{ g Si}}{60.085\text{ g SiO}_2}\right)\times\left(\frac{1\text{ mol Si}}{28.086\text{ g Si}}\right) = 0.932\text{ mol Si}$$

$$\text{mol Pb} = (29\text{ g PbO})\times\left(\frac{207.2\text{ g Pb}}{223.2\text{ g PbO}}\right)\times\left(\frac{1\text{ mol Pb}}{207.2\text{ g Pb}}\right) = 0.130\text{ mol Pb}$$

Therefore, the Pb : Si ratio is 0.130 : 0.932 = **1: 7.17.**

22-53. Since the formulas are so similar, we will start by determining the relative chemical amounts of $MgCO_3$ and $CaCO_3$. In exactly 100 grams of dolomite, there will be 45.7 g of $MgCO_3$ and 54.3 g of $CaCO_3$. Then:

$$MgCO_3\text{: } 45.7\text{ g MgCO}_3\times\left(\frac{1\text{ mol MgCO}_3}{84.31\text{ g MgCO}_3}\right) = 0.542\text{ mol MgCO}_3$$

$$CaCO_3\text{: } 54.3\text{ g CaCO}_3\times\left(\frac{1\text{ mol CaCO}_3}{100.087\text{ g CaCO}_3}\right) = 0.542\text{ mol CaCO}_3$$

There are equal chemical amounts of both compounds. So we can write the empirical formula of dolomite as $MgCO_3 \bullet CaCO_3$, or **$CaMg(CO_3)_2$**.

22-55. Beryllia is an amphoteric oxide, which can behave as an acid or a base (see Chapter 4-6). Like another amphoteric oxide, alumina (Al_2O_3), beryllia can react with either aqueous acid or base, or even with water:

With acid: $BeO\ (s) + 2\ H^+\ (aq) \rightarrow H_2O\ (l) + Be^{2+}\ (aq)$

With base: $BeO\ (s) + 2\ OH^-\ (aq) + H_2O\ (l) \rightarrow Be(OH)_4^-\ (aq)$

With water: $BeO\ (s) + H_2O\ (l) \rightarrow Be(OH)_2\ (s)$

This last reaction is probably the source of volatile beryllium that the book mentions.

22-57. $Si_3N_4\ (s) + 12\ HF\ (aq) \rightarrow 3\ SiF_4\ (g) + 4\ NH_3\ (g)$

This, and many other reactions involving the formation of Si-F bonds, is driven by the strength of the Si-F linkage.

CHAPTER 23 - CHEMICAL PROCESSES

23-1. In a batch process, the reactants are all put into a single reactor and the reaction is allowed to proceed. The product or products are removed only after the completion of the process. Thus, a batch process has a discrete beginning, middle, and end. A continuous process is characterized by the continual addition of one or more of the reactants to some reactor, which contains embedded in it the heaters, pressurizers, catalysts, etc., needed to produce the product or products. The product or products are removed continuously also, though a separate purification step may still be required.

23-3. Geochemical processes are not driven by any "requirements," while biochemical processes must meet the needs of the organism they support. Thus, although both geochemical and biochemical processes must obey the laws of thermodynamics, only biochemical processes often exhibit high selectivity associated with a specific goal. Since organisms are also under time pressures, biochemical processes must often be very fast. Geochemical processes can be very slow, though exceptions are known, such as the eruption of a volcano. The process diagram for the conversion of igneous calcium carbonate might look something like:

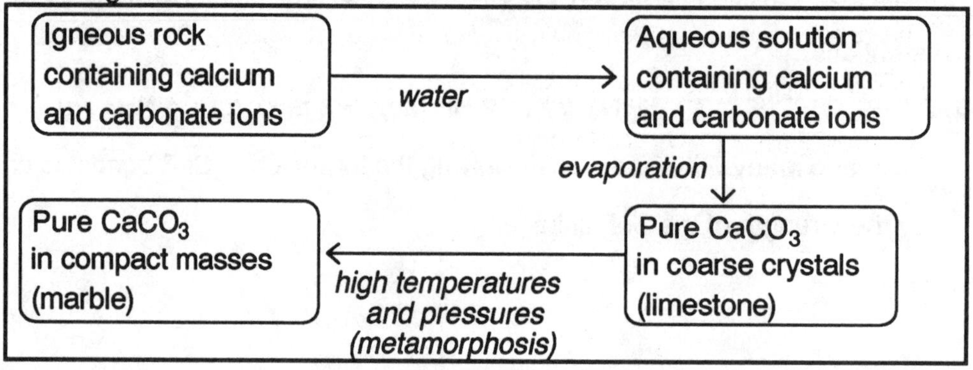

23-5. (a) Pure sulfur is obtained directly from mining the S *(s)* formed by reduction of calcium sulfate (gypsum) by methane in the presence of carbon dioxide.

(b) Elemental carbon is the major constituent of coal, itself produced by the geochemical and biochemical conversion of biomass.

(c) Molybdenum is a less-common metal, and as such is rarely obtained as in its own ores. It is often obtained as a constituent of other ores, especially in igneous rocks. Certain exceptional deposits of MoS_2 do, however, exist.

23-7. Lead sulfate will deposit in the presence of lead (II) ions -- the likely product of the oxidation of lead -- and this will coat the lead that makes up the chamber.

23-9. The following observations about the direct process suggest certain improvements, given the reaction stoichiometry and thermodynamics.

$$SO_2\,(g) + {}^1/_2\,O_2\,(g) \rightarrow SO_3\,(g) \qquad \Delta H^o = -98.9 \text{ kJ}$$

OBSERVATION		POSSIBLE IMPROVEMENT
There are fewer particles of gas products than gaseous reactants	⇒	Increase the reaction pressure
Reaction is exothermic	⇒	Cool the reaction / lower the temperature
SO_3 *(g)* is more soluble than SO_2 *(g)* in H_2SO_4 *(aq)*	⇒	Include H_2SO_4 *(aq)* in the unit if it is done in a batch process; pass gases over water before recycling in a continuous process. This will remove SO_3 selectively

23-11. The reaction must convert SO_2 *(g)* into SO_3 *(g)* or H_2SO_4 *(aq)*, either of which contains sulfur (VI). A balanced aqueous reaction with H_2O_2 is:

$$SO_2\,(g) + H_2O_2\,(aq) \rightarrow HSO_4^-\,(aq) + H^+\,(aq)$$

23-11. (continued)

In this case, the free energy calculation is as follows:

$$\Delta G^o_f = \Delta G^o\,(HSO_4^-\,(aq)) + \Delta G^o(H^+\,(aq)) - \Delta G^o(SO_2\,(g)) - \Delta G^o(H_2O_2\,(g))$$

$$= (1\text{ mol} \times -755.91\,\frac{\text{kJ}}{\text{mol}}) + (1\text{ mol} \times 0.00\,\frac{\text{kJ}}{\text{mol}})$$

$$- (1\text{ mol} \times -300.19\,\frac{\text{kJ}}{\text{mol}}) - (1\text{ mol} \times -134.03\,\frac{\text{kJ}}{\text{mol}}) = \mathbf{-321.7\ kJ}$$

Note that the sulfuric acid will completely ionize to hydrogen ion and hydrogen sulfate. This reaction would be spontaneous; and aqueous H_2O_2 would work to oxidize SO_2 to SO_3, at least thermodynamically.

23-13. The answer for this comes from the many reactions discussed in section 23-2.

Extraction of ore:	$ZnS\,(s) + {}^3/_2\,O_2\,(g) \rightarrow ZnO\,(s) + SO_2\,(g)$
Direct oxidation of SO_2:	$SO_2\,(g) + {}^1/_2\,O_2\,(g) \rightarrow SO_3\,(g)$
Dissolution in water:	$SO_3\,(g) + H_2O\,(l) \rightarrow H_2SO_4\,(aq)$
Overall:	$H_2O\,(l) + ZnS\,(s) + 2\,O_2\,(g) \rightarrow ZnO\,(s) + H_2SO_4\,(aq)$

23-15. This is both an oxidation-reduction and an acid base reaction. In balancing it, we treat elemental phosphorus as having a simple formula "P". One may use half reactions for greatest insight, even though the reaction is done directly. Note that this is a reaction in aqueous acid.

Oxidation: $4\,H_2O\,(l) + P\,(s) \rightarrow H_3PO_4\,(aq) + 5\,H^+\,(aq) + 5\,e^-$

Reduction: $2\,e^- + 2\,H^+\,(aq) + H_2SO_4\,(aq) \rightarrow SO_2\,(g) + 2\,H_2O\,(l)$

The oxidation reaction is multiplied by 2 and the reduction reaction is multiplied by 5 to cancel the electrons (H^+ cancels in the process, too.)

Overall: $2\,P\,(s) + 5\,H_2SO_4\,(aq) \rightarrow 2\,H_3PO_4\,(aq) + 5\,SO_2\,(g) + H_2O\,(l)$

23-17. The best industrial starting materials for almost any inorganic acid are often sulfuric acid and an ore. In the case of these minerals and acids:

$$CaF_2\,(s) + H_2SO_4\,(l) \rightarrow 2\,HF\,(g) + CaSO_4\,(s)$$

$$2\,NaCl\,(s) + H_2SO_4\,(l) \rightarrow 2\,HCl\,(g) + Na_2SO_4\,(s)$$

23-19. The Kraft process is used in converting wood pulp into paper. An interesting aspect is the use of organic matter to reduce sulfate to sulfide. In that step "[C]" stands for many different compounds, all of which serve as reductants of sulfate, yielding CO_2 also. Together, the important individual steps are:

Synthesis of sodium sulfate:

$$H_2SO_4\ (aq) + 2\ NaOH\ (aq) \rightarrow 2\ H_2O\ (l) + Na_2SO_4\ (s)$$

Reduction of sodium sulfate:

$$Na_2SO_4\ (s) + 2\ [C] \rightarrow Na_2S\ (s) + 2\ CO_2\ (g)$$

23-21. Disulfuric acid is made up of sulfuric acid and sulfur trioxide. When it reacts with water, we can envision it splitting into its components followed by hydration of SO_3 to give H_2SO_4: $H_2S_2O_7\ (s) + H_2O\ (l) \rightarrow 2\ H_2SO_4\ (l)$

23-23. Note that the phrase "amount of fixed nitrogen" refers to elemental N, which is appropriate because the emitted nitrogen is in a variety of substances. Also note that, 2×10^8 kg is equal to 2×10^{11} g and, as discussed in problem 16-21, 1 year is equal to 3.16×10^7 sec. In this case:

$$\left(\frac{2\times10^{11}\text{g N}}{1\text{ year}}\right)\times\left(\frac{1\text{ mol N}}{14.00674\text{ g N}}\right)\times\left(\frac{6.0221\times10^{23}\text{N atoms}}{1\text{ mol N}}\right)\times\left(\frac{1\text{ year}}{3.16\times10^{7}\text{ s}}\right)$$

$= \mathbf{3 \times 10^{26}}$ **N atoms** $\mathbf{s^{-1}}$

23-25. *Synthesis of lime:* $CaCO_3\ (s) \rightarrow CaO\ (s) + CO_2\ (g)$

Synthesis of calcium carbide:

$$CaO\ (s) + 3\ C\ (s) \rightarrow CaC_2\ (s) + CO\ (g)$$

Fixation of nitrogen into calcium cyanamide:

$$CaC_2\ (s) + N_2\ (g) \rightarrow CaCN_2\ (s) + C\ (s)$$

Hydrolysis of calcium cyanamide:

$$CaCN_2\ (s) + 4\ H_2O\ (l) \rightarrow Ca(OH)_2 + CO_2\ (g) + 2\ NH_3\ (g)$$

Overall: $CaCO_3\ (s) + 2\ C\ (s) + N_2\ (g) + 4\ H_2O\ (l)$

$$\rightarrow Ca(OH)_2\ (s) + 2\ CO_2\ (g) + CO\ (g) + 2\ NH_3\ (g)$$

23-25. (continued)

The data in the appendix give *for this reaction*: ΔH = **+374.4 kJ.** The reaction has two moles of ammonia; for each molecule of ammonia, the enthalpy change is ΔH = **+187.2 kJ mol^{-1}**.

23-27. Since the Haber-Bosch process has fewer gas molecules in the product than there are in the reactants, it will go more to the product if the pressure is raised. On the other hand, this creates engineering and safety issues. Concerning temperature, the text shows that the reaction is exothermic. It will go more to the product if the temperature is kept lower, regardless of the pressure. But, finally, the reaction will go more quickly at **higher** temperatures.

23-29. All of the steps in the Ostwald process are exothermic. So higher conversions are favored by **lower** temperatures.

23-31. These reactions involve the same half reaction for the nitric acid:

$$1\ e^- + H^+\ (aq) + HNO_3\ (aq) \rightarrow NO_2\ (g) + H_2O\ (l)$$

The reactions for the metal both follow the same pattern: $M\ (s) \rightarrow M^{3+} + 3\ e^-$

These are combined in the right amounts to cancel the electrons:

$$3\ H^+\ (aq) + 3\ HNO_3\ (aq) + Cr\ (s) \rightarrow Cr^{3+}\ (aq) + 3\ NO_2\ (g) + 3\ H_2O\ (l)$$

$$3\ H^+\ (aq) + 3\ HNO_3\ (aq) + Fe\ (s) \rightarrow Fe^{3+}\ (aq) + 3\ NO_2\ (g) + 3\ H_2O\ (l)$$

23-33. 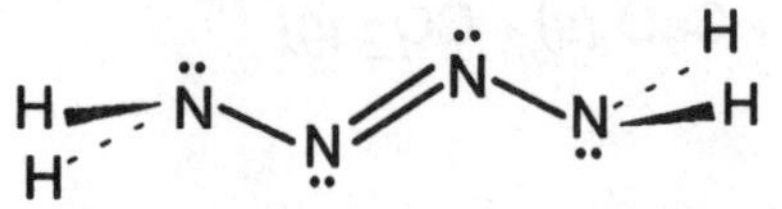

23-35. Specifying pH = 14 means that the reaction will occur with a standard 1 M concentration of hydroxide ion, and that ammonia will not be protonated. The disproportionation reaction would be:

$$3\ N_2H_4\ (aq) \rightarrow N_2\ (g) + 4\ NH_3\ (aq)$$

$\Delta\mathcal{E}^o = \mathcal{E}^o(N_2 \mid N_2H_4) - \mathcal{E}^o(N_2H_4 \mid NH_3) = 0.1\ V - (-1.16\ V) = +\ 1.3\ V$

A positive potential indicates the disproportionation reaction will be spontaneous. Hydrazine is thermodynamically **unstable** in aqueous base.

23-37. This kind of reaction is known as a "con-proportionation" because two oxidation states of nitrogen are present in the reactants and only one oxidation state of nitrogen is present among the products.

Oxidation: $N_2H_4\,(l) \rightarrow N_2\,(g) + 4\,H^+\,(aq) + 4\,e^-$

Reduction: $10\,e^- + 2\,HNO_3\,(l) + 10\,H^+\,(aq) \rightarrow N_2\,(g) + 6\,H_2O\,(l)$

Combined: $4\,HNO_3\,(l) + 5\,N_2H_4\,(l) \rightarrow 7\,N_2\,(g) + 12\,H_2O\,(l)$

$$\Delta H^o = 12\,\Delta H_f^o\,(H_2O\,(l)) + 7\,\Delta H_f^o\,(N_2\,(g)) - 5\,\Delta H_f^o\,(N_2H_4\,(l)) - 4\,\Delta H_f^o\,(HNO_3\,(l))$$

$$= (12\text{ mol} \times -285.83\,\frac{\text{kJ}}{\text{mol}}) + (7\text{ mol} \times 0.00\,\frac{\text{kJ}}{\text{mol}})$$

$$- (5\text{ mol} \times +50.63\,\frac{\text{kJ}}{\text{mol}}) - (4\text{ mol} \times -174.10\,\frac{\text{kJ}}{\text{mol}}) = \mathbf{-2986.71\text{ kJ}}$$

23-39. This process is not described in the chapter, but we can come up with a plan by working backwards ("retrosynthetically" in the language of modern synthetic chemistry) from our target to our starting material through pathways we know:

$N_2O_4 \Rightarrow NO_2 \Rightarrow$ NO and $O_2 \Rightarrow NH_3$ and $O_2 \Rightarrow N_2$ and H_2

We can then reconstruct the synthesis in the forward direction:

Ammonia synthesis: (Haber-Bosch process) $N_2\,(g) + 3\,H_2\,(g) \rightarrow 2\,NH_3\,(g)$

Nitrogen oxide synthesis: (Pt catalyzed) $4\,NH_3\,(g) + 5\,O_2\,(g) \rightarrow 4\,NO\,(g) + 6\,H_2O\,(g)$

Nitrogen dioxide synthesis: $2\,NO\,(g) + O_2\,(g) \rightarrow 2\,NO_2\,(g)$

Condensation of nitrogen dioxide: $2\,NO_2\,(g) \rightarrow N_2O_4\,(s)$

23-41. TNT by itself does not have all the oxygen required for complete combustion of its carbon to carbon dioxide. Getting full combustion requires an oxidizing agent. Ammonium nitrate is an excellent oxidant and powerful explosive in its own right. Its decomposition ($NH_4NO_3 \rightarrow N_2 + 2\,H_2O + {}^3/_2\,O_2$) also liberates oxygen gas to serve to complete the oxidation of the CO produced from TNT to CO_2.

23-43. (a) Aspirin is at a lower free energy than coal, hydrogen, and air. Coal, hydrogen, and the oxygen in air are all high-free energy species. As is mentioned in the text, they can serve as useful raw materials for the synthesis of intermediate free energy substances, like aspirin.

(b) Virtually any mixture, especially of salts in water, is a lower free energy than the separated components. Sea water is at lower free energy in this case.

(c) Carbon dioxide and water are at the lowest free energy of any carbon, hydrogen, and oxygen containing species. They are at lower free energy than vitamin A and oxygen.

23-45. This question, in both its parts, was answered in the "Chemistry in Progress" module at the end of Chapter 12 in the text. Plants use the energy of the sun, which they collect as light energy, to drive the processes of their life cycles. This coupling of a non-spontaneous process to a spontaneous one is the key to many processes. Included are the processes by which animals use the liberation of chemical energy available in their food (ultimately, plants) to drive their own, otherwise non-spontaneous biochemical pathways.

23-47. Over history, the following sources have been important sources of S for sulfuric acid. Note that one source, elemental sulfur, has been prominent in two different eras. In chronological order:

1a. Elemental sulfur, easily extracted.

2. Sulfide ores, as by-product of metal processing (early 19th century)

1b. Elemental sulfur, extracted from earth by the Frasch process (1890s)

3. Recovery of sulfur from fossil fuels as hydrogen sulfide (1970s)

4. Scrubbing of SO_2 from gases with hydrogen sulfide (Claus process , 1970s)

23-49.

Process	ΔH^o (kJ)	ΔS^o (J K^{-1})	ΔG^o (kJ)
$SO_2\ (g) + {}^1/_2\ O_2\ (g) \rightarrow SO_3\ (g)$	-98.89	-196.49	-70.89
$SO_2\ (g) + NO_2\ (g) \rightarrow SO_3\ (g) + NO\ (g)$	-63.63	-20.76	-35.63

Oxidation of SO_2 by O_2 has a larger driving force at room temperature than oxidation by NO_2. Therefore, the NO_2 reaction will function best if it is a catalytic pathway linked to the reoxidation of NO to NO_2 by O_2. Note, however, that the NO_2 reaction will become thermodynamically superior to the direct reaction of SO_2 by O_2 at higher temperatures because the NO_2 reaction is less endothermic.

23-51. An electrolysis reaction that makes $S_2O_8^{2-}$ from SO_4^{2-} will use the reaction as an anode connected to a hydrogen half-cell as the cathode. Then, for the overall reaction

$$2\ SO_4^{2-}\ (aq) + 2\ H^+\ (aq) \rightarrow S_2O_8^{2-} + H_2\ (g)$$

we have $\Delta\mathcal{E}^o = \mathcal{E}^o(H^+ \mid H_2) - \mathcal{E}^o(S_2O_8^{2-} \mid SO_4^{2-}) = 0.00\text{ V} - (+2.0\text{ V}) = -2.0\text{ V}$

The number of electrons transferred in this case, *n*, is 2.

In the Nernst equation:

$$\Delta\mathcal{E} = -2.0\text{ V} - \frac{0.0592\text{ V}}{2}\log\left(\frac{[S_2O_8^{2-}](P_{H_2})}{[SO_4^{2-}]^2[H^+]^2}\right)$$

$$= -2.0\text{ V} - \frac{0.0592\text{ V}}{2}\log\left(\frac{(0.5)(0.10)}{(1.0)^2(1.0)^2}\right)$$

$$= -2.0\text{ V} - (-0.04\text{ V}) = -1.96\text{ V}$$

The electrolysis unit must provide an electrical potential sufficient to overcome this thermodynamic limitation, or a potential of at least **+1.96 V.**

23-53. *Precipitation*: The product must be a sparingly soluble sulfate if it is to precipitate in the presence of the high concentration of hydrogen ions generated

$$Pb^{2+}\ (aq) + H_2SO_4\ (aq) \rightarrow PbSO_4\ (s) + 2\ H^+\ (aq) \qquad K = 1.5 \times 10^{-6}$$

23-53. (continued)

Acid base reaction: The "pickling" of steel, for example to dissolve iron oxide:

$$Fe_2O_3\ (s) + H_2SO_4\ (aq) \rightarrow 2\ Fe^{3+}\ (aq) + 6\ SO_4^{2-}\ (aq) + 6\ H_2O\ (l)$$

Oxidation-reduction reaction: The strong acid properties of sulfuric acid will cause many metals to oxidize, as in Charles' process for manufacturing hydrogen gas for balloons in the eighteenth century (problem 5-52):

$$Fe\ (s)\ +3\ H_2SO_4\ (aq) \rightarrow Fe^{2+}\ (aq) + 6\ SO_4^{2-}\ (aq) + H_2\ (g)$$

23-55. (a) We determine the free energy change at 1000 K by assuming that the enthalpy and entropy changes of the reaction are independent of temperature.

$$\Delta H^o = \Delta H_f^o\ (CO_2\ (g)) + 2\ \Delta H_f^o\ (H_2O\ (l)) + 4\ \Delta H_f^o\ (SO_2\ (g))$$

$$- 4\ \Delta H_f^o\ (SO_3\ (g)) - \Delta H_f^o\ (CH_4\ (g))$$

$$= (1\ mol \times -393.51\ \frac{kJ}{mol}) + (2\ mol \times -241.82\ \frac{kJ}{mol}) + (4\ mol \times -293.83\ \frac{kJ}{mol})$$

$$- (4\ mol \times -395.72\ \frac{kJ}{mol}) - (1\ mol \times -74.81\ \frac{kJ}{mol}) = -406.78\ kJ = -406{,}780\ J$$

$$\Delta S^o = S^o\ (CO_2\ (g)) + 2\ S^o\ (H_2O\ (l)) + 4\ S^o(SO_2\ (g))$$

$$- 4\ S^o(SO_3\ (g)) - S^o(CH_4\ (g))$$

$$= (1\ mol \times 213.63\ \frac{J}{mol\text{-}K}) + (2\ mol \times 188.72 \frac{J}{mol\text{-}K}) + (4\ mol \times 248.11 \frac{J}{mol\text{-}K})$$

$$- (4\ mol \times 256.65\ \frac{J}{mol\text{-}K}) - (1\ mol \times 186.15\ \frac{J}{mol\text{-}K}) = 370.76 \frac{J}{K}$$

At 1000 K : $\Delta G^o = -406{,}780\ J - (1000\ K \times 370.76 \frac{J}{K}) = -777{,}540\ J =$ $\mathbf{-777.54\ kJ}$

(b) For the critic's reaction:

$$\Delta H^o = \Delta H_f^o\ (CO_2\ (g)) + \Delta H_f^o\ (H_2O\ (l)) + \Delta H_f^o\ (H_2S\ (g))$$

$$- \Delta H_f^o\ (SO_3\ (g)) - \Delta H_f^o\ (CH_4\ (g))$$

$$= (1\ mol \times -393.51\ \frac{kJ}{mol}) + (1\ mol \times -241.82\ \frac{kJ}{mol}) + (1\ mol \times -20.63\ \frac{kJ}{mol})$$

$$- (1\ mol \times -395.72\ \frac{kJ}{mol}) - (1\ mol \times -74.81\ \frac{kJ}{mol}) = -185.43\ kJ = -185{,}430\ J$$

23-55. (continued)

$$\Delta S^o = S^o(CO_2\ (g)) + S^o(H_2O\ (l)) + S^o(H_2S\ (g)) - S^o(SO_3\ (g)) - S^o(CH_4\ (g))$$

$$= (1\text{ mol} \times 213.63\ \frac{J}{\text{mol-K}}) + (1\text{ mol} \times 188.72\frac{J}{\text{mol-K}})$$

$$+ (1\text{ mol} \times 205.68\frac{J}{\text{mol-K}}) - (1\text{ mol} \times 256.65\ \frac{J}{\text{mol-K}})$$

$$- (1\text{ mol} \times 186.15\ \frac{J}{\text{mol-K}}) = 165.23\frac{J}{K}$$

At 1000 K : ΔG^o = -185,430 J - (1000 K × 165.23$\frac{J}{K}$) = -350,700 J = **-350.70 kJ**

(c) It seems there is more driving force for your proposed reaction, until you realize that the free energy change *per mole of SO_3* is only -194 kJ for your reaction, while it is -351 kJ for the critic's reaction. Thus, in the presence of methane as reducing agent, H_2S is a more favored substance than SO_2. Still, in terms of the conversion of SO_3, your product -- SO_2 -- may be an intermediate on the path to more highly reduced H_2S. Perhaps the right conditions (catalysts, etc.) can stop the reaction at SO_2.

23-57. The basic repeat unit of a polymer indicates its empirical formula. In this drawing (lone pairs are omitted) two of the repeat units are indicated in the brackets.

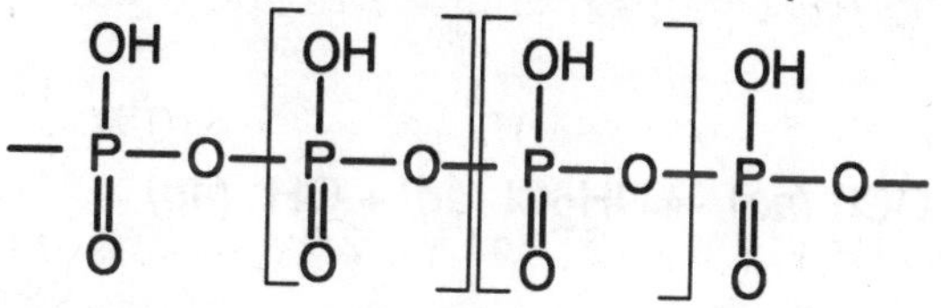

The bracketed atoms are "HPO_3" units, the empirical formula for metaphosphoric acid.

23-59. To rewrite the formula for an analysis of P_2O_5 content, we must pull that formula unit out of the rest of the formula. For superphosphate, the overall formula has 7 moles of $CaSO_4 \cdot 2\ H_2O$ (gypsum) 3 moles of $Ca(H_2PO_4) \cdot H_2O$:

$$(CaSO_4 \cdot 2\ H_2O)_7(Ca(H_2PO_4)_2 \cdot H_2O)_3 = Ca_{10}P_6S_7O_{69}H_{46}$$

$$Ca_{10}P_6S_7O_{69}H_{46} = (P_2O_5)_3(Ca_{10}S_7O_{54}H_{46})$$

The molar mass of "$(P_2O_5)_3$" is 425.835 g mol^{-1}. The molar mass of "$Ca_{10}P_6S_7O_{69}H_{46}$" is 1961.41 g mol^{-1}.

23-59. (continued)

The mass fraction of "P_2O_5" in superphosphate is $\frac{425.835}{1961.41} = 0.2171$, so regular superphosphate is **"21.7% P_2O_5."** Triple superphosphate has a phosphorus content about three times (actually 2.6 times) this amount, whence its name.

23-61. The Haber-Bosch process is very energy intensive, both in the actual hydrogen and nitrogen reaction and in the need to make high-free-energy hydrogen gas, which is usually done with coal and water as the starting materials.

23-63. This is a reaction where two different nitrogen oxidation states become one. For urea, the oxidation state of N is -3 (treating carbon as C (+4) in comparison with the related carbonic acid) and in nitrogen dioxide the oxidation state of N is +4.

The balanced reaction is: $4\ (NH_2)_2CO + 6\ NO_2 \rightarrow 7\ N_2 + 4\ CO_2 + 8\ H_2O$

For the reaction of NO, the nitrogen begins in the +2 oxidation state and we have: $2\ (NH_2)_2CO + 6\ NO \rightarrow 5\ N_2 + 2\ CO_2 + 4\ H_2O$

23-65. The suggestion of an NH_2Cl intermediate indicates the following possible reaction scheme:

chlorination of ammonia:

$$NH_3\ (aq) + OCl^-\ (aq) \rightarrow NH_2Cl\ (aq) + OH^-\ (aq)$$

coupling to hydrazine:

$$NH_3\ (aq) + NH_2Cl\ (aq) + OH^-\ (aq) \rightarrow N_2H_4\ (aq) + Cl^-\ (aq) + H_2O(l)$$

Hydroxide is also an intermediate in this case. This reaction is related to the very dangerous reaction that can result when household ammonia and chlorine bleach are mixed.

23-67. (a)

$$\Delta G^o = 4\,\Delta G_f^o\,(Fe_3O_4\ (s)) + 2\,\Delta G_f^o\,(H_2O\ (l)) + \Delta G_f^o\,(N_2\ (g))$$
$$- 6\,\Delta G_f^o\,(Fe_2O_3\ (s)) - \Delta G_f^o\,(N_2H_4\ (l))$$
$$= (4\text{ mol} \times -1015.5\ \frac{kJ}{mol}) + (2\text{ mol} \times -237.18\ \frac{kJ}{mol}) + (1\text{ mol} \times 0.00\ \frac{kJ}{mol})$$
$$- (6\text{ mol} \times -742.2\ \frac{kJ}{mol}) - (1\text{ mol} \times +128.1\ \frac{kJ}{mol}) = \mathbf{-211.26\ kJ}$$

(b) Including concentrated acid would result in two possible problems. First, the acid might actually dissolve some of the metal oxides. Second, the hydrazine would now be present as hydrazinium ion, $N_2H_5^+$. The simple reaction stoichiometry would then become:

$$6\,Fe_2O_3\ (s) + N_2H_5^+ \rightarrow 4\,Fe_3O_4\ (s) + N_2\ (g) + 2\,H_2O\ (l) + H^+\ (aq)$$

This reaction is less favored in the presence of high concentrations of hydrogen ion, so hydrazine is a poorer reducing agent under strong acid conditions.

CHAPTER 24 - CHEMISTRY OF THE HALOGENS

24-1. The determination of the equilibrium constant requires the standard free energy change for this reaction, which is calculated as follows:

$$\Delta G^o = 2\,\Delta G_f^o(OCl^-\ (aq)) + \Delta G_f^o(H_2O\ (l)) - 2\,\Delta G_f^o(OH^-\ (aq)) - \Delta G_f^o(Cl_2O\ (g))$$

$$(2\text{ mol} \times -36.8\frac{kJ}{mol}) + (1\text{ mol} \times -237.18\ \frac{kJ}{mol})$$

$$-\ (2\text{ mol} \times -157.24\frac{kJ}{mol}) - (1\text{ mol} \times +97.9\ \frac{kJ}{mol}) = -94.2\text{ kJ} = -94{,}200\text{ J}$$

This means that, per mole of reaction, $\Delta G^o = -94{,}200\text{ J mol}^{-1}$

$$K = e^{-\left(\Delta G^o/RT\right)} = e^{-\left(-94{,}200\text{ J mol}^{-1}/8.3145\text{J mol}^{-1}\text{ K}^{-1} \times 298.15\text{ K}\right)}$$

$$= e^{+38.00} = 3.2 \times 10^{16}$$

24-3. The Solvay and the Leblanc processes both convert sodium chloride and calcium carbonate into sodium carbonate and other materials. For the Solvay process, the "other materials" are the simple by-product calcium chloride required by the stoichiometry. The Solvay process does employ carbon dioxide and ammonia to form important intermediates, but these are recovered and recycled. It is much easier to produce pure product from the Solvay process, which goes through the selective formation of sodium hydrogen carbonate. The Leblanc process achieves the transformation through the use of expensive sulfuric acid and coke (carbon). These additional reactants also contribute to the by-products calcium sulfide, hydrochloric acid, and sodium hydroxide, all of which must be separated from the sodium carbonate product.

24-5. For this thermochemical analysis, we will treat the reaction in the following manner:

$$2\ NaCl\ (s) + H_2SO_4\ (l) + 2\ C\ (s) + CaCO_3\ (s)$$

$$\rightarrow 2\ HCl\ (g) + CaS\ (s) + 2\ CO_2\ (g) + Na_2CO_3\ (s)$$

24-5. (continued)

With so many reactants and products, it is best to determine the enthalpy change in a tabular format:

Substance	Stoichiometric coefficient n	$\Delta H_f^o \left(\frac{kJ}{mol}\right)$	$n \times \Delta H_f^o$
2 HCl	+2 mol	-92.31	-184.62 kJ
CaS	+1 mol	-482.4	-482.4 kJ
2 CO_2	+2 mol	-393.51	-787.02 kJ
Na_2CO_3	+1 mol	-1130.68	-1130.68 kJ
NaCl	-2 mol	-411.15	+822.30 kJ
H_2SO_4	-1 mol	-813.99	+813.99 kJ
C	-1 mol	0.00	0.00 kJ
$CaCO_3$	-1 mol	-1206.92	+1206.92 kJ
		TOTAL:	**+258.5 kJ**

The reaction is endothermic; it will give more product at higher temperatures.

24-7. Chlorous acid (pK_a = 1.96) is much stronger than hypochlorous acid (pK_a = 7.53). Only chlorous acid is competent to convert sodium fluoride directly to hydrofluoric acid (pK_a = 3.18).

24-9. Both calcium and carbonate ions are possible impurities in NaOH made from $Ca(OH)_2$ and Na_2CO_3. Since electrolytic sodium hydroxide is made with only water and sodium chloride, neither calcium nor carbonate will be an impurity.

24-11. The moles of Br_2 available in the sea water is half the number of moles of Br^-:

$$\left(0.0036\frac{\text{mol Br}^-}{\text{L}}\right)\times\left(1000\ \text{m}^3\right)\times\left(\frac{10\text{dm}}{\text{m}}\right)^3\times\left(\frac{1\ \text{L}}{\text{dm}^3}\right)\times\left(\frac{1\ \text{mol Br}_2}{2\ \text{mol Br}^-}\right) = 1800\ \text{mol Br}_2$$

There is a 1 : 1 ratio of Cl_2 : Br_2 in this process, so we need 1800 mol Cl_2.

At STP this is: 1800 mol Cl_2 × (22.4 L mol^{-1}) = **40,000 L** of gaseous chlorine

24-13. (a) Chlorine has a +1 oxidation state in Cl_2O

(b) The oxyacid formed is the one with Cl(+1) -- **hypochlorous acid.**

24-15. For the disproportionation reaction, the first reaction will be the "cathode", the second the "anode." Then the standard cell potential will be;

$$\Delta \mathcal{E}^o = \mathcal{E}^o (ClO_2 \mid ClO_2^-) - \mathcal{E}^o (ClO_3^- \mid ClO_2)$$

$$= 0.954 \text{ V} - (-0.25 \text{ V}) = \mathbf{+1.204 \text{ V}}$$

A positive cell potential indicates the reaction is spontaneous. **ClO_2 is unstable with respect to disproportionation in aqueous base.**

24-17. As was discussed with carbon in the text, the small size and high electronegativity of fluorine mean its bond to Si will be stronger than that of Cl.

24-19. (a) *Oxidation of oxide to oxygen:*

$$2\ SrO\ (s) + 2\ F_2\ (g) \rightarrow 2\ SrF_2\ (s) + O_2\ (g)$$

(b) *Oxidation of oxygen to O(+2)*

$$O_2\ (g) + 2\ F_2\ (g) \rightarrow 2\ OF_2\ (g)$$

(c) *Oxidation of U(+4) to U(+6), its maximum oxidation state*

$$UF_4\ (s) + F_2\ (g) \rightarrow UF_6\ (s)$$

(d) *Oxidation of chloride to chlorine*

$$2\ NaCl\ (s) + F_2\ (g) \rightarrow 2\ NaF\ (s) + Cl_2\ (g)$$

24-21. All we need here is the molar ratio of F to Na, beginning from the mass ratio:

$$\left(\frac{2.48 \text{ g F}}{1.00 \text{ g Na}}\right) \times \left(\frac{22.990 \text{ g Na}}{1 \text{ mol Na}}\right) \times \left(\frac{1 \text{ mol F}}{18.998 \text{ g F}}\right) = \frac{3.00 \text{ mol F}}{1 \text{ mol Na}}$$

Therefore, the stoichiometry requires three F's for every Na, something possible only with the acid fluoride **NaF•2 HF**

24-23. The empirical formula of a binary compound can be determined by a ratio analysis, as in problem #21. Here we may assume that we have a sample of exactly 100 g, which will contain 38.35 g Cl and 61.65 g F:

$$\left(\frac{61.65 \text{ g F}}{38.35 \text{ g Cl}}\right) \times \left(\frac{35.4527 \text{ g Cl}}{1 \text{ mol Cl}}\right) \times \left(\frac{1 \text{ mol F}}{18.998 \text{ g F}}\right) = \frac{3.00 \text{ mol F}}{1 \text{ mol Cl}}$$

24-23. (continued).

The empirical formula is then ClF_3, which has a formula mass of 92.45.

The gas density data provide a means to directly determine the molar mass of the compound: $4.13 \text{ g L}^{-1} \times 22.4 \text{ L mol}^{-1} = 92.5 \text{ g mol}^{-1}$.

This value is equal to the formula mass. The molecular formula is **ClF_3**.

24-25. (a) OF_2: Bent, with an F-O-F angle slightly less than 109.5°. SN (oxygen) = 4.

(b) BF_3: Trigonal planar, with F-B-F angles equal to 120°. SN(boron) = 3.

(c) BrF_3: "T"-shaped, with all the atoms lying in a plane and F-Br-F angles between the central and outer F's of slightly less than 90°. SN(bromine) = 5.

(d) BrF_5: Square pyramid, with F-Br-F angles slightly less than 90°. SN(bromine) = 6.

(e) Pentagonal bipyramid, with F-I-F angles in the equatorial plane of $360/5 = 72°$. SN(I) = 7.

(f) Octahedral, with all F-Se-F angles equal to 90°. SN(Se) = 6.

24-27. (a)

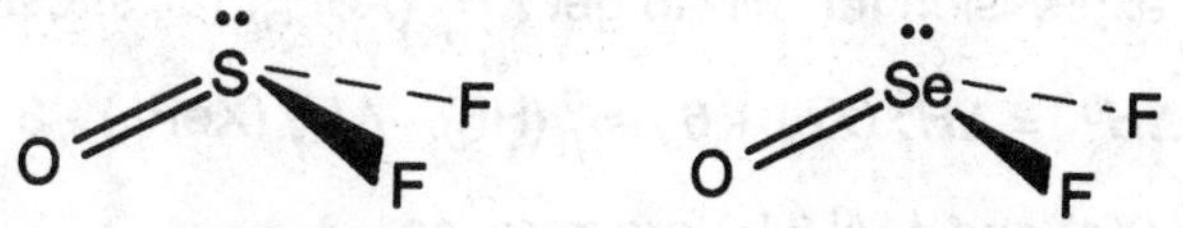

Pyramidal Pyramidal

There will be a steric number of 4 in each case about the central atoms.

(b) A Lewis base is defined as a molecule that is capable of donating an electron pair. In this case, thionyl difluoride acts as a **Lewis base.**

24-29. The autoionization in this case involves the transfer of F^-:

$$2\ BrF_3 \rightleftarrows BrF_4^- + BrF_2^+$$

This is a Lewis acid-base reaction (see problem No. 4-43), with the electron pairs on the Lewis base fluoride being transferred from one BrF_3 to another. The bromine centers -- in BrF_3 and BrF_2^+ -- are Lewis acids.

24-31. The boiling points will increase as the ionic character of the bonding increases.

b.p.(PtF_6) < b.p.(PtF_4) < b.p.(CaF_2).

24-33. The explosive decomposition of tetrafluoroethylene proceeds according to the stoichiometry: $C_2F_4\ (g) \rightarrow C\ (s) + CF_4\ (g)$

For this,
$$\Delta H^o = \Delta H_f^o(C\ (s)) + \Delta H_f^o(CF_4\ (g)) - \Delta H_f^o(C_2F_4\ (g))$$
$$= (1\text{ mol} \times 0.00\frac{\text{kJ}}{\text{mol}}) + (1\text{ mol} \times -925\frac{\text{kJ}}{\text{mol}}) - (1\text{ mol} \times -651\frac{\text{kJ}}{\text{mol}})$$

= -274 kJ. This is the heat released for 1 mol of C_2F_4.

The molar mass of C_2F_4 is 100.01 g mol^{-1} and 1.00 kg is equal to 1000 g. So the enthalpy change for the decomposition of 1.00 kg of C_2F_4 is:
$$\Delta H = 1000\text{ g } C_2F_4 \times \left(\frac{1\text{ mol } C_2F_4}{100.01\text{ g } C_2F_4}\right) \times \left(\frac{-274\text{kJ}}{1\text{ mol } C_2F_4}\right)$$

= -2740 kJ.

This is the opposite to the heat absorbed by the surroundings, **+2740 kJ.**

24-35. The enthalpy change for this reaction includes the quantity we seek, so we can rearrange the expression for ΔH^o to get ΔH_f^o (XeF_6) (all substances are gases):
$$\Delta H^o = \Delta H_f^o(Xe) + 6\,\Delta H_f^o(HF) - \Delta H_f^o(XeF_6) - 3\,\Delta H_f^o(H_2)$$

Note that ΔH_f^o (Xe) and ΔH_f^o (H_2) are zero, so:
$$\Delta H^o = 6\,\Delta H_f^o(HF) - \Delta H_f^o(XeF_6)$$
$$\Delta H^o - 6\,\Delta H_f^o(HF) = -\Delta H_f^o(XeF_6)$$
$$6\,\Delta H_f^o(HF) - \Delta H^o = \Delta H_f^o(XeF_6)$$

When we write this to solve for ΔH_f^o (XeF_6), we get:
$$1\text{ mol } XeF_6 \times \Delta H_f^o(XeF_6) = 6\,\Delta H_f^o(HF) - \Delta H^o$$
$$= (6\text{ mol} \times -271.1\frac{\text{kJ}}{\text{mol}}) - 1282\text{ kJ} = -345\text{ kJ}$$
$$\Delta H_f^o(XeF_6) = \mathbf{-345\ \frac{kJ}{mol}}$$

24-35. (continued)

(b) For thermochemical purposes, we may calculate the enthalpy of formation for XeF_6 by comparing the bond enthalpies for the Xe-F bonds formed and the F-F bonds destroyed.

We can consider the formation of Xe-F as a two step cycle. In the first step, we "invest" the enthalpy of 3 F-F bonds and in the second step we "gain" the enthalpy of six Xe-F bonds.

$$3\ \text{F-F} \rightarrow 6\ \text{F} \qquad \Delta H_1 = 3 \times \text{F-F enthalpy} = 3\ \text{mol} \times 158\ \frac{\text{kJ}}{\text{mol}} = +474\ \text{kJ}$$

$$6\ \text{F} + \text{Xe} \rightarrow XeF_6 \qquad \Delta H_2 = -6 \times \text{Xe-F enthalpy}$$

$$3\ \text{F-F} + \text{Xe} \rightarrow XeF_6 \qquad \Delta H = \Delta H_1 + \Delta H_2 = \Delta H_f^o(XeF_6)$$

This last equation can be rearranged to obtain ΔH_2:

$$\Delta H_2 = \Delta H_f^o(XeF_6) - \Delta H_1 = (1\ \text{mol} \times -345\ \frac{\text{kJ}}{\text{mol}}) - 474\ \text{kJ} = -819\ \text{kJ}$$

Then: $\Delta H_2 = -6 \times \text{Xe-F enthalpy} = -819\ \text{kJ}$

Xe-F bond enthalpy $= -(819/6) =$ **136 kJ**

24-37. $\Delta H^o = \Delta H_f^o(XeOF_4\ (l)) + 2\ \Delta H_f^o(HF\ (g)) - \Delta H_f^o(XeF_6\ (g)) - \Delta H_f^o(H_2O\ (l))$

$$= (1\ \text{mol} \times 148\frac{\text{kJ}}{\text{mol}}) + (2\ \text{mol} \times -271.1\frac{\text{kJ}}{\text{mol}})$$

$$- (1\ \text{mol} \times -298\frac{\text{kJ}}{\text{mol}}) - (1\ \text{mol} \times -285.83\frac{\text{kJ}}{\text{mol}}) = \mathbf{+190\ kJ}$$

24-39. Oxidation: This is the opposite of the reduction of permanganate to manganese(II) ion, which was treated in problem 13-9b:

$$Mn^{2+}\ (aq) + 4\ H_2O\ (l) \rightarrow 5\ e^- + 8\ H^+\ (aq) + MnO_4^-\ (aq)$$

Reduction: $XeO_6^{4-} \rightarrow Xe$

Add H_2O to balance O: $XeO_6^{4-} \rightarrow Xe + 6\ H_2O$

Add H^+ to balance H: $12\ H^+ + XeO_6^{4-} \rightarrow Xe + 6\ H_2O$

Add e^- to balance charge: $8\ e^- + 12\ H^+ + XeO_6^{4-} \rightarrow Xe + 6\ H_2O$

Add appropriate phase descriptions:

$$8\ e^- + 12\ H^+\ (aq) + XeO_6^{4-}\ (aq) \rightarrow Xe\ (g) + 6\ H_2O\ (l)$$

24-39. (continued)

Overall: The least common multiple of 5 and 8 is 40, so we must multiply the oxidation reaction by 8 and the reduction reaction by 5. When common substances are removed from both sides of the reaction, we get:

$5\ XeO_6^{4-}\ (aq) + 8\ Mn^{2+}\ (aq) + 2\ H_2O\ (l) \rightarrow 4\ H^+\ (aq) + 8\ MnO_4^-\ (aq) + 5\ Xe\ (g)$

24-41. Bromine will also be an oxidizing bleach, but because bromine is a weaker oxidant than chlorine ($\mathcal{E}^o\ (Cl_2 \mid Cl^-) = +1.358$ V and $\mathcal{E}^o\ (Br_2 \mid Br^-) = +1.065$ V), it will be a weaker bleach than chlorine.

24-43. $\Delta H^o = \Delta H_f^o\ (Cl_2\ (g)) + \Delta H_f^o\ (H_2O\ (l)) - {}^1/_2\ \Delta H_f^o\ (O_2\ (g)) - 2\ \Delta H_f^o\ (HCl\ (g))$

$$= (1\ \text{mol} \times 0.00 \frac{\text{kJ}}{\text{mol}}) + (1\ \text{mol} \times -241.82 \frac{\text{kJ}}{\text{mol}})$$

$$- ({}^1/_2\ \text{mol} \times 0.00 \frac{\text{kJ}}{\text{mol}}) - (2\ \text{mol} \times -92.31 \frac{\text{kJ}}{\text{mol}}) = -57.2\ \text{kJ} = -57{,}200\ \text{J}$$

$\Delta S^o = S^o\ (Cl_2\ (g)) + S^o\ (H_2O\ (l)) - S^o(O_2\ (g)) - 2\ S^o(HCl\ (g))$

$$= (1\ \text{mol} \times 222.96 \frac{\text{J}}{\text{mol-K}}) + (1\ \text{mol} \times 188.72 \frac{\text{J}}{\text{mol-K}})$$

$$- ({}^1/_2\ \text{mol} \times 205.03 \frac{\text{J}}{\text{mol-K}}) - (2\ \text{mol} \times 186.80 \frac{\text{J}}{\text{mol-K}}) = -64.44 \frac{\text{J}}{\text{K}}$$

The reaction is run at 450 °C, which is equal to 723 K. Assuming that ΔH and ΔS do not change from their standard state values:

$$\Delta G \approx \Delta H^o - T\,\Delta S^o = -57{,}200\ \text{J} - (723\ \text{K} \times -64.44 \frac{\text{J}}{\text{K}}) = -10{,}610\ \text{J}$$

This is equal to a free energy change per mole of reaction of -10,610 J mol^{-1}

The equilibrium constant is then

$$K = e^{-(\Delta G/RT)} = e^{-\left(-10{,}610\ \text{J mol}^{-1}/8.3145\ \text{J mol}^{-1}\ \text{K}^{-1} \times\ 723\ \text{K}\right)} = e^{+1.765}$$

$= \mathbf{5.84}$

(b) The H-Br bond is weaker than the H-Cl bond by 66 kJ mol^{-1}. The Br-Br bond is weaker than the Cl-Cl bond by 50 kJ mol^{-1}. Although we are making a weaker bond in Br_2, it is so much easier to break H-Br bonds that we expect the reaction to have a **larger** equilibrium constant with bromine.

24-45. The chlor-alkali reaction is given in the text as:

$$2\ H_2O\ (l) + 2\ Cl^-\ (aq) \rightarrow 2\ OH^-\ (aq) + H_2\ (g) + Cl_2\ (g)$$

$$\Delta G^o = +422\text{ kJ} = +422{,}000\text{ J.}$$

For this reaction, the number of electrons transferred $n = 2$. The standard cell potential for this reaction is:

$$\Delta\mathcal{E}^o = -\frac{\Delta G^o}{n\mathcal{F}} = -\frac{422{,}000\text{ J}}{(2\text{ mol e}^-)\times(96{,}485\text{C (mol e}^-)^{-1})} = -2.19\ \frac{\text{J}}{\text{C}} = \mathbf{-2.19\ V.}$$

A potential of at least 2.19 V must be applied to the cell to cause the reaction to proceed from left to right.

24-47. The article must be referring to the weight of the product. There are 2 moles of sodium hydroxide (caustic soda) made for every 1 mole of Cl_2.

One mole of Cl_2 has a mass of 70.9 g.

Two moles of NaOH have a mass of 2 mol × 40.00 g mol^{-1} = 80.00 g.

The theoretical mass ratio of NaOH : Cl_2 is 80.0 : 70.9 = 1.13. Thus, we expect about 13% more NaOH than Cl_2, by weight. The "as usual" must also refer to a typically lower actual yield of NaOH.

24-49. As we did in problem No. 23-39, we can work this out "retrosynthetically" by going backwards from F_2 to CaF_2.

$$F_2 \Rightarrow HF \Rightarrow CaF_2$$

We can then reconstruct the synthesis in the forward direction:

Extraction of HF from CaF_2 (fluorspar):

$$CaF_2\ (s) + H_2SO_4\ (aq) \rightarrow CaSO_4\ (s) + 2\ HF\ (g)$$

Electrolysis of HF:

$$2\ HF\ (g) \rightarrow F_2\ (g) + H_2\ (g)$$

24-51. As discussed in problem #31, the fluoride ion is a Lewis base because it has lone pair electrons to donate to other atoms and molecules. In accepting two fluoride ions TiF_4 acts as a Lewis acid.

24-53. There are several non-standard units in this problem. Let's clarify them first.

The market value of gold is \$350 (troy oz)$^{-1}$ × (1 troy oz/31.3 g) = \$11.18 g^{-1}.

A 1000 g piece of quartz has 1000 g × 0.001% = 1000 g × 0.00001 = 0.01 g Au and essentially 1000 g of SiO_2. The value of the gold in the quartz is then \$11.18 g^{-1} × 0.01 g = \$0.11.

The reaction has to destroy all of the SiO_2 in the quartz. The mass of HF required is:

$$1000\text{ g }SiO_2 \times \left(\frac{1\text{ mol }SiO_2}{60.065\text{ g }SiO_2}\right) \times \left(\frac{4\text{ mol HF}}{1\text{ mol }SiO_2}\right) \times \left(\frac{20.006\text{ g HF}}{\text{mol HF}}\right) = 1332\text{ g HF}$$

The HF is sold as a commercial solution. The density of the solution is 1.17 g cm^{-3}, or 1,170 g L^{-1}. Then the amount of the solution needed is:

$$1332\text{ g HF} \times \left(\frac{100\text{ g solution}}{50\text{ g HF}}\right) \times \left(\frac{1\text{ L solution}}{1{,}170\text{ g solution}}\right) = 2.28\text{ L solution}$$

This will cost 2.28 L × \$0.25 L^{-1}= \$0.57. This is more than the value of the gold that could be recovered.

24-55. 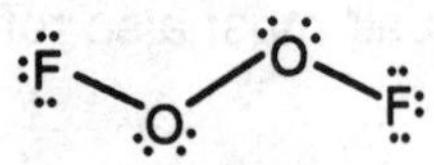

The bond order for all the bonds is 1. The geometry will be bent around both oxygens, with O-O-F angles slightly less than 109.5^{o}. It is analogous to the compound of oxygen and hydrogen called hydrogen peroxide.

24-57. 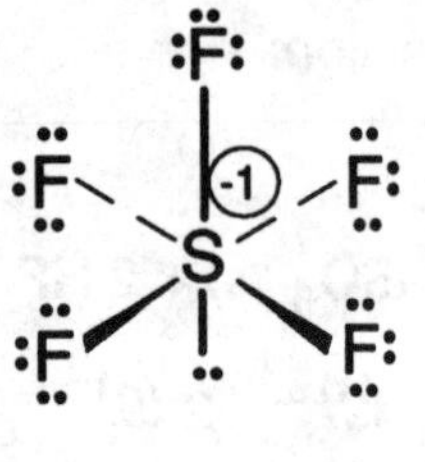

The geometry is a square pyramid, based on an SN = 6 for the sulfur with one lone pair. The F-S-F angles will be less than 90°, because of the extra volume of the lone pair on the sulfur.

24-59. Teflon is a polymer of tetrafluoroethylene. It has no chlorine. The empirical formula of teflon is CF_2, with a formula mass of 50.007 g mol^{-1}. The theoretical mass fraction of fluorine is:

$$\left(\frac{2 \text{ mol F}}{1 \text{ mol CF}_2}\right) \times \left(\frac{18.998 \text{ g F}}{1 \text{ mol F}}\right) \times \left(\frac{1 \text{ mol CF}_2}{50.007 \text{ g CF}_2}\right) = \frac{0.7598 \text{ g F}}{1 \text{ g CF}_2}.$$

This corresponds to a mass percentage of 76.0%. There was far too little fluorine found in the original sample, possibly because of the challenge of completely degrading such a famously inert substance as Teflon.

24-61. The standard molar free energy of formation of XeF_4 *is* the standard free energy change for this reaction, because ΔG_f^o for both Xe and F_2 will be zero. Thus,

$$\Delta G^o = \Delta G_f^o (XeF_4\ (g)) = 1 \text{ mol} \times -134 \frac{\text{kJ}}{\text{mol}} = -134 \text{ kJ} = -134{,}000 \text{ J}.$$

This is equal to a free energy change per mole of reaction of -134,000 J mol^{-1}

Then:

$$K = e^{-\left(\Delta G^o / RT\right)} = e^{-\left(-134{,}000 \text{ J mol}^{-1} / 8.3145 \text{ J mol}^{-1} \text{ K}^{-1} \times 298 \text{ K}\right)} = e^{+54.1}$$

$$= \mathbf{3.07 \times 10^{23}}$$

CHAPTER 25 - FROM PETROLEUM TO PHARMACEUTICALS

25-1. An octane number of 100 means a gasoline burns with the same amount of knocking as the reference compound *iso*-octane. If a compound burns with *less* knocking than *iso*-octane, then it will have an octane number exceeding 100.

25-3. (a) The formation of cyclopropane can be thought of as occurring through the atomization of C and H and then the recombination of these atoms into C_3H_6.

ATOMIZATION STEPS

$$3\ H_2\ (g) \rightarrow 6\ H\ (g) \quad 6\ \Delta H^o_f(\text{H},\ g) = 6\ \text{mol} \times +217.96\ \frac{\text{kJ}}{\text{mol}} = +1307.76\ \text{kJ}$$

$$3\ C\ (s) \rightarrow 3\ C\ (g) \quad 3\ \Delta H^o_f(\text{C},\ g) = 3\ \text{mol} \times +716.682\ \frac{\text{kJ}}{\text{mol}} = +2150.046\ \text{kJ}$$

BOND FORMING STEPS

$$3\ C\ (g) + 3\ H\ (g) \rightarrow 6\ \text{C-H} \quad -6\ \text{B.E.(C-H)} = -6\ \text{mol} \times 413\ \frac{\text{kJ}}{\text{mol}} = -2478\ \text{kJ}$$

$$3\ C\ (g) \rightarrow 3\ \text{C-C} \quad -3\ \text{B.E.(C-C)} = -3\ \text{mol} \times 348\ \frac{\text{kJ}}{\text{mol}} = -1044\ \text{kJ}$$

$$\text{TOTAL}\ \Delta H^o = -64\ \text{kJ}$$

(b) The combustion reaction will have an enthalpy change related to the standard enthalpy of formation of the reactants and products (all substances are gases): $\Delta H^o = 3 \times \Delta H^o_f(CO_2) + 3 \times \Delta H^o_f(H_2O) - 3 \times \Delta H^o_f(O_2) - \Delta H^o_f(C_3H_6)$

$$1 \times \Delta H^o_f(C_3H_6) = 3 \times \Delta H^o_f(CO_2) + 3 \times \Delta H^o_f(H_2O) - 3 \times \Delta H^o_f(O_2) - \Delta H^o$$

$$= 3\ \text{mol} \times (-393.51\frac{\text{kJ}}{\text{mol}}) + 3\ \text{mol} \times (-241.82\frac{\text{kJ}}{\text{mol}})$$

$$- 3\ \text{mol} \times (0.0\frac{\text{kJ}}{\text{mol}}) - (-1959\ \text{kJ}) = +53\ \text{kJ}$$

$$\Delta H^o_f(C_3H_6) = +53\ \text{kJ mol}^{-1}$$

(c) Cyclopropane lies at an enthalpy +117 kJ mol^{-1} higher than expected on the basis of "normal" bond enthalpies. This represents the compound's strain energy.

25-5. Decane has 10 carbon atoms, so the products of cracking into molecules with equal numbers of carbon atoms will give two chains of 5 carbons each. The alkane product will have the formula $C_nH_{2n+2} = C_5H_{12}$. The alkene product will have the formula $C_nH_{2n} = C_5H_{10}$. The chemical equation for this is:

$$C_{10}H_{22} \rightarrow C_5H_{10} + C_5H_{12}$$

(b) Assuming the product alkene is a straight chain, there are two possible isomers: 1-pentene ($H_2C{=}CHCH_2CH_2CH_3$) and 2-pentene ($H_3CCH{=}CHCH_2CH_3$). 2-pentene will also exist as *cis* and *trans* isomers.

25-7.

(a)

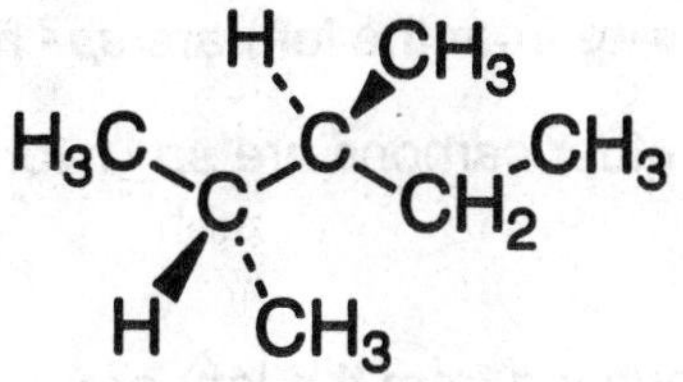

(b)

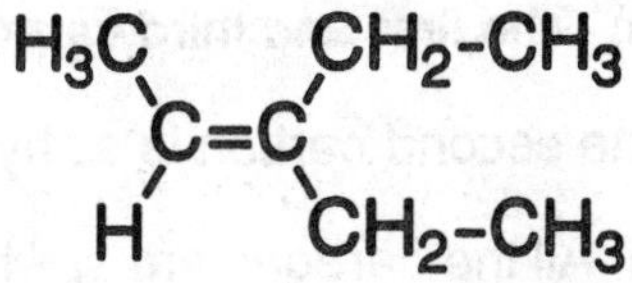

(c)

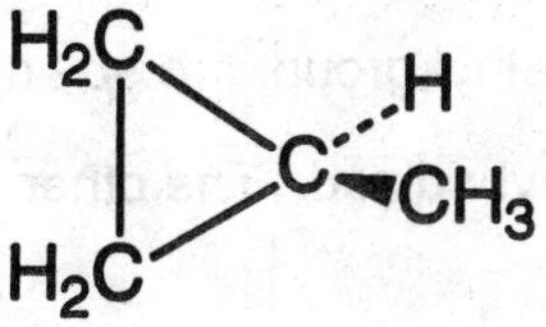

(d)

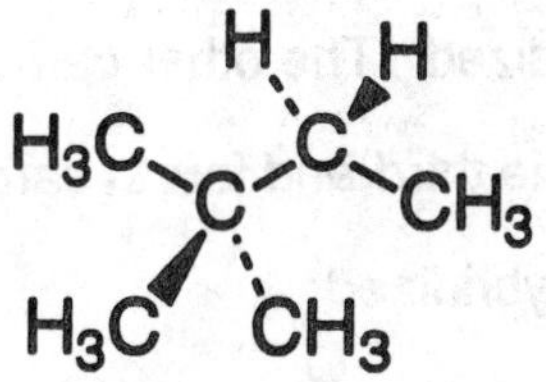

(e)

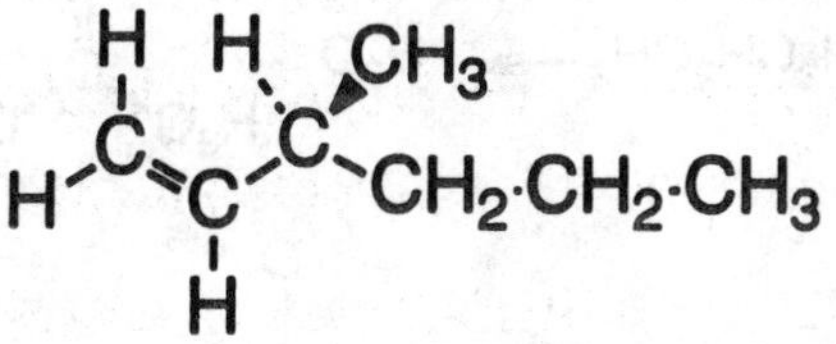

(f)

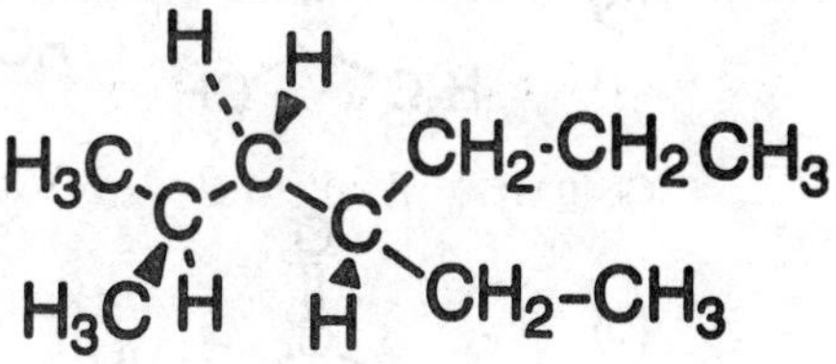

(g)

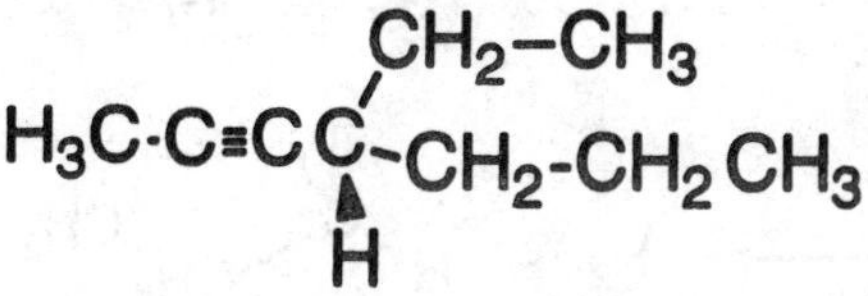

25-9. 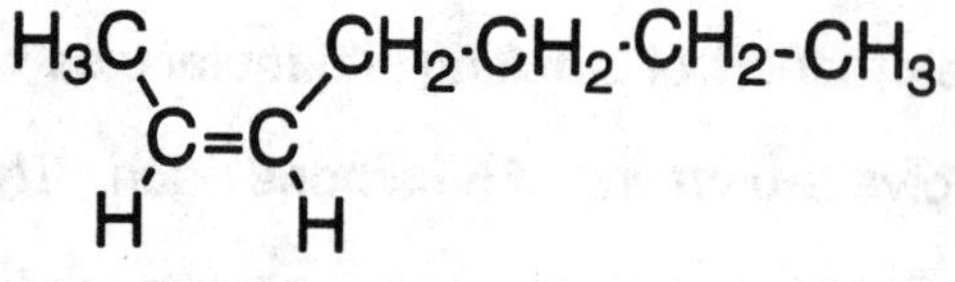 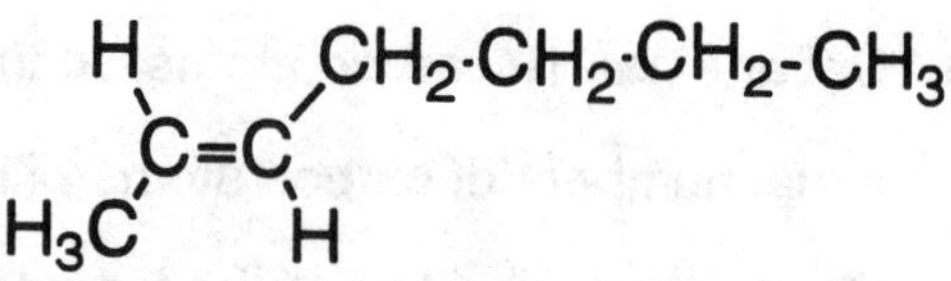

25-11. (a) 1,2-hexadiene (b) 1,3,5-hexatriene

(b) 2-methylhexene (d) 3-hexyne

25-13. Hybridization for carbon can be assigned based on the number of bound atoms:

2 bound atoms .... *sp* hybrid

3 bound atoms .... sp^2 hybrid

4 bound atoms .... sp^3 hybrid

(a) The first and third carbon atoms (counting from the left) are sp^2 hybridized. The second carbon is *sp* hybidrized. The other carbons are sp^3 hybridized

(b All the carbons are sp^2 hybridized.

(c) The first and second carbon atoms (counting from the left) are sp^2 hybridized. The other carbons, including the methyl group, are sp^3 hybridized

(d) The third and fourth carbon atoms are sp^2 hybridized. The other carbons are sp^3 hybridized

25-15. (a)

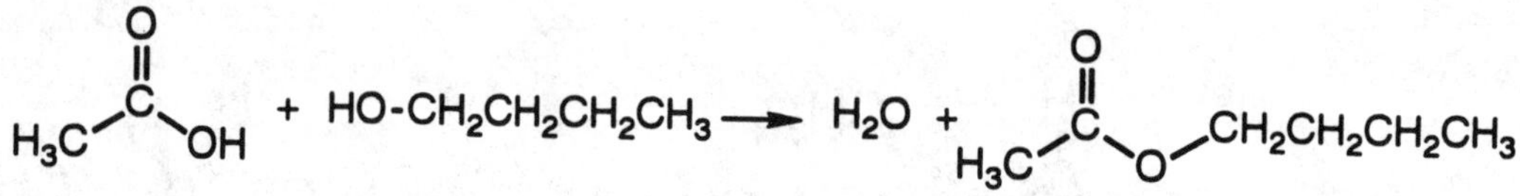

(b)

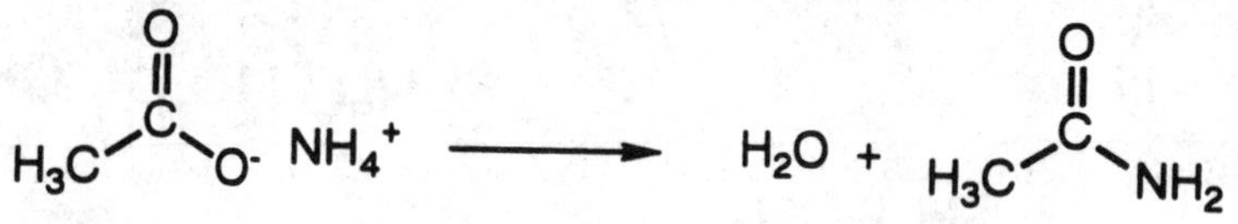

(c)

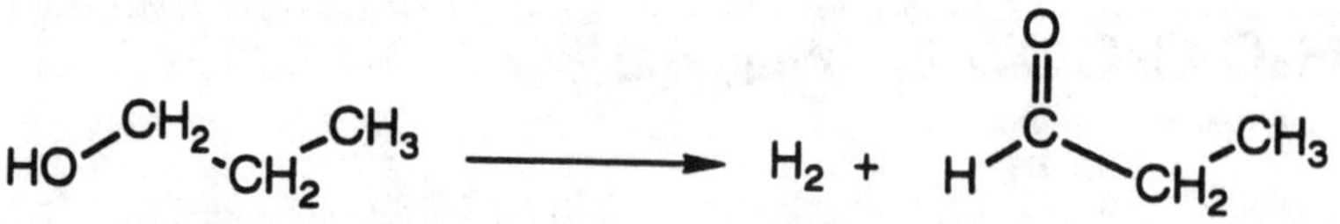

(d)

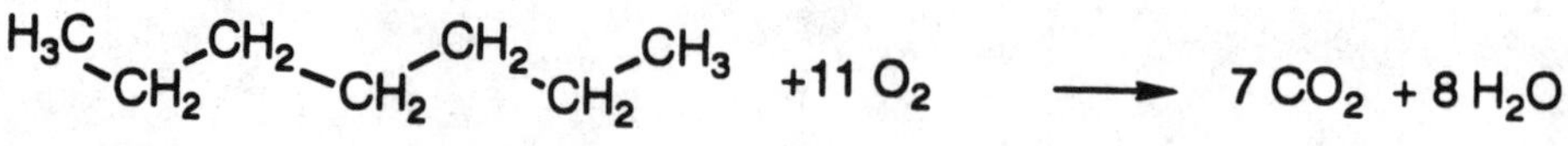

25-17. (a) *Addition of bromine:* $CH_2=CH_2 + Br_2 \rightarrow CH_2BrCH_2Br$

Removal of HBr: $CH_2BrCH_2Br \rightarrow CH_2=CHBr + HBr$

(b) *Addition of water:* $CH_3CH_2CH=CH_2 + H_2O \rightarrow CH_3CH_2CH_2CH_2OH$

(requires acid catalyst)

(c) *Dehydration of 2-propanol:* $CH_3CH(OH)CH_2 \rightarrow H_2O + CH_3COCH_3$

(requires mild acid catalyst)

25-19. $R\text{-}COOH + HO\text{-}CR_3'' \rightarrow RCOOCR_3''$

The use of R denotes a variable group; most any carboxylic acid will under some reaction like this. The R" designation on the alcohol indicates that it is a *different* group, anything but hydrogen.

25-21. In large scale problems like this, it is often best to work entirely in kilograms instead of grams. The molar mass of ethylene is 28.0538 g mol^{-1}, or 0.0280538 kg mol^{-1}, and the molar mass of ethylene dichloride ($C_2H_4Cl_2$) is 98.959 g mol^{-1}, or 0.098959 kg mol^{-1}. The synthesis of one mole of ethylene dichloride requires one mole of ethylene.

The mass of ethylene required to yield 6.26×10^9 kg of ethylene dichloride is:

$$6.26 \times 10^9 \text{ kg } C_2H_4Cl_2 \times \left(\frac{1 \text{ mol } C_2H_4Cl_2}{0.098959 \text{ kg } C_2H_4Cl_2}\right) \times \left(\frac{1 \text{ mol } C_2H_4}{1 \text{ mol } C_2H_4Cl_2}\right) \times \left(\frac{0.0280538 \text{ kg } C_2H_4}{1 \text{ mol } C_2H_4}\right)$$

$$= 1.775 \times 10^9 \text{ kg } C_2H_4.$$

This represents $\dfrac{1.775 \times 10^9 \text{ kg } C_2H_4}{15.87 \times 10^9 \text{ kg } C_2H_4} = 0.01118 =$ **11.2%** of all production

The synthesis of ethylene dichloride involves the addition of chlorine to ethylene. Therefore, the mass of product that does *not* come from ethylene must come from chlorine.

$$\text{mass } Cl_2 + \text{mass } C_2H_4 = \text{mass } C_2H_4Cl_2$$

$$\text{mass } Cl_2 = \text{mass } C_2H_4Cl_2 - \text{mass } C_2H_4$$

$$= 6.26 \times 10^9 \text{ kg} - 1.775 \times 10^9 \text{ kg } C_2H_4$$

$$= \mathbf{4.49 \times 10^9 \text{ kg } Cl_2}$$

25-23. (a) Acid:

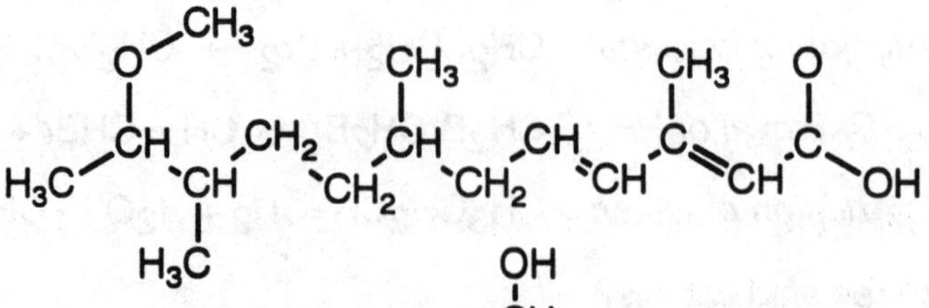

Alcohol:

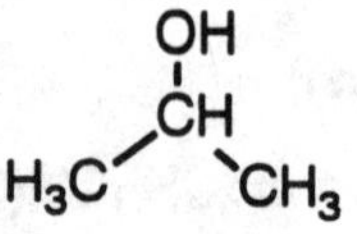

2-propanol

(b)

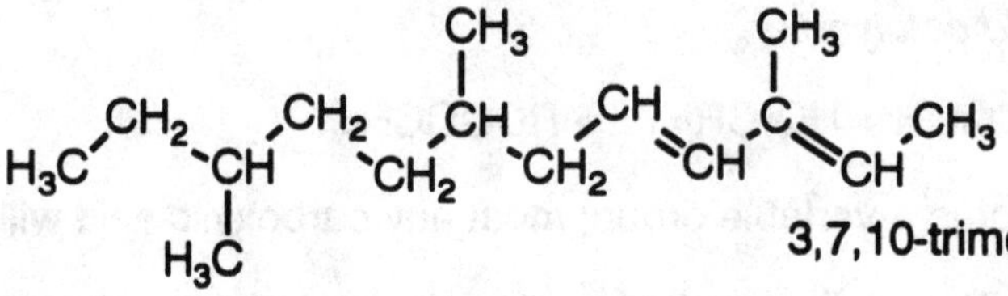

3,7,10-trimethyl-2,4-dodecadiene

25-25. (a) Aspirin has a molecular formula of $C_9H_8O_4$. The molar mass of this is $180.16\ g\ mol^{-1}$.

(b) For 325 mg of aspirin, there will be 0.325 g of aspirin, containing

$$\frac{0.326\ \text{g aspirin}}{180.16\ \text{g mol}^{-1}\ \text{aspirin}} = 1.80 \times 10^{-3}\ \text{mol aspirin}$$

25-27.

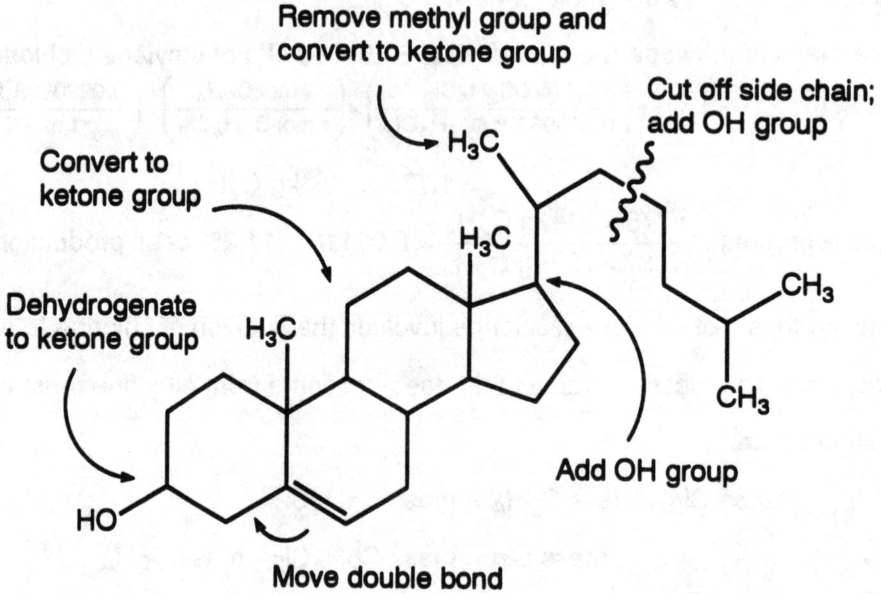

25-29. Combustion of heptane: $C_7H_{16}\ (g) + 11\ O_2\ (g) \rightarrow 7\ CO_2\ (g) + 8\ H_2O\ (g)$

Combustion of isooctane: $C_8H_{18}\ (g) + 11^1/_2\ O_2\ (g) \rightarrow 7\ CO_2\ (g) + 9\ H_2O\ (g)$

In determining the standard enthalpy change for the combustion reactions, we may ignore the oxygen, which has a $\Delta H_f^o = 0$.

The standard enthalpy for combustion of heptane (all substances are gases):

$$\Delta H^o = 7\ \Delta H_f^o(CO_2) + 8\ \Delta H_f^o(H_2O) - \Delta H_f^o(C_7H_{16})$$

$$= (7\text{ mol} \times -393.51\ \frac{\text{kJ}}{\text{mol}}) + (8\text{ mol} \times -241.82\ \frac{\text{kJ}}{\text{mol}}) - (1\text{ mol} \times -187.82\ \frac{\text{kJ}}{\text{mol}})$$

=- 4501.31 kJ

The standard enthalpy for combustion of heptane (all substances are gases):

$$\Delta H^o = 8\ \Delta H_f^o(CO_2) + 9\ \Delta H_f^o(H_2O) - \Delta H_f^o(C_7H_{16})$$

$$= (8\text{ mol} \times -393.51\ \frac{\text{kJ}}{\text{mol}}) + (9\text{ mol} \times -241.82\ \frac{\text{kJ}}{\text{mol}}) - (1\text{ mol} \times -224.13\ \frac{\text{kJ}}{\text{mol}})$$

= - 5136.64 kJ

(b) Note that this question only asks which give more heat per gallon. We need to determine the relative heat per volume, and this will not be keyed to any unit system. So we might as well ask the relative heat delivered per liter. Moreover, the relative densities will be independent of the units used, so if the relative mass of one gallon of isooctane : one gallon heptane = 5.77 lb : 5.71 lb = 1.0105 : 1, then this will be the ratio of the relative mass of one liter of each.

$$\frac{\Delta H\ L^{-1}\text{ isooctane}}{\Delta H\ L^{-1}\text{ heptane}} = \frac{\Delta H\text{ mol}^{-1}\text{ isooctane}}{\Delta H\text{ mol}^{-1}\text{ heptane}} \times \frac{\text{g mol}^{-1}\text{ heptane}}{\text{g mol}^{-1}\text{ isooctane}} \times \frac{\text{g L}^{-1}\text{ isooctane}}{\text{g L}^{-1}\text{ heptane}}$$

$$= \frac{5136.64\text{ kJ}}{4501.31\text{ kJ}} \times \frac{100.204\text{ g mol}^{-1}}{114.231\text{ g mol}^{-1}} \times 1.0105$$

$$= 1.011$$

There is **1.1%** more heat given off in the combustion of 1 gallon of isooctane than in the combustion of one gallon of heptane.

25-31.

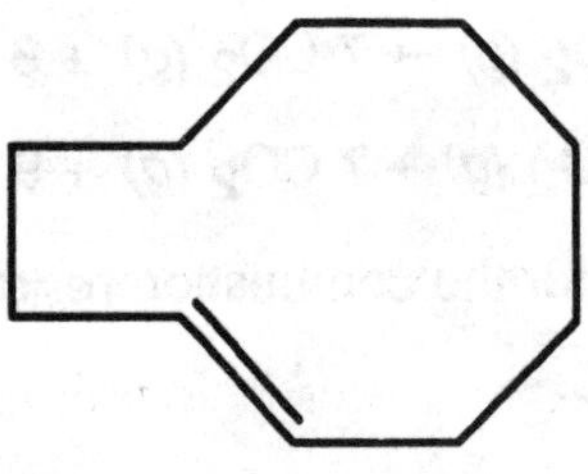

trans - cyclododecene

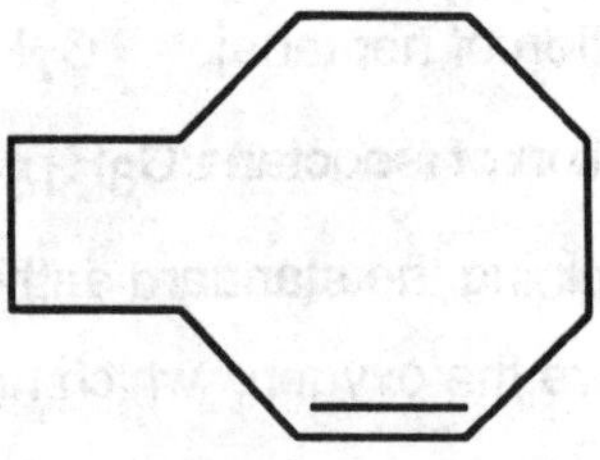

cis - cyclododecene

25-33. The alkene content can be increased by catalytic cracking of longer chain hydrocarbons into shorter chain alkenes and alkanes (see problem 25-5b). Both alkenes and aromatics can also be made from alkanes by dehydrogenation, removing H_2 from one or more C-C bond to give C=C double bonds.

25-35. *Dehydration* is the removal of *water*, as in the conversion of an alcohol to an alkene: $RCH_2CH_2OH \rightarrow H_2O + RCH{=}CH_2$.

Dehydrogenation is the removal of *hydrogen*, as in the conversion of heptane into heptene: $C_5H_{11}CH_2CH_3 \rightarrow H_2 + C_5H_{11}CH{=}CH_2$.

25-37. (a)

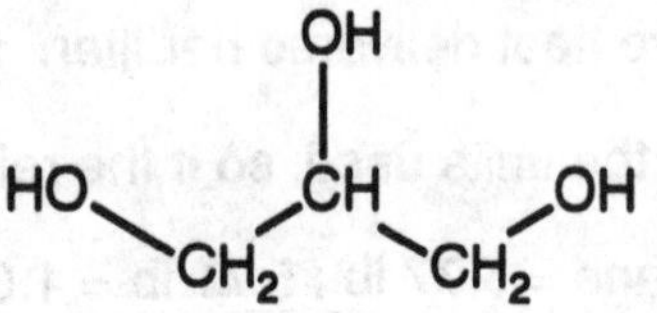

(b) The reaction of glycerol and stearic acid to give tristearin is an esterification reaction, whether three ester linkages are formed from the acid groups and three alcohol groups. Tristearin is a tri-ester.

25-39. Both pharmaceuticals and pesticides must be biologically active, preferably in as specific a manner as possible. In many cases, the strategy for delivery of the compound to the target is similar: utilizing the organism's own pathways for taking in compounds as a means for getting it to accept a molecule that doesn't, in a basic sense, "belong" in its system. Hence, mimicking the organism's own chemicals is important in delivery of both kinds of chemicals.

25-39. (continued)

Also, the development of both requires a careful examination of the purpose of the compound and also any possible side-effects. Pharmaceuticals are under particular pressure to do one and only one thing in the organism they are given to. This objective may be different for different drugs, and one must carefully consider how to get the pharmaceutical to the target tissue, and what will happen to the pharmaceutical in the body's metabolism. This is in contrast to the objective of a pesticide. It has a very simple objective: killing the target by any means possible. Therefore, pesticides can have a variety of effects, and this makes many of them genuinely broad spectrum in their target. However, side effects outside of the target organism may be more important than the short term goal of killing a pest. Hence, many pesticides are toxic to other organisms, and this severely restricts their usefulness.

CHAPTER 26 - POLYMERS: NATURAL AND SYNTHETIC

26-1. Addition polymerization is the linkage of many monomer units without loss of any atoms. For 1,1-dichloroethylene, this reaction is:

$$n\ Cl_2C{=}CCH_2 \rightarrow (CCl_2CH_2)_n$$

26-3. The starting monomer is the empirical formula of the polymer, if we assume growth by addition polymerization. In this case the monomer would be **CH_2O**, which is the molecular formula of formaldehyde.

26-5. (a) Condensation polymerization is the linkage of many monomer units *with* loss of some atoms. Polyglycine is built up of peptide linkages, themselves formed from an amino group and a carboxylic acid group with the splitting off of water:

$$H_2N{-}CH_2{-}COOH + H_2N{-}CH_2{-}COOH \longrightarrow H_2O + H_2N{-}CH_2{-}CO{-}NH{-}CH_2{-}COOH$$

(b) The repeat unit is $(NH\text{-}CH_2\text{-}C(O))$, which has a formula of C_2H_3NO. Note that this has a formula of glycine ($C_2H_5NO_2$) - water (H_2O). The structure of two repeat units is:

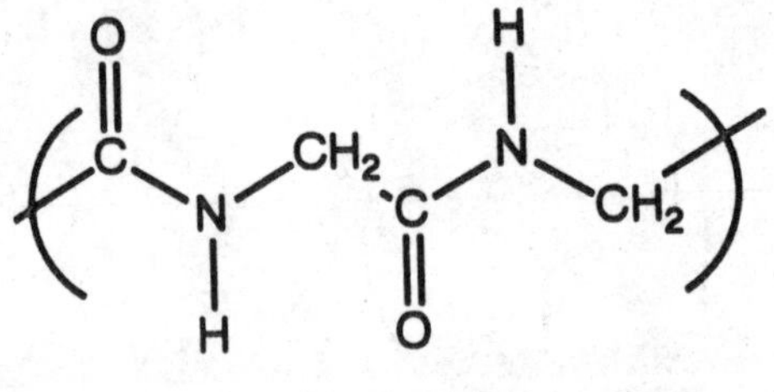

26-7. The initiator reacts with one monomer unit to form the "living polymer" based on continuous regeneration of the same anion for further polymerization. For sodium amid and acrylonitrile, this will be:

$$NaNH_2 + H_2C{=}CHCN \rightarrow H_2NCH_2CH^{-}(CN)\ Na^{+}$$

The same anionic functional group is generated by butyl lithium and acrylonitrile.

26-9. Because a polypeptide has a direction to it -- determined by the carboxylic acid end and the amino end of the whole molecule -- the three positions in a linear peptide are unique (this is not true for circular polypeptides, however). Therefore, the sequence "A-B-C," where A, B, and C are three different amino acids, is different from the sequence "C-B-A."

In such a case, we can determine the total number of possible sequences by considering the probability of any single one of them. There is a $^1/_3$ rd chance of finding a given amino acid at any one position. So the probability of finding three specific amino acids at three specific positions is $^1/_3 \times ^1/_3 \times ^1/_3 = ^1/_{27}$. If any one sequence has a probability of $^1/_{27}$ of being present, there must be 27 different sequences. This reasoning is similar to that used in problem 12-67, which dealt with flips of a coin.

26-11. The pentapeptide in question has the following structure.

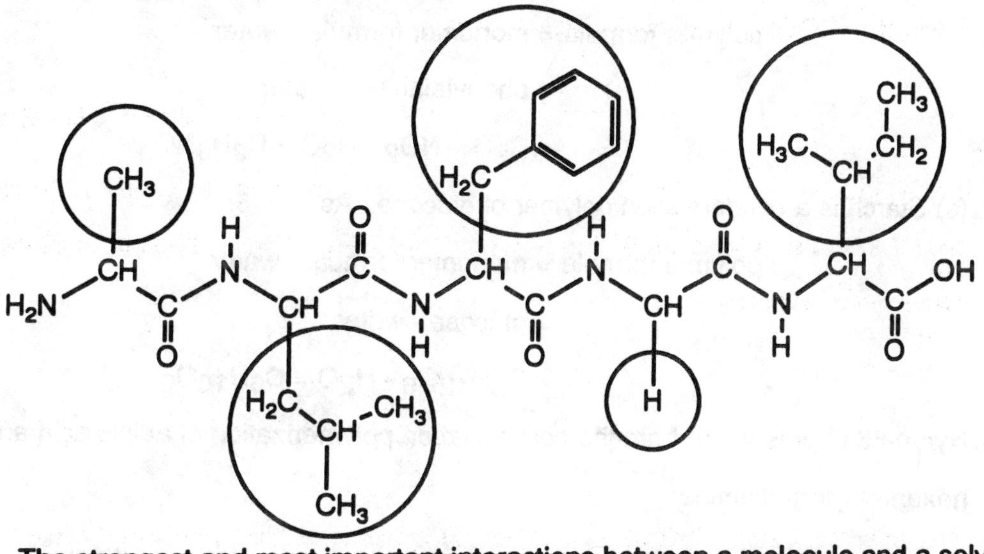

The strongest and most important interactions between a molecule and a solvent will involve the functional groups on the outside of the molecule. For a polypeptide, these groups are the amino acid side chains, outlined with circles above. In this example they contain carbon and hydrogen only. These will interact more strongly with a hydrocarbon solvent, in this case **octane**.

26-13. In its ring form, β-galactose will have the form shown below. The five asymmetric carbon centers are marked with asterisks.

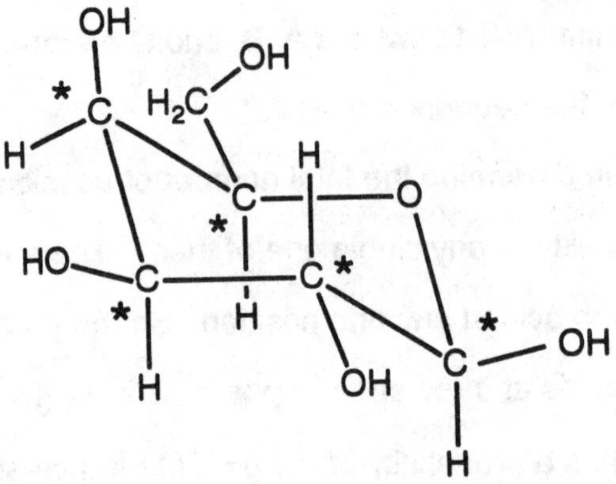

26-15. A polymer built of phenylalanine units will be made by condensation polymerization. Recall from problem No. 5(b) that the empirical formula for such a polymer is the empirical formula of the monomer minus water. In this case:

polymer formula = monomer formula - water

= phenylalanine - water

= $C_9H_{11}NO_2 - H_2O$ = $\mathbf{C_9H_9NO}$

26-17. (a) Starch is a condensation polymer of glucose. As in #15:

polymer formula = monomer formula - water

= glucose - water

= $C_6H_{12}O_6 - H_2O$ = $\mathbf{C_6H_{10}O_5}$

26-19. Nylon-66 fiber is made from the condensation polymerization of adipic acid and hexamethylenediamine:

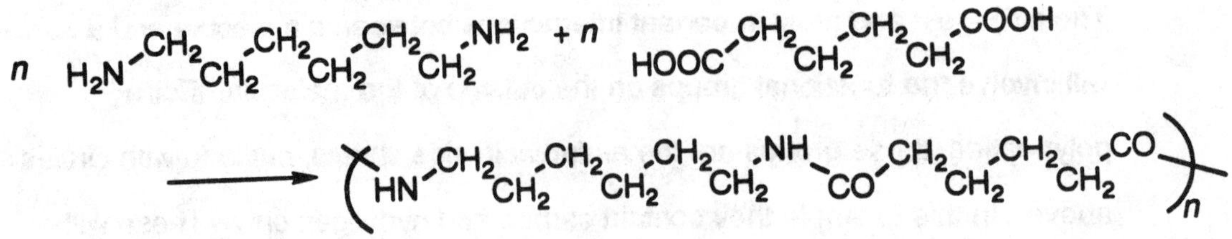

26-19. (continued)

Note that the repeat unit of the polymer, indicated in the product, has a formula of $C_{12}H_{22}O_2N_2$. The molar mass of this repeat unit is 226.32 g. Each repeat unit is built of one adipic acid and one hexamethylenediamine. note also that 1.00×10^3 kg = 1.00×10^6 g.

$$\text{Moles of repeat unit} = \frac{1.00 \times 10^6 \text{ g repeat unit}}{226.32 \text{ g mol}^{-1} \text{ repeat unit}} = 4418.5 \text{ mol repeat unit}$$

This is also the number of moles of adipic acid (molar mass 146.14 g mol^{-1}) and hexamethylenediamine (molar mass 116.21 g mol^{-1}) needed to make the nylon. Therefore:

$$4418.5 \text{ mol adipic acid} \times 146.14 \text{ g mol}^{-1} = \mathbf{646{,}000 \text{ g adipic acid}}$$

$$4418.5 \text{ mol hexamethylenediamine} \times 146.14 \text{ g mol}^{-1} = \mathbf{513{,}000 \text{ g}} \text{ hexamethylenediamine}$$

26-21. A branch point in a polymer occurs when a single carbon atom is bound to more than two chains, usually when it has three or more other carbon atoms bound to it. In diamond, each carbon is bound to four other carbons, forming four "chains" branching off each carbon atom.

26-23. Because polyethylene is an addition polymer, the mass of ethylene required for to make polyethylene is equal to the mass of the product (assuming 100% yields). In this case, then, 4.37 billion kilgrams of ethylene is needed for all the low-density polyethylene. Note that this mass is equal to 4.37×10^9 kg or 4.37×10^{12} g of ethylene. Then:

$$4.37 \times 10^{12} \text{ g } C_2H_4 \times \left(\frac{1 \text{ mol } C_2H_4}{28.05376 \text{ g } C_2H_4}\right) \times \left(\frac{22.4 \text{ L } C_2H_4}{1 \text{ mol } C_2H_4}\right) = 3.49 \times 10^{12} \text{ L}$$

There are 1000 L in a cubic meter, so this is equal to 3.49×10^9 m^3, the equivalent of a 1 meter high bubble of ethylene gas over an area 59 km on a side.

26-25. The butyl lithium is needed to create the first side of an anionic living polymer based on acrylonitrile. Once butyl lithium adds to an acrylonitrile monomer, then polymerization can proceed. The butyl lithium is not released; it is a permanent "cap" on the polymer. Hence, though it may form a very small part of the mass of the product polymer, the butyl lithium **is consumed** in the reaction, so it is not a catalyst.

26-27. For these polymers, the direction of growth may be as important as the stoichiometry. An arrow is used to indicate this in the following diagrams of a polymer based on butadiene ("B") and vinylchloride ("V"):

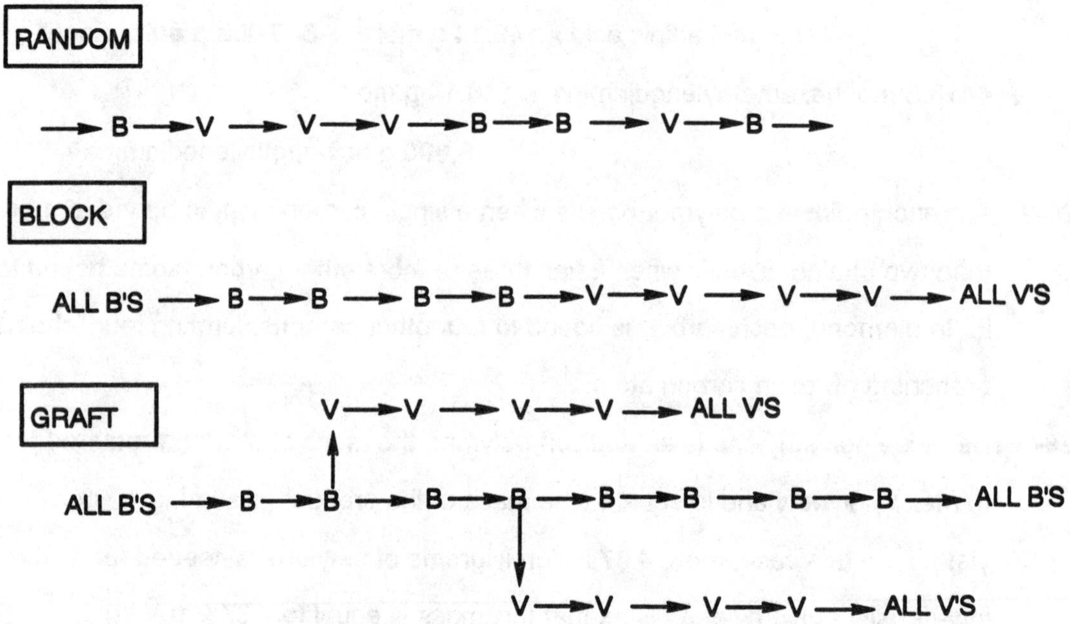

26-29. This is the same as problem #9 earlier, except there is now a $^1/_2$ chance of finding a given amino acid at a given site. The probability of any single polypeptide being formed is then:

$(^1/2) \times (^1/2) \times (^1/2) \times (^1/2) \times \ldots \times (^1/2) = (^1/2)^{22} = {}^1/4{,}194{,}304$.

By the same rationale given earlier, there are 4,194,304 different polypeptides that can form.

26-31. The mass of Fe in one mole of hemoglobin is:

$$65{,}000 \text{ g hemoglobin} \times \frac{0.00344 \text{ g Fe}}{1 \text{ g hemoglobin}} = 223.6 \text{ g Fe}$$

This corresponds to $223.6 \text{ g} / 55.847 \text{ g mol}^{-1} = 4.00 \text{ mol Fe}$.

There are four moles of iron in one mole of hemoglobin, so there are four atoms of iron in one molecule of hemoglobin.

26-33. L-sucrose is the enantiomer of D-sucrose, so the structure of L-sucrose is:

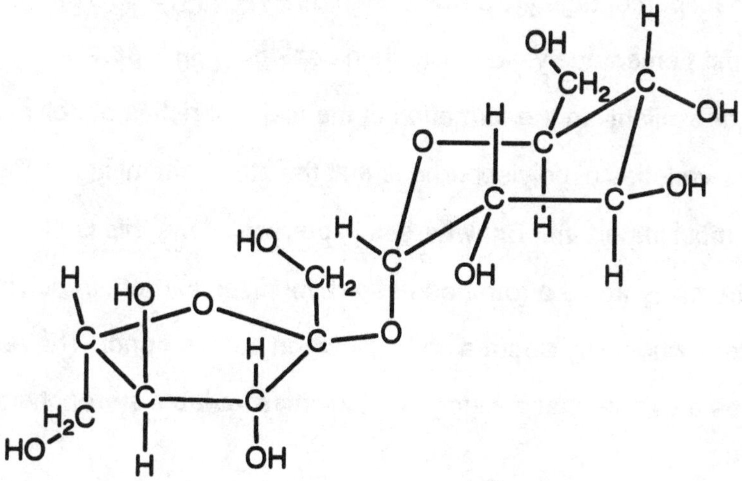

26-35. The name ethylene dichloride refers to the chemical "$C_2H_4Cl_2$" (see problem No. 25-21). Its conversion to vinyl chloride involves the loss of on mole of HCl per mole of vinyl chloride. We can then think of the synthesis of PVC by the *overall* equation:

$$n\, C_2H_4Cl_2 \rightarrow (C_2H_3Cl)_n + n\, HCl$$

We need to determine the mass of PVC that could theoretically be obtained from the indicated amount of ethylene dichloride. For this problem, we might as well remain in the mass units given -- pounds.

26-35. (continued)

The relative mass of equal chemical amounts of ethylene dichloride and PVC will be equal to the ratio of the molar mass of their empirical units.

$$\text{theoretical yield of PVC} = \text{mass of ethylene dichloride} \times \frac{\text{mass } C_2H_3Cl}{\text{mass } C_2H_4Cl_2}$$

$$= 950 \text{ lb } C_2H_4Cl_2 \times \frac{62.498 \text{ lb } C_2H_3Cl}{98.0592 \text{ lb } C_2H_4Cl_2}$$

$$= 600 \text{ lb } C_2H_3Cl = \mathbf{600\ lb\ PVC}$$

The highest percentage yield would then be $^{550}/_{600}$ = **91.7%.**

The lowest percentage yield would then be $^{500}/_{600}$ = **86.7%.**

26-37. The major similarity in the formation of the major varieties of polypropylene and the major varieties of polyisoprene is that the stereochemistry of the growing chain is most important. But whereas in polypropylene this is the stereochemistry about a tetrahedral *sp*^{3} hybridized carbon, in polyisoprene this is the stereochemistry about a carbon-carbon double bond. The relevant structures are (note that a wiggly line indicates variable stereochemistry):

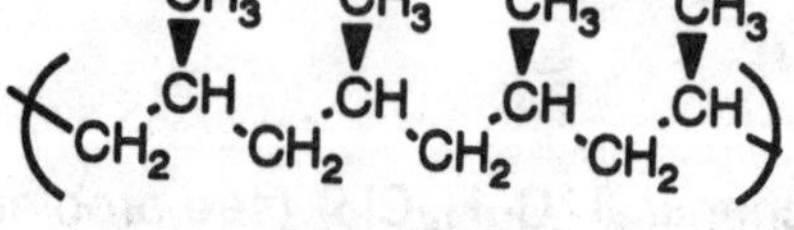

ISOTACTIC

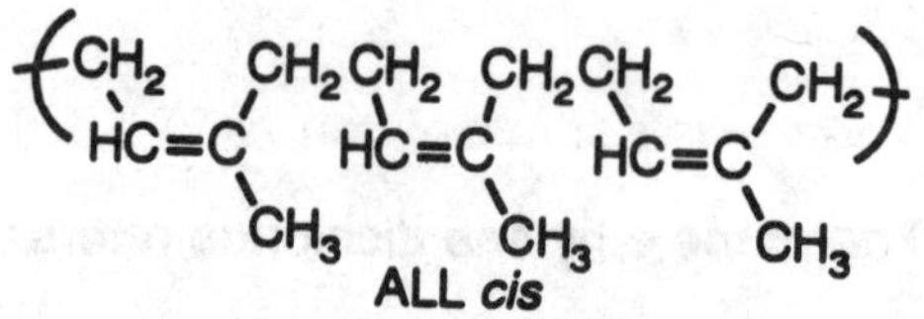

ALL *cis*

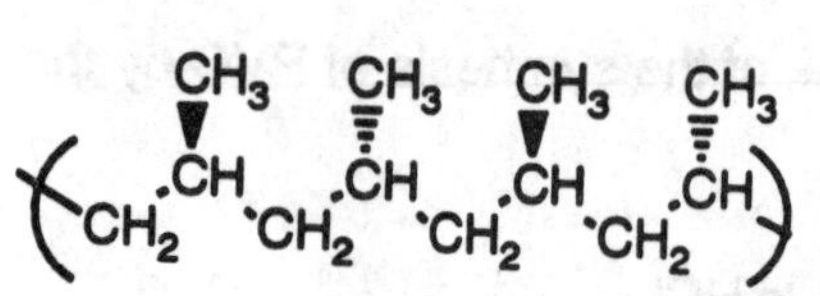

SYNDIOTACTIC

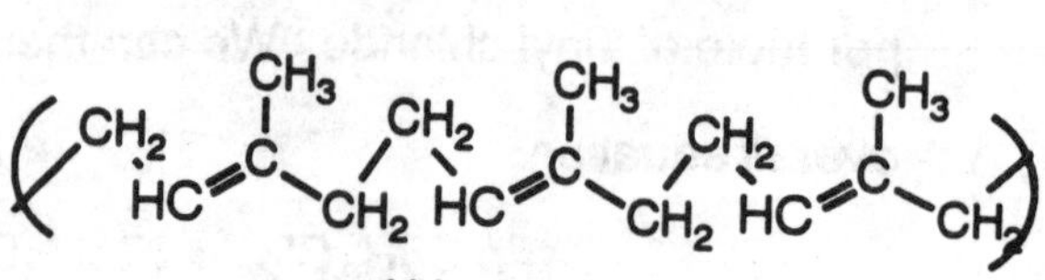

ALL *trans*

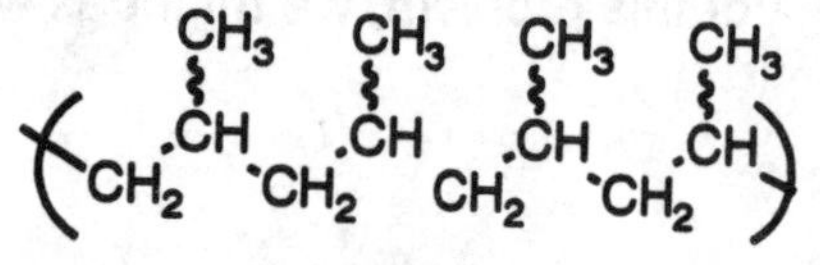

ATACTIC

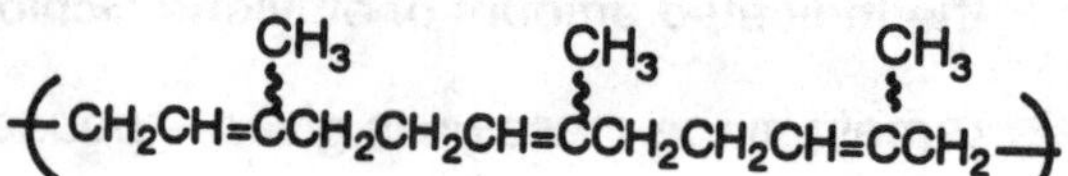

MIXED *cis* and *trans*

APPENDIX A - SCIENTIFIC NOTATION AND EXPERIMENTAL ERROR

A-1. (a) 5.82×10^{-4} (b) 1.402×10^{3}

(c) 7.93 (d) -6.59300×10^{3}

(e) 2.530×10^{-3} (f) 1.47

A-3. (a) 0.000537 (b) 9,390,000

(c) -0.00247 (d) 0.006020

(e) 20,000

A-5. All four are given from biggest to smallest.

1.90×10^{2}	>	9.7×10^{-2}	>	-4.10×10^{-2}	>	-4.10×10^{-2}
190	>	0.097	>	-0.00410	>	-490

A-7. 746,000,000 kg

A-9. (a) The **135.64 g** value seems much too large. It should be discarded.

(b) The average of the six valid measurements is **111.34 g.**

(c) The standard deviation σ is **0.22 g.**

A-11. The measurements in problem 9 are reported to a precision of one part out of 10^{5}. The measurements in problem 10, to one part out of 10^{3}. The measurements in problem 9 are more precise.

A-13. (a) Five (b) Three (c) Two or three

(d) Three (e) Four

A-15. We will retain the notation system used in each part.

(a) 14 L (b) -0.0034 ^{o}C (c) 34016

(d) 3.4×10^{2} miles (e) 6.2×10^{-27} J

A-17. 2,997,215.55

A-19. We report the "raw" value first, then the value to the proper number of significant figures.

(a) $-167.254 = -167.25$

(b) $75.50 = 76$

(c) A clearer layout of this is:

$$3.2156 \times 10^{15} - 0.04631 \times 10^{15} = 2.16929 \times 10^{15} = 3.1693 \times 10^{15}$$

(d) As in (c):

$$0.241 \times 10^{-25} - 7.83 \times 10^{-25} = -7.589 \times 10^{-25} = -7.59 \times 10^{-25}$$

A-21. (a) $-8.4008 = -8.40$

(b) $0.14735 = 0.147$

(c) $3.2446 \times 10^{-12} = 3.24 \times 10^{-12}$

(d) $4.464 \times 10^{13} = 4.5 \times 10^{13}$

A-23. The formula for the area of a triangle is:

$$\text{Area} = \frac{1}{2} \times \text{base} \times \text{altitude}$$

$$= \frac{1}{2} \times (42.07\ \text{cm}) \times (16.0\ \text{cm})$$

$$= 336.56\ \text{cm}^2 = 337\ \text{cm}^2$$

APPENDIX B - S.I. UNITS AND THE CONVERSION OF UNITS

B-1. (a) $65.2 \text{ nanograms} \times \left(\frac{10^{-9} \text{ grams}}{\text{nanograms}}\right) \times \left(\frac{1 \text{ kg}}{1000 \text{ grams}}\right) = \mathbf{6.52 \times 10^{-11} \text{ kg}}$

(b) $88 \text{ picoseconds} \times \left(\frac{10^{-12} \text{ seconds}}{1 \text{ picosecond}}\right) = \mathbf{8.8 \times 10^{-11} \text{ s}}$

(c) $5.4 \text{ terawatts} \times \left(\frac{10^{12} \text{ watts}}{1 \text{ terawatt}}\right) \times \left(\frac{1 \text{ kg m}^2 \text{ s}^{-3}}{1 \text{ watt}}\right) = \mathbf{5.4 \times 10^{12} \text{ kg m}^2 \text{ s}^{-3}}$

(d) $17 \text{ kilovolts} \times \left(\frac{1000 \text{ volts}}{1 \text{ kilovolt}}\right) \times \left(\frac{1 \text{ kg m}^2 \text{ s}^{-3} \text{ A}^{-1}}{1 \text{ volt}}\right) = \mathbf{1.7 \times 10^{4} \text{ kg m}^2 \text{ s}^{-3} \text{ A}^{-1}}$

B-3. $1 \text{ Wb} = 1 \text{ Vs} = 1 (\text{kg m}^2 \text{ s}^{-3} \text{ A}^{-1}) (\text{s}) = \mathbf{1 \text{ kg m}^2 \text{ s}^{-2} \text{ A}^{-1}}$

B-5. We should first note what each value is on a common scale, the liter:

$100 \text{ cm}^3 = 0.100 \text{ L}$ $500 \text{ mL} = 0.500 \text{ L}$

$100 \text{ dm}^3 = 100 \text{ L}$ $1.5 \text{ gall} = 5.678 \text{ L}$

$100 \text{ cm}^3 < 500 \text{ mL} < 1.5 \text{ gall (US)} < 100 \text{ dm}^3 < 150 \text{ L}$

B-7. The general formula is: $^{o}\text{C} = \frac{5\ ^{o}\text{C}}{9\ ^{o}\text{F}}\left(t_{^{o}F} - 32\ ^{o}\text{F}\right)$

(a) 4983 ^{o}C

(b) 37.0 ^{o}C

(c) The boiling point of water at 1 atm pressure is 212 ^{o}F.

Then ^{o}C = 111 ^{o}C

(d) -40. ^{o}C (This is the only temperature where the two scales are exactly equal.)

B-9. (a) 5256 K

(b) 310 K

(c) 384 K

(d) 233 K

B-11.

Physical Quantity	Name of Unit	Value in Familiar Units
volume	m^3	264.1722 gall (US)
length	m	39.37008...in
mass	kg	2.2046226 lb
energy	J	0.2390057... cal

B-13. (a) $\left(55.0\,\frac{\text{miles}}{\text{hr}}\right)\times\left(\frac{1609.344\text{ m}}{\text{mile}}\right)\times\left(\frac{1\text{ hour}}{3600\text{ s}}\right) = \mathbf{24.6\ m\ s^{-1}}$

(b) $\left(1.51\,\frac{\text{g}}{\text{cm}^3}\right)\times\left(\frac{1\text{ kg}}{1000\text{ g}}\right)\times\left(\frac{100\text{ cm}}{1\text{ m}}\right)^3 = \mathbf{1.51\times10^{3}\ kg\ m^{-3}}$

(c) $\left(1.6\times10^{-19}\text{C Å}\right)\times\left(\frac{1\text{ A}}{1\text{ C-s}^{-1}}\right)\times\left(\frac{1.0\times10^{-10}\text{m}}{1\text{ Å}}\right) = \mathbf{1.6\times10^{-29}\ A\ s\ m}$

(d) $\left(0.15\,\frac{\text{mol}}{\text{L}}\right)\times\left(\frac{1\text{ L}}{1\text{ dm}^3}\right)\times\left(\frac{10\text{ dm}}{\text{m}}\right)^3 = \mathbf{1.5\times10^{2}\ mol\ m^{-3}}$

(e) $\left(5.7\times10^3\,\frac{\text{L atm}}{\text{min}}\right)\times\left(\frac{1\text{ dm}^3}{1\text{ L}}\right)\times\left(\frac{10\text{ m}}{10\text{ dm}}\right)^3\times\left(\frac{101{,}325\text{ Pa}}{1\text{ atm}}\right)\times\left(\frac{1\text{ kg m}^2\text{ s}^{-2}}{1\text{ Pa}}\right)\times\left(\frac{1\text{ min}}{60\text{ s}}\right)$

$= 9.6\times10^3\text{ kg m}^2\text{ s}^{-3} = \mathbf{9.6\times10^{3}\ W}$

B-15. Lb in^{-3} and μ L^{-1} are obviously mass + volume units. For the others:

$$\text{Pa m}^2\text{ s}^{-2}\times\left(\frac{1\text{ kg m}^2\text{ s}^{-2}}{1\text{ Pa}}\right) = \text{kg m}^4\text{ s}^{-4}$$

$$\text{J m}^{-1}\text{ s}^{-2}\times\left(\frac{1\text{ kg m s}^{-2}}{1\text{ J}}\right) = 1\text{ kg s}^{-4}$$

These are not density units.

B-17. $(1\text{ kw-h})\times\left(\frac{1000\text{ w}}{\text{kw}}\right)\times\left(\frac{1\text{ kg m}^2\text{ s}^{-3}}{1\text{ w}}\right)\times\left(\frac{3600\text{ s}}{\text{hr}}\right)$

$= 3.6\times10^6\text{ kg m}^2\text{ s}^{-2} = 3.6\times10^6\text{ J}$

15.3 kw-h = $\mathbf{5.51\times10^{7}\ J}$

B-19. $(404\text{ in}^3)\times\left(\frac{2.54\text{ cm}}{1\text{ in}}\right)^3\times\left(\frac{1\text{ L}}{1000\text{ cm}^3}\right) = \mathbf{6.62\ L}$

APPENDIX C - MATHEMATICS FOR GENERAL CHEMISTRY

C-1. (a) $\text{slope} = \dfrac{\text{change in distance}}{\text{change in time}} = \dfrac{150 \text{ miles} - 75 \text{ miles}}{3.0 \text{ h} - 1.5 \text{ h}} = 50 \dfrac{\text{miles}}{\text{hour}}$

C-3. (a) Slope = 4 Intercept = -7

(b)

$$7x - 2y = 5$$
$$-2y = -7x + 5$$
$$y = +\frac{7}{2}x - \frac{5}{2}$$

Slope = $\frac{7}{2}$ Intercept = $-\frac{5}{2}$

(c)

$$3y + 6x - 4 = 0$$
$$3y = -6x + 4$$
$$y = -2x + \frac{4}{3}$$

Slope = -2 Intercept = $\frac{4}{3}$

C-5.

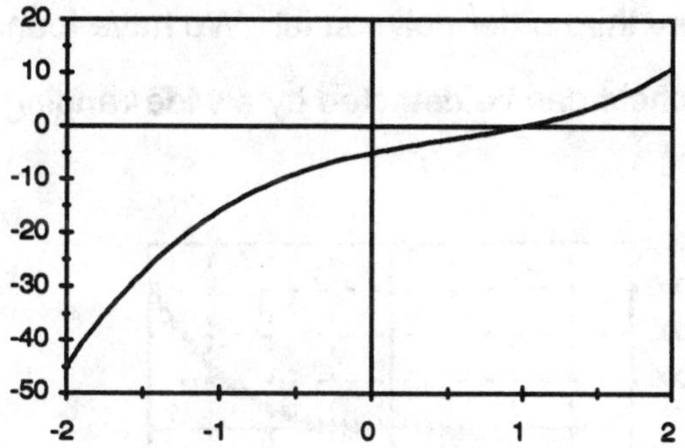

This is not a straight line!

C-7. (a) $7x + 5 = 0$

$$7x = -5$$
$$x = -\frac{5}{7}$$

(b) $-4x + 3 = 0$

$$-4x = -3$$
$$x = \frac{3}{4}$$

(c) $-3x = -2$

$$x = \frac{2}{3}$$

C-9. (a) $a = 4$; $b = 7$; $c = -5$

$$x = \frac{-7 \pm \sqrt{(7)^2 - 4(4)(-5)}}{8}$$

$$= \frac{-7 \pm \sqrt{129}}{8} = \frac{-7 \pm 11.36}{8} = \mathbf{+0.5447 \text{ and } -2.295}$$

(b) $2x^2 = -3 - 6x$

$2x^2 + 6x + 3 = 0$ $a = 2$; $b = 6$; $c = 3$

ROOTS: $x =$ **-0.6340 and -2.366**

(c) $2x + \frac{3}{x} = 6$

$2x^2 + 3 = 6x$

$2x^2 - 6x + 3 = 0$ $a = 2$, $b = -6$; $c = 3$.

ROOTS: $x =$ **+0.6340 and +2.366**

C-11. (a) We will try an assumption that $x << 2.00$:

$x\,(2.00)^2 \approx 2.6 \times 10^{-6}$

$x \approx 1.65 \times 10^{-7}$. This is sufficient to justify the assumption

There are three roots to every third order polynomial. We have found one by approximation of small *x*. Others can be detected by a wide-ranging graph of the function:

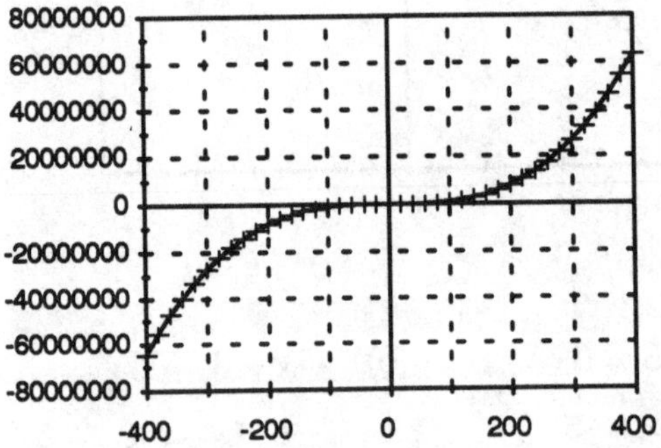

There is clearly only one real root. The other two roots must be complex.

C-11. (b) We will start with an assumption of x small.

$$x\ (3.00)\ (2.00) \sim 0.230$$

$$x = 0.046$$

This is **not** small enough to justify the assumption. So we will use it as a key for a solution by successive approximation.

$$x(3.00 - 7(0.046))(2.00 + 2\ (0.046)) \sim 0.230$$

$$x\ (2.678)\ (2.092) = 0.230$$

$$x = 0.043$$

A third iteration using 0.-43 as the key gives x = 0.041. Further iterations refine this value to **0.0407.**

We must check for other roots here, too. A narrow range graph of the function looks like:

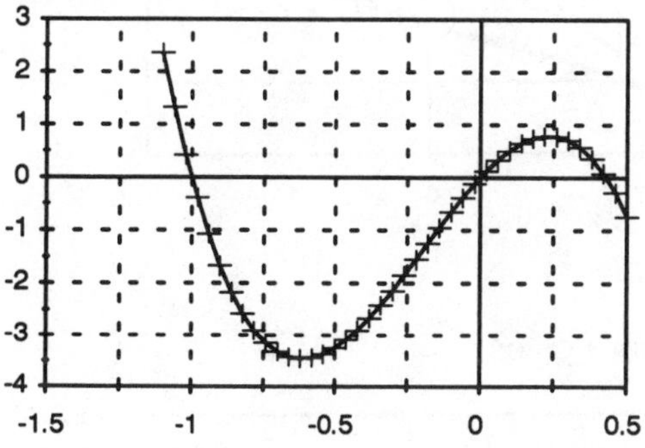

We can see that there are two other real roots -- around 0.40 and -1.00. Using these values as seeds for a series of iterations yields the roots x = +**0.399** and x = **-1.011**.

C-11. (c) A graph of the function over a wide range looks like this:

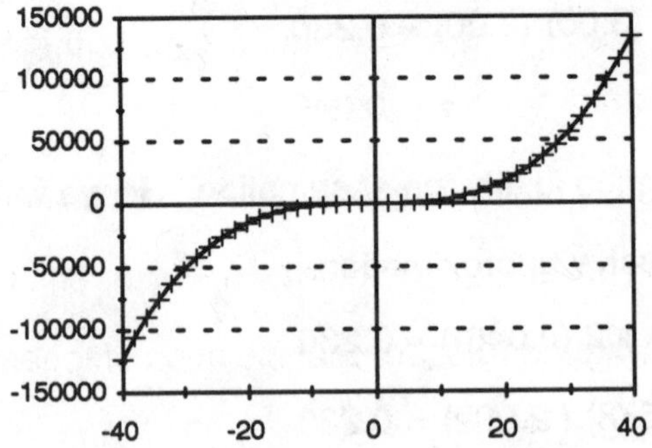

We can "zoom in" to get a better view of the intercept point:

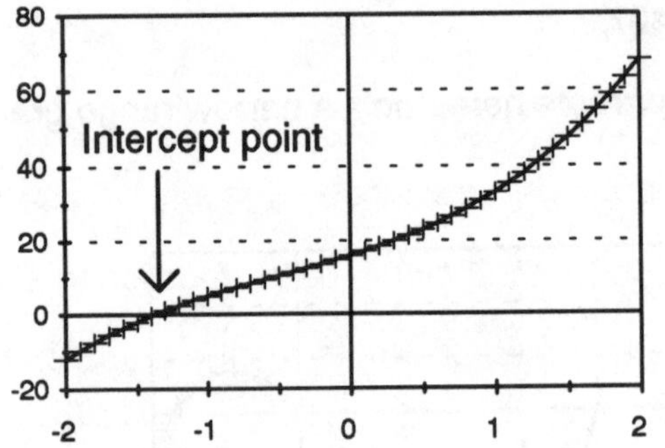

And zooming in even more gives:

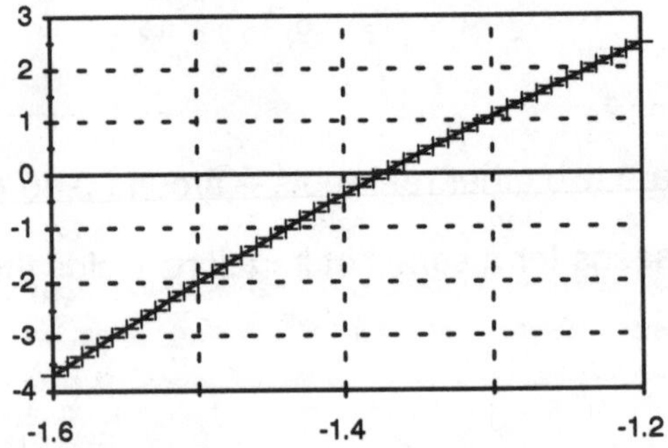

From this we can see that a solution to the equation occurs at $x \approx -1.37$. More precise graphing yields a root at x = **-1.3723**.

C-13 (a) 4.551 (b) 1.53×10^7 (c) 2.57×10^8 (d) -48.7264

C-15. The number x with the common logarithm 0.4793 is the number x in the equation:

$$\log_{10} x = 0.4793$$

$$x = 10^{+0.4793} = \mathbf{3.015}$$

C-17. Many calculators will not accept exponents beyond 99. But we can solve this equation in parts, using the rules for manipulation of logarithms:

$$\log_{10} (3.00 \times 10^{121}) = \log_{10} (3.00) + \log_{10} (10^{121})$$

C-19. In a logarithmic function, the "power of 10" determines the number *before* the decimal. The pre-exponential determines the number *after* the decimal.

Therefore: $\log_{10} (5.64 \times 10^7) = 7 + .751 = \mathbf{7.751}$

$$\log_{10} (5.64 \times 10^{-3}) = -3 + .751 = \mathbf{-2.249}$$

C-21. The requirement that the argument of a logarithm -- base 10 or otherwise -- be greater than 0 restricts the domain of the function to $x > 1$ so that $\ln x > 0$. A wide graph of the function yields the graph on the left.

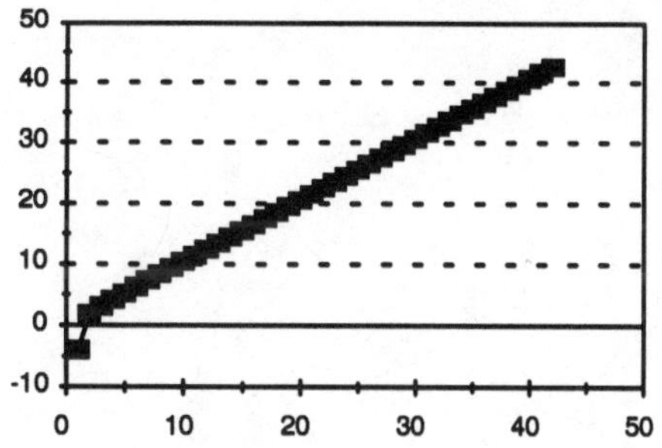

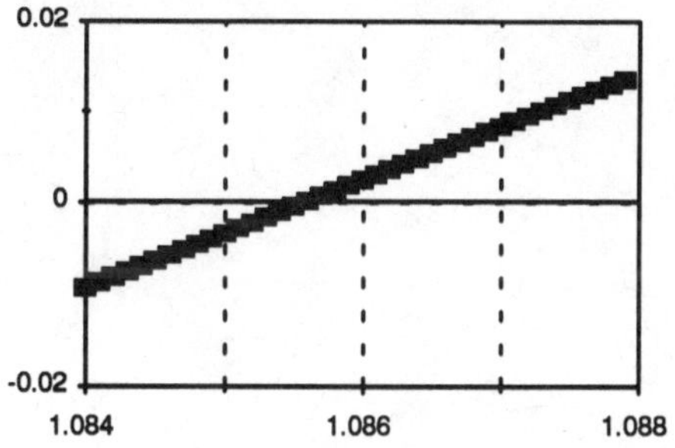

We can see that the function does have an intercept -- at about 1.2. Zooming in, we find from the graph on the right that the intercept is closest to $x = 1.086$.

C-23. (a) The total mass of the system is 24.60 g + 17.2 g + 0.0020 g = 41.802 g

Note that the last two digits in the total mass are not significant, but they *should* be retained in calculations of ratios, to avoid round-off errors..

$$\text{mass fraction of water} = \frac{24.60\ \text{g}}{41.802\ \text{g}} = 0.588$$

$$\text{mass fraction of NaCl} = \frac{17.2\ \text{g}}{41.802\ \text{g}} = 0.411$$

$$\text{mass fraction of mercury} = \frac{0.0020\ \text{g}}{41.802\ \text{g}} = 4.8 \times 10^{-5}$$

(b) the total volume is 32.614147 mL. The volume fractions are 0.756 water, 0.244 NaCl, and 4.5×10^{-6} mercury.

(c) ppmv = volume fraction $\times\ 10^6$ = 4.5 ppmv

(d) ppbm mass fraction $\times\ 10^9$ = 48,000 ppbm